Contributions to the History of Geology

Volume 1
American Mineralogical Journal
. . . to Elucidate the Mineralogy and Geology of the United States
Conducted by Archibald Bruce
With an introduction by John C. Greene
Foreword by George W. White
Volume 1 (all published) 270 p. + index. New York 1810-1814

Volume 2
C. F. Volney
View of the Soil and Climate of the United States of America
Translated, with occasional remarks by C. B. Brown
With an introduction by George W. White
XXVIII, 446 p. + 2 maps + 2 plates. Philadelphia 1804

Volume 3
Monthly American Journal of Geology and Natural History
Conducted by G. W. Featherstonhaugh
With an introduction by George W. White
Volume 1 (all published) 576 p. Philadelphia 1831-1832

Volume 4
Nicolaus Steno 1638-1686
The Prodromus of Nicolaus Steno's Dissertation concerning a Solid Body enclosed by Process of Nature within a Solid
An English version with an introduction and explanatory notes by John Garrett Winter
With a foreword by William H. Hobbs
With an introduction by George W. White
University of Michigan, Humanistic Studies. Vol. XI, part 2. 1916 and 1930

Volume 5
James Hutton
System of the Earth, 1785; Theory of the Earth, 1788; Observations on Granite, 1794; together with Playfair's Biography of Hutton
With an introduction by Victor A. Eyles
With a foreword by George W. White

Volume 6
David Thomas
Travels through the Western Country in the Summer of 1816
With an introduction by John W. Wells
With a foreword by George W. White

Volume 7
Robert Boyle
An Essay About the Origine & Virtues of Gems
With an introduction by A. F. Hagner
With a foreword by George W. White

Volume 8
Johann David Schöpf
Geology of Eastern North America, An annotated translation of Beyträge zur Mineralogischen Kenntniss des Östlichen Theils von Nord-Amerika und seiner Gebürge, 1787, by Edmund M. Spieker. With a foreword by George W. White. To which is added a facsimile of the Beyträge.

CONTRIBUTIONS

TO THE

HISTORY OF GEOLOGY

Edited by

George W. White

Research Professor of Geology
University of Illinois

Volume 8

Portrait of Johann David Schöpf

Geology of Eastern North America

By

Johann David Schöpf

An annotated translation of
Beyträge zur Mineralogischen Kenntniss
des Ostlichen Theils von Nord-Amerika
und seiner Gebürge, 1787

By

Edmund M. Spieker
The Ohio State University

With a Foreword by
George W. White
University of Illinois

[With a Facsimile Reprint of the Original German Text]

HAFNER PUBLISHING COMPANY
New York
1972

Published by
HAFNER PUBLISHING COMPANY, INC.
866 Third Avenue
New York, N.Y. 10022

Library of Congress Catalog Card Number: 78-183010

Printed in U.S.A. by
NOBLE OFFSET PRINTERS, INC.
NEW YORK, N.Y. 10003

Contents

Editor's Foreword

by

GEORGE W. WHITE

The first book on the geology of the United States, *Beyträge zur mineralogischen Kenntniss des östlichen Theils von Nord-Amerika und seiner Gebürge,* by the young German military surgeon and naturalist, Johann David Schöpf, was published in 1787. It has never been reprinted and has never before been translated into English. This early work has been known to most geologists only from a few brief notes in secondary publications; only a very few have seen an actual copy of the book.

Other volumes in the Series, *Contributions to the History of Geology,* are facsimile reproductions of rare early works in English, especially (but not exclusively) early American works. Because of its particular importance this work in German is included in the Series, both in facsimile of the original and in an annotated translation. (The facsimile is not exactly the size of the original, in which the width of printing on the page is 81 mm). This first book on American geology is a perceptive record of geological observations, together with an attempt to explain the origin of many of the geological features. Schöpf's book is an outstanding example of pre-Wernerian and pre-Huttonian geology, and as such is important not only to American geologists and historians of geology, but also to historians of geology in general.

One of the important features of Schöpf's book is the number of authors to whom he refers in his descriptions and explanations. These references enable us to recognize his breadth of knowledge and his acquaintance with current geological literature. The references, unlike those of many others of the time, are generally precise enough to identify editions and sometimes pages. Professor Spieker has dealt with these in his notes and has provided an annotated bibliography of the books, journals, and maps cited by Schöpf, who was well acquainted with Continental literature and with the American descriptions of Catesby, Evans, Kalm, Stork, Pownall, and Chastellux, and his summaries of them are accurate and fair.

Schöpf's *Beyträge* shares with Lewis Evans' *Analysis* and *Map*, 1755, the topmost place in early geological Americana. Evans little book is not primarily on geology, but it contains much of geological importance; his map is almost, but not quite, a geological map. Schöpf's book is designedly a book on geology (he wrote another on his travels) ; it contains data from which a map could have been drawn, had he chosen to do so. Evans' *Map* and *Analysis* are rare, but not unobtainable to a resourceful (and resource full!) seeker, but Schöpf's book is far more difficult to find. The Ohio State University Orton Memorial Library of Geology is fortunate indeed to have a fine copy in original boards, which was used in the preparation of this volume.

It is most appropriate that Dr. Edmund M. Spieker, longtime distinguished Research Professor of Geology at the Ohio State University, and officer of the United States Geological Survey, should be the translator and editor of this work. Professor Spieker is known for his work in historical, stratigraphic, structural, tectonic, and economic geology. He has been a geological explorer in Alaska, in western Canada, and in the western United State. He is intimately acquainted with the geology of the eastern United States through his early residence and academic study in Baltimore, which was one of the centers from which Schöpf traveled. He has seen most of the territory traversed by the German physician and naturalist and can thus assess the accuracy of these reports. Professor Spieker's long interest in the history of geology and his linguistic ability in several languages further add to the good fortune of having him translate and provide extensive notes for this work. He has determined the routes of Schöpf's travels and has described them in detail in the Introduction. We are indebted to Mr. Leslie R. Lewis, University of Illinois Geology Department cartographer, for skillfully drafting the map that accompanies this volume.

Translator's Introduction

by

EDMUND M. SPIEKER

HISTORICAL SIGNIFICANCE

This work, the first serious and comprehensive treatise on the geology of North America,[1] has long lain in neglect. For over fifty years after it appeared there was no evidence that anybody in America was aware of it, and more than a century passed before it gained substantial notice in our literature. In 1842 Samuel L. Dana exhibited a copy of the book (from the library of the Boston Society of Natural History, possibly then a recent acquisition) at a meeting of the American Association of Geologists (1843) and a German-speaking member was asked to study it and report, but nothing further seems to have come of this. Not until 1894 was the work effectively brought to the attention of American geologists, when George Huntington Williams (1894) published an article appreciative of Schöpf and his accomplishment, and since then little more has been done to make it known in America. In the first version of his detailed history Merrill (1906) passed it over in bare mention because it was not published in America. In the later edition (Merrill 1924, 1964) he gave somewhat fuller account, but added little to what Williams had already brought out, and in neither case did he give any reference to Williams. Morrison (1911, 1968), in the introduction to his translation of Schöpf's *Reise* (Schöpf 1788), mentioned the *Beyträge* and quoted two sentences from Williams.

---

[1] Several earlier travellers and surveyors, for example Kalm and Evans (cited herein farther on) had included mention of sundry geologic features in their reports, and Jean Étienne Guettard (1752) even attempted a geologic map, but none of these accounts can justly be called comprehensive. Guettard, as a matter of fact, was never in America. (For further comment on this, see note 9.)

1

The work is listed in the bibliographies of Darton (1896), Goode (1886), and Nickles (1923). More recently it has been noted in a few publications on the early history of science in America (Browning 1931; White 1953; Hindle 1956; White and Slanker 1962; Stuckey 1965), and Schöpf is listed in *World Who's Who in Science* (Marquis, Chicago 1968, p. 1500) with mention of the *Beyträge,* but otherwise the press of America has been silent on the subject.

This general default, to put it mildly, seems passing strange. Especially is it puzzling when we realize that Schöpf's work on the *materia medica* of North America (Schöpf 1787) was not only known here, but for many years was the accepted authority on the subject, and this can mean nothing less than its presence on the bookshelves of contemporary American physicians.[2] Initially the deficiency may have been merely a matter of isolationary provincialism, but this can hardly be the whole story, for later pioneers such as Maclure and Eaton were familiar with work in Germany, at least to the extent that they adopted Werner's system. There may have been a touch of chauvinism—unwillingness to accredit a foreigner for pioneering work on American soil. The book may, indeed, have come out in a very small edition (bibliophiles now rate it as exceedingly rare) and any copies that came to America may simply not have fallen into the hands of naturalists interested in the earth. At all events, whatever may have been the cause of it all, today we can only deplore the effect that the work failed of its author's principal aim. It undoubtedly did serve well in its time to inform European readers about currently interesting features of the New World, but Schöpf's stated intention was to pave the way toward more advanced work on

[2] It might be noted, however, that the *Materia Medica* is couched entirely in Latin, *lingua franca* to the educated physician of the day, whereas the German of the *Beyträge* may well have been a sealed book to those naturalists and other cultivated gentry here who should have read it. The study of modern languages was not yet general in America—the first college department was established at William and Mary in 1779. Further, despite the strong German element in the early population of the central colonies, there may have been few or no naturalists there in the late 18th century who were able to read standard German with ease. Schöpf is known to have corresponded with the pioneer American botanist G. H. E. Muhlenberg (Hindle 1956 p. 307) but apparently not with any naturalist interested in the earth. The whole question of possible language barrier, however, is necessarily speculative.

American geology, and it is more than slightly pathetic to read the modest words of hope with which he introduced and closed his work.

But, for all that it had no known influence on the advancement of American geology, the book is still no mere antiquarian curiosity. It is important as a clear record of the way in which a highly intelligent and broadly cultured naturalist of the late 18th century observed and thought originally and independently about features that were soon to become the major substance of geology proper. As we read his pages we must keep it constantly in mind that Schöpf was doing this work at the very time when the science of geology was in process of being born. Let us look at a few dates. Schöpf was in America from mid-1777 to early 1784, and nearly all of the work reported in the *Beyträge* was done within the last eight months of that period. Werner started his epoch-making activity in the lecture room at Freiberg in 1775, not long before Schöpf's departure for America, but he did not develop and promulgate his famous system with its associated concepts until later years. (His *Kurze Klassifikation* came out in 1786 and 1787, the latter the year of the *Beyträge,* and he never did publish most of the concepts.) Hutton published the first volume of his great *Theory of the Earth* in 1785, but the full work did not appear until 1795. (Incidentally, anent the general weariness among intellectuals with "theories of the Earth" that was a major cause of the failure that initially attended Hutton's *magnum opus,* it is of more than passing interest to read Schöpf's acid remarks on interpretation of the earth in the last pages of his book.) The significance of what Lehmann and Füchsel had done in 1756 and 1762 had not yet been widely noticed or appreciated (and was not, in fact, until 1830—see Geikie 1905). It was a time of ferment for our nascent science, one fraught with importance for later developments, and Schöpf's groping for explanations of what he saw in our Coastal Plain, Piedmont, and Appalachians is of great interest as a definite record of the thinking among natural scientists of the time, as well as a tribute to the ability of one man in a new and largely unexplored field, for many of Schöpf's ideas were on the right track toward our present picture, and some may be regarded as remarkably foresighted. The work is therefore of no mean importance in the general history of geology.

It is especially important, indeed, as an example of independent geologic reasoning in America before the imperious influence of Werner exerted its unfortunate effects. Schöpf's thinking was to some extent controlled by ideas he had acquired in Europe, but at least it was not overborne by the powerful picture set forth by the pontiff of Freiberg. After reading the *Beyträge* through one comes out with the impression of an open mind, candidly willing to admit itself unable to reach solid answers to many major questions, but presciently fertile in suggestions as to others that have turned out to be valid. Had Schöpf's attitude and approach (and his body of knowledge) been followed by the first American pioneers, the history of our geology would almost certainly have been very different and probably more fortunate than it was for more than half a century after his time.

Schöpf was no Hutton, nor yet a Werner, although he was a better scientist than Werner, humbly cautious and analytical where Werner was autocratically, narrowly, and unyieldingly dogmatic, and he knew enough chemistry to realize that granite and gneiss were "no products of water." Further, he understood several principles that Hutton was even then laying down in his great foundation of modern geology.

Schöpf's book has long been hard to come by, and when in 1942 the Orton Memorial Library of Geology at the Ohio State University acquired a copy for its growing rare book collection I realized that it ought to be translated and so made generally available. I actually began the work at that time, but soon had to lay it aside under pressure of other duties, and did not take it up again until recently. And in this aspect of the undertaking I am greatly indebted to Professors George W. White and Aurèle LaRocque for stimulation and encouragement without which I might not have ventured to complete the task.

BIOGRAPHICAL SKETCH[3]

Johann David Schöpf was born March 8, 1752, at Wunsiedel, a little town in the Fichtelberg nearly 20 miles northeast of Bay-

---

[3] The biographical sketch here offered is taken mainly from the account by Friedrich Ratzel in the *Allgemeine Deutsche Biographie*, vol. 32, pp. 350-352, 1891, and in part from the entry on Schöpf in Meusel, *Lexikon der vom Jahr 1750 bis 1800 verstorbenen Teutschen Schriftsteller*, vol. XII pp. 364-365, Leipzig, 1812, reprod. Hildesheim, 1968.

reuth. He was the son of a prosperous merchant, and he enjoyed a comfortable upbringing and a good education. In the vicinity of Wunsiedel there are many mines and quarries, and young Schöpf early developed strong interest in minerals and mining, and in the forests round about he was attracted to the general study of nature as well. After tutorial instruction at home his father sent him to the gymnasium at Hof, and upon graduation there in 1770, to the University of Erlangen, where he undertook the curriculum in medicine.

However, he did not look forward with any enthusiasm at all to the practice of medicine, especially in a small town, and following the inclinations of his youth, he broadened his studies so as to be prepared for wider-ranging and more varied activities in natural science, working in mineralogy and mining, botany and zoology, as well as at his medical studies. At the university his principal teacher in natural science was Schreber,[4] but he also had much stimulation and help from Esper.[5] In 1773 he passed his examinations at Erlangen, and then went to Berlin, where he attended lectures on forestry. He was rounding himself out, we see, as a naturalist in addition to his competence in medicine.

In 1774 he set out on travels through the Erzgebirge and Bohemia to Prague, Vienna, Idria, Trieste, Venice, and Padua, seeking communication with scholars wherever he went, visiting mines and quarries, and even tarrying for periods of study at the

[4] Johann Christian Daniel Schreber, born at Weissensee, Thuringia January 17, 1739, died at Erlangen December 10, 1810, went to Uppsala at the age of 21 to study under Linnaeus, and on his return to Erlangen introduced the Linnaean system into Europe. He has been called the "German Linnaeus." He taught not only botany and physiology but a wide range of other subjects —political economy, agriculture, technology—and he doubtless inspired Schöpf to use the Linnaean nomenclature for minerals and rocks. He knew astronomy, Greek, Hebrew, and he wrote classic Latin. However, he was a dry teacher, unapproachable, and he had few close friends. He rose rapidly into prominence, becoming President of the Carolinian-Leopoldian Academy of Science, and was elevated to the nobility as Imperial Councillor. He was either member or honorary member of most of the scientific societies of Europe.

[5] Johann Friedrich Esper (1732-1781) was by profession a clergyman (as were many if not most naturalists of the time) but also very active and competent at general nature study. In 1759 he published a paper on the transit of Venus, and in later years explored the caves in the Muggendorf region, discovering many animal remains. He also published several papers on mineralogy and petrography. The whole of his work gained him considerable fame.

universities of Vienna and Prague. He returned through Switzerland and in 1776 presented and defended his dissertation[6] at Erlangen, and attained the doctorate.

He was still loath to set out as a medical practitioner, and (inveterate traveller that he turned out to be) was on the point of taking off for India when he was offered the post of chief surgeon to the Ansbach "Hilfstruppen" that had been engaged by King George III of England to help put down the rebellion in the American colonies. Attracted by the prospect of visiting the New World, he accepted, and bearing the commission from the Hofrath Schreber mentioned in his preface to the *Beyträge,* left for America March 7, 1777. He arrived in New York on June 4, and spent the next six years in the British military garrisons, mainly at New York and Philadelphia, active at his surgical work, at communication with other physicians, and as far as possible at studies in natural history. During this period he saw only Rhode Island, "York Island," a bit of Long Island, and Philadelphia; his job kept him pretty well limited to the British army posts, and he had very little time for any kind of geologizing. Immediately at the end of the war, however, in late July 1783, he set out from New York on his journey, which took him as far west as Pittsburgh and as far south as St. Augustine, on a network of routes through Pennsylvania, Maryland, and northern Virginia and a fairly direct course along the Atlantic Coast to Charleston, whence he went by sea to St. Augustine and thence to the Bahamas. Some details of these travels are reviewed farther on in this introduction. He crossed the Atlantic in a small sailing vessel and in July 1784 arrived in London, almost exactly a year after his departure from New York. He travelled rather thoroughly in England, then made his way in leisurely fashion across western

---

[6] The title of Schöpf's dissertation is *De medicamentorum mutatione in corpore humano praecipue a fluidis.* It is of only marginal interest, to be sure, in the present essay, yet it is hard to avoid wondering just what this document contains. It was prepared, let us recall, at the very time when modern chemistry was beginning to take form, largely through the genius of Lavoisier, and it is doubtful that Schöpf could have known much (for all that he was a "modern" of his time and unquestionably a progressive) about what was happening to the phlogiston theory and other notions of mid-18th century chemistry, and thus about the real nature of chemical reaction. It would be most interesting to see what his ideas were, and this might well be a fit subject for investigation by some medical historian.

Europe (he stayed three weeks in Paris) and reached Bayreuth in October of 1784.

At his homecoming he was happy to be close again to his relatives, sorely missed for so long, to renew old acquaintances and to make new friends, and he passed the years 1785 to 1800 peacefully, consorting with honest and sincere people of all classes, busy and happy at work and pleasure ordained to his own desire and taste. This quiet and fruitful life was interrupted by only two trips to Italy and one to Holland. In 1785 he was appointed court and military physician, and district medical officer, but the duties of these posts left him enough free time to write abundantly about all aspects of his American experience.

He became a member of several learned societies, and his abilities were increasingly recognized until in 1795 he was appointed President of the Medical College of Ansbach, and in 1797 President of the combined medical schools of Ansbach and Bayreuth. He was probably well on the way toward greater fame and recognition, but unfortunately he was soon stricken by illness, described by Ratzel as a protracted disease of the throat (almost certainly cancer) that brought him to premature death on September 10, 1800, midway in his forty-ninth year, just at the time when a man of his type is likely to be in his prime, at the height of his powers.

Schöpf was appreciated in Germany, at least, and not only as a competent medical man, administrator, and naturalist, either; also as a progressive, in general a member of the *avant-garde*. Ratzel said this: "Versatility, lively and unprejudiced comprehension, sharp observation and apposite judgment stamp Schöpf as an interesting representative of the more liberal intellectual trend that was making headway even in Germany at the close of the 18th century." Although we are concerned here mainly with his work on North American geology, we may well set this achievement in its proper human environment, and admire its author as a man of parts worthy of notice in any age.

SCHÖPF'S PREPARATION AND SCHOLARLY BACKGROUND FOR HIS GEOLOGIC WORK

In Schöpf's day students of the earth were trained primarily in mineralogy, and anything of what later came generally to be called geology was commonly included under that heading, as witness the title of the *Beyträge*, which specifies only mineralogy whereas the book is much more a treatment of general geology than of mineralogy proper. Schöpf was well grounded in mineralogy, but beyond that and more important for the larger aspects of his venture, he was remarkably well acquainted with the literature that dealt with geology as such. His footnotes and many remarks in his text show that he was familiar with a wide variety of essentially geologic treatises, including such European works as those of de Saussure, Pallas, von Beroldingen, and Buffon as well as the accounts of American geology by Evans, Kalm, Catesby, Stork, Robin, and Carver.

He was evidently not acquainted, however, with the works of Lehmann, Füchsel, and Arduino that later came to be appreciated as monuments in the early development of geology, but, as noted specifically farther on, neither were most if not all of the other natural philosophers in his time.

It is very doubtful that he knew anything about Werner, whose publication was about simultaneous with the *Beyträge*. His obvious care and honesty in matters bibliographic virtually rule out any such possibility.

Schöpf was, however, thoroughly familiar with the works of Evans and Pownall, but these he did not see until he had already crossed the mountains "for the second time" and thus had completed the major part, perhaps all of his field observations west of the Coastal Plain. He expressed pleasure at seeing so many of his observations confirmed by theirs, and we may therefore assume that he actually derived little if anything from their work. It is further worthy of record that he said these publications were rare (even then!) in America.

It might possibly be thought that Schöpf gained some of his geologic ideas from Ferber's account of his travels in Italy (Ferber 1776; Ford 1966), a work that has apparently suffered a general oblivion similar to that of Schöpf's *Beyträge* in America. In this work Ferber introduced several sound geologic concepts, including that of the basement complex and the recognition that strata now dipping steeply and even overturned must originally have been horizontal, and he gave clear account of Arduino's classification. But the only actual evidence we have that Schöpf might have been familiar with this work is the mention of Ferber's name, quoted from Schreber, in the preface to the

Beyträge. Against the idea is the fact that Schöpf nowhere cites either Ferber or Arduino, and once more we must observe that his documentation is otherwise so thorough that it is hard to believe him capable of so important an omission. Further, if he had known of Arduino's classification it seems hardly possible, the good scientist and scholar he obviously was, that he would not have used it, but his only approach to such order is his recognition of the crystalline rocks as primitive. It does seem strange, that Schöpf, familiar at least with Ferber's name, would not have looked up the work, especially considering his broad acquaintance otherwise with the literature, but despite this disturbing thought I feel virtually certain that he did not draw from Ferber.

Schöpf's command of the literature, then, was remarkable even for an erudite natural scientist of his time. And in this quarter it is certainly worthy of note that his references, even though commonly abbreviated, are generally clear enough to be recovered, and by no means can this be said for most natural philosophers of the time.

Over and above these matters of general preparation in knowledge of mineralogy and geology we might note that Schöpf brought to his task a mind sharpened in powers of observation by his youthful predilections toward natural history and his studies and experiences in medicine and surgery. He had trained himself, and had been trained, to look carefully for detail as well as at the larger outlines of what lay before him; this attribute is more amply discussed farther on, in my evaluation of the *Beyträge.* And as regards the medical element, although it is not exactly germane to the present concern, it is worth noting here that many of us today may not realize how many medical men contributed to early American geology, and how many actually became geologists of note (Browning 1931).

SCHÖPF'S OTHER AMERICAN WORK

In addition to the work here presented Schöpf published a number of articles and books on other features of America—climate, meteorology, illnesses, materia medica, agriculture, frogs, fishes, turtles; and he wrote a manuscript on the birds that was somehow lost. And the work on geology was not his only pioneering accomplishment. The treatise on fishes (Schöpf 1788) was "the first special ichthyological paper ever written in America or concerning American species" (Goode 1901), and the work on materia medica (Schöpf 1787) not only enjoys the same distinction, but, as already noted, was the standard work on the subject here for many years, well into the 19th century. His treatise on turtles was recognized by Goode as "one of the earliest monographs of the Testudinata." These and his other scientific works are listed in the bibliography at the end of this introduction. The only reason why he did not write about American forests, for which task he was eminently prepared, was because he felt that his friend von Wangenheim had satisfactorily covered the subject. All in all our author was a productive and versatile scientist.

Most notably, however, Schöpf got out a detailed narrative and descriptive account of his travels (Schöpf 1788b) —regarded by Ratzel as his *magnum opus* (in which judgment I concur) — that has been rendered into English (Morrison 1911, 1968),[7] and here we find a fuller profile of the man than in any of the other works. Whereas the *Beyträge* is strictly professional in form and tone, and is devoted exclusively to the business in hand, the *Reise,* in much freer atmosphere, reveals a highly talented man of parts, endowed with wisdom remarkable for his years and possessed of a keen sense of humor, master of a dry wit that enlivens his pages and belies his own appraisal of the work in his preface as merely a body of "simple facts and * * * arid observations." In this work Schöpf talks freely about all aspects of the new-born nation that he observed as he rode through cultivated districts and wildernesses, tarried in principal cities, sojourned at night with farmers and backwoodsmen as well as in taverns and, in a few cases, the homes of the well-to-do, visited most assiduously all of the mines, quarries, mills and other such operations that he could reach, criticizing favorably as well as otherwise as he commented on American *mores,* language, politics, professions, industry—hardly anything did he miss—as viewed by a cultured European. His expostulations over the language of the

---

[7] Morrison's translation was issued in an edition supported by subscription (copies obtainable in 1911 from the translator for $5.00 the pair) and it soon became a rare book. The reissue in 1968 by Bergman is therefore a real boon to all who would gain further acquaintance with Schöpf and his accomplishments.

Germans in Pennsylvania are priceless. His strictures on the prevalent waste and devastation in the forests hit a weakness in the American economy that is only now being partly remedied. He appreciated highly the culture in cities like Philadelphia (but spotted the clannishness that still lingers in that metropolis) and noted candidly the lack of it where, all too often, he found it; on this score he was downright rough on the descendants of his compatriots who became known as the Pennsylvania Dutch, and compared them most unfavorably with the people of English extraction. But, as we do today, he admired their skill and neatness in farming. He found the southern farmers far less industrious and efficient than those of the north, and the land-owners more indolent, but on the other hand he esteemed the gracious living of the upper-class whites in the south and he liked Charleston, for example, better in some ways than he did Philadelphia; he found life there more cheerful and pleasant. He spoke critically of the slaves, but he ascribed their deficiencies—laziness, dirtiness, ignorance, superstition, unreliability, and immorality —entirely to poor upbringing, and he anticipated modern anthropologists and sociologists by concluding that the blacks are not inherently or basically inferior to the whites.

In the principal cities Schöpf became acquainted with many prominent citizens, some of whose names still shine bright in the annals of American history. Especially is this true of Philadelphia, for which he mentions some twenty outstanding men with whom he had various degrees of association (see Morrison 1911, 1968, vol. 1, pp. 74-86, 89-97). Naturally the largest number of these were medical men, and at the head of the list the distinguished Benjamin Rush, widely remembered pioneer in American medicine. Benjamin Franklin, President of the Philosophical Society, was in France during and after the war, and Schöpf thus missed the opportunity he would certainly have had and enjoyed to meet the famous American scientist, philosopher, inventor, statesman, and diplomat, but he did know Dr. Bond, vice-president of the society when Franklin was President, and "had several times the pleasure of enjoying his society." Among others with whom he associated were David Rittenhouse, the noted surveyor-astronomer and leading citizen of Pennsylvania, and the botanist William Bartram, son of John, the famous explorer, along with other botanists and gardiners of the time. He commented on the collection[8] of the Swiss painter Eugène du Simitière (in the *Beyträge* he mispelled the name Sumetiere and Morrison, 1911 p. 85, made it Sumitiere) and was more favorable in his estimate of it than have been some other critics (Hindle 1956, p. 261). He visited the house of Charles William Peale, but may not have actually met the famous painter of the Washington portraits.

For Baltimore the only figure he mentions is Dr. Carl Friedrich Wiesenthal, a highly cultured and competent physician as well as a charming personality and a major figure in the history of the city (Cunz 1948). Schöpf appreciated Dr. Wiesenthal's fine qualities just as thoroughly as have later writers on Baltimore.

His presence in Pittsburgh was noted by the historian of that city (Killikelly 1906) but the account is limited to quotation of his own unfavorable criticism of the people there as published in the *Reise*.

In Richmond he witnessed Albert Gallatin's appearance before the Virginia Assembly to lay claims for supplies furnished in the western theater of war.

Strangely, although he spent more time in Charleston than in any other American city, he says nothing specifically about the people he met there; he notes only that he attended meetings of the South Carolina legislature (Morrison 1911-1968, p. 197).

Among the multitude of features described in the *Reise* are many references to geology additional to those embodied in the present work, and especially, descriptions of mines and their histories. Anyone who desires to become familiar with all of Schöpf's geological observations must therefore read the *Reise* as well as the *Beyträge*.

All in all his picture of the land and its people, his sage comments on the conditions he observed, and the wide range of subjects he covered not only reveal him as a person of capacious and well-stocked mind and a warmly outgoing human being, but also constitute an important contribution to history. All this, let us bear in mind, he accomplished in his early thirties; he was only 25 when he left Germany for America. He was remarkably

---

[8] du Simitière was a painter of Swiss origin who gathered a collection of mineralogical and geological specimens and other "curiosities" that was unfortunately lost after the niggardly Assembly of Pennsylvania refused a modest appropriation to buy it for the University. (See Morrison 1911 or 1968, vol. 1, pp. 85-86.)

mature for his years. And as to his person, a portrait of him (frontispiece) reveals a profile not unlike that of George Washington, only with more strongly jutting jaw, a countenance of the kind most of us associate with strength of character and general competence.

Finally, it might be noted that the fate of the *Reise* in Europe seems to have been similar to that of the *Beyträge* in America. Ratzel (1891, p. 352), after admiring the *Reise* said that it "has become unjustly forgotten." Now, however, thanks to the recent reprint of Morrison's translation, any readers familiar with English can enjoy it as thoroughly as might have those who missed it in the past.

SCHÖPF'S GEOLOGY VIS-A-VIS THAT OF LATER PIONEERS

When we compare his achievement in geology with that of the pioneers who later went over the same ground, Schöpf comes out remarkably well.

The next important work to appear was that of the Comte de Volney (1803), a distinguished French scholar, naturalist, and explorer who spent three years in America from 1795 to 1798 and in 1796 travelled widely through the region between Canada and Virginia and went as far west as Louisville and Vincennes in the Ohio and Wabash valleys, and Detroit on the Great Lakes. His book was promptly translated into English, and a facsimile of this version is now generally available (Volney-Brown 1804-1968).

Volney's account is by no means as comprehensive as that of Schöpf, but it is important because it covers territory west of the Allegheny Plateau that was not reached by Schöpf (nor by his successor Maclure, either) and it contains excellent analysis of the terraces in the valleys of the Ohio and other rivers, and of Niagara Falls, with sound interpretation of the histories of these features. Less than a quarter of Volney's book is devoted to geology (the remainder deals with climate, diseases in relation to geography, the Indians and their ways of life, and the Miami language), and this is about three-quarters as long as Schöpf's treatise, but in general quality it falls considerably short of measuring up to Schöpf. And in places it harbors curious error. For example, impressed by the relation between earthquakes and volcanoes and ascribing the disturbed strata of the mountains to earthquakes, Volney reported basalt from the Alleghenies (*op. cit.*, 1804, p. 54) and he thought that the basin of Lake Ontario must be the crater of an extinct volcano (*ibid.*, p. 99). As we shall see in the next section of this commentary, Schöpf had dealt with this problem much more effectively.

It seems certain that Volney did not know of Schöpf's work. He gave credit in the body of his text to several earlier observers such as Kalm and Evans, but there is not a single specific reference to literature in the whole section on geology, and in view of this bibliographic deficiency there might be room for suspicion that he deliberately ignored Schöpf, the German. But this is hardly likely. Volney was an accomplished scholar, and when we consider Schöpf's clear statements about the absence of volcanic products in the mountains, it is highly probable that Volney would have attempted to justify his identification of basalt there far more fully than he did, but he merely said "we find basaltic masses in the vallies of the Allegheny" (*op. cit.*, p. 54). Further, there are differences in interpretation that he would almost certainly have mentioned had he been familiar with Schöpf's work, and it is inconceivable that his treatment of the rocks and minerals would not have been better. There are other comparisons that might be invoked, but I think this enough to support the conclusion that Volney, like all others interested in American geology at the time (and for long years thereafter) was unaware of Schöpf's signal accomplishment.

On the question of priority the work with which Schöpf's may be most aptly compared is that of Maclure (1809) which has long been accepted as the first comprehensive work on American geology, and which early gained for its author the sobriquet "Father of American Geology."

Examined candidly, Maclure's achievement, granted its primal effect and its importance otherwise, does not measure up in many respects, notably in thoroughness, to that of Schöpf—and Maclure had much more time and better facility for his observations. He is said to have "crossed and recrossed the Allegheny Mountains no less than fifty times" (Morton 1841). The one outstanding superiority of Maclure's offering, and the one generally remembered, is his map, the first of its kind to be attempted in the

United States,[9] and anent this we must note that Schöpf, probably as an original thought, suggested the value of such a colored chart and regretted his own inability to present one. In professional aspect Maclure's treatise is better organized, for his plan is Wernerian and he cast what he saw in the framework rigidly set out by the great German master (but, as we shall see shortly, he shied away from Werner's interpretations). In this quarter his product was more detailed than that of Schöpf, for he recognized individual formations where Schöpf lumped such ingredients into the categories of his major rock belts; but when we look at Schöpf's work as a whole we see a much more thorough and extensive treatment. In volume alone it goes far beyond Maclure, more than six times as long; Maclure's report of 1809 comes to about 5,750 words, whereas Schöpf's work in the German totals some 36,000, and in the English of this translation, about 35,000. Length in itself is of course no measure of excellence, but even when we discount some of Schöpf's wordiness we find solid substance on every page of his book. His descriptions of rocks and minerals are far fuller than those of Maclure, and he recognized some major geologic features, such as the Fall Line and the Schooley Peneplain, that Maclure does not mention. Further, Schöpf attempted, at least, to explain most of the things he saw, whereas Maclure modestly abstained from any such essay. In adopting Werner's system he says clearly that he does not "mean to enter into the origin or first creation of the different sub-

---

[9] Guettard's map (1756) has been called the first geological map of North America (Ireland, H. A., *Geol. Soc. Am. Bull.* vol. 54, p. 1257, 1943; Wells, J. W., *Wash. Acad. Sci. Jour.* vol. 49, pp. 198-199, 1959; Osborne, F. F., *Naturaliste Canadien*, vol. 95, pp. 1189-1193, 1968), and in a certain sort of liberal view this judgment may be acceptable. Although priority in geologic mapping is no particular concern of the present essay, some readers may object to my rating of Maclure's map, and I must explain that I make a distinction between a map produced from data acquired at second or third hand and one made on the ground by the person who actually did the field work and saw, studied, and identified the rock units whose outlines he delineated; such a man is more surely entitled to be called the author of the map and the map itself is entitled to superior rating. (I make this distinction, indeed, between Guettard's own maps of France and America, the first of which I consider a genuine geologic map, solidly based; the second, however, rather a sort of "ghost production"—for Guettard had not seen the terrain concerned and could not be absolutely sure of what he was putting down.) Maclure's map was the first produced in America by the man who did the work on the ground himself, and so is the first of its kind.

stances" or into agents that may have modified them; "I am equally ignorant," he says, "of the relative periods of time in which these modifications or changes may have taken place; such speculations are beyond my range, and pass the limits of my inquiries" (Maclure 1809, p. 427). (Incidentally, the sentiment expressed in this quotation easily inspires doubt that Maclure should be called an actual Wernerian; see White, 1970; Spieker 1971). And, shortly after these remarks, he concludes his paper with a modest statement, similar to that of Schöpf, that his work will "call forth the attention of those possessed of more talents and industry for the accurate investigation of this interesting subject." Maclure's worthy aspiration was realized, but Schöpf's was not.

APPRAISAL OF THE WORK

Schöpf's accomplishment may be evaluated in its three major categories: first, description; second, recognition of geologic entities; and third, interpretation. It may also be rated as an achievement in field work.

Most of the work, about three-quarters, is devoted to description, and the description is generally good. Here Schöpf reveals himself as a sharp and thorough observer. From the tiniest crystal in a hand specimen out to the entire form of eastern North America he took in what lay before him, and he gave good account of it. Williams (1894 p. 593) admired his portrayal of the rocks around Baltimore, and the present-day reader may do likewise for those rocks familiar to him in other parts of the terrain Schöpf covered. All his descriptions of rocks and minerals are excellent in the terms of his time; he was thorough and meticulous in listing all the properties then (and many of them still) thought important, and this part of his work was not equalled until well after the American pioneers began their work a quarter of a century later. For the most part he used the Linnaean system of mineral nomenclature, and, as we have already seen, in this he was almost certainly influenced by his teacher, the Hofrath Schreber, "the German Linnaeus."

He was more thorough in naming minerals than he was for the many crystalline rock species he described, but he did specify granite, gneiss, schist, and serpentine. Some of his "granite" is evidently pegmatite, but according to the Oxford dictionary this word did not enter the literature until 1832, and Schöpf evidently thought of the rock as a member of his "granite family."

In general his descriptions show that he knew what to look for. Although primarily a medical man, he was trained in general ,biology, forestry, mineralogy, and mining, and as already noted, his preparation in all these fields equipped him well for careful observation. Further, he brought to his task a mind sharpened by discussion of matters both scientific and philosophic with many thinkers in various parts of Europe—and America. This last was undoubtedly of great importance in controlling the facts he gathered, for by and large we see what we are prepared to see, and a man who brings to a mission like that of Schöpf a background in thinking about nature will perceive things to which the man equipped with merely factual knowledge may well be blind. Schöpf's descriptions prove abundantly that he was well prepared.

The major geologic features that he identified were both geomorphic and petrographic-stratigraphic. He recognized the Fall Line and the Schooley Peneplain, and he outlined the principal belts of bedrock from the Coastal Plain westward to the Allegheny Plateau.

He was not the first to spot the Fall Line—that feature had been noted by observers from Thomas Hariot and Captain John Smith to Lewis Evans (see White, 1952, 1953a, 1953b, 1953c) but he gave thorough account of it and probably did so independently; we have already noted that he did not see Evans's writings until after he had done his own field work. He recognized the fact that all the streams issuing from the interior go over waterfalls along a slightly sinuous but definite line at the inner margin of the Coastal Plain, and he listed the evidence for this fully, methodically, and clearly. Further, he correctly correlated this line with the appearance of the first hard-rock belt encountered going inward from the coast, and he understood that the hard-rock basement must continue seaward under the sedimentary strata of the Coastal Plain. Here he was definitely the pioneer—his was the first analysis of the evidence on this question, and the first sound conclusion. He was the first, in other words, to recognize the crystalline basement complex.

Rather more remarkable was his comprehension of the geo-

morphic feature that we today call the Schooley Peneplain. He
saw that in grand outline the surface of the eastern United States
is merely a vast plain sloping gently southeastward, into which
the longitudinal valleys of the mountain belts have been cut to
form the present relief. He probably did not understand the
origin of this old plain, but he detected its existence, and this in
itself was a notable achievement. Here he was taking the first
essential step in the development of any branch of science—the
observation and recording of significant fact—and throughout the
history of science this has commonly been a feat of no mean
order. At the very present day, indeed, geologists working in
many quarters of the subject are able to do little if anything
more than to ferret out the important facts. Schöpf's accomplishment in discerning the major peneplain of the eastern United
States was the sort of thing that would distinguish any scientist
of the present age. And it was not, as a matter of fact, until more
than a century later that the Schooley Peneplain was again clearly
recognized, and given its name (Davis 1889) and that at a time
when geology had advanced far toward maturity and standing as
a science.

One possible qualification should be noted here. Lewis Evans
had already detected this old plain (Pownall 1776; White 1951)
and the question arises whether Schöpf made his observation
independently or took it from Evans without giving proper
credit. After weighing the available evidence I am inclined to
decide in favor of Schöpf. This item must have been one of those
in his own work that he was glad to find confirmed in Evans's
report. He quoted Evans liberally where he felt it advisable to
extend and support his own work, and he obviously respected
Evans's accomplishment in general. Further, he reveals his attitude toward plagiarism when he says, in minatory terms, that
Pownall took his work "word for word" from Evans. We are
probably safe in accepting the discernment of the Schooley Peneplain as one of Schöpf's original accomplishments.

However, while Evans is momentarily in view, we might note
that he conceived the origin of the valleys cut into the old plain
in terms more nearly valid than those proposed by Schöpf. Evans
said (Pownall, 1776, p. 29; White 1951, p. 153) ". . . the highest
Mountains themselves, as they now appear, were formerly but
one large Plain, inclining with a considerable Slant toward the

Sea; that this has been worn into its present Appearance of Ridges, with Vales between them, by the Rains of the Heavens and Waters of the Earth washing the Soil from the upper Parts, and carrying it down Seawards." Whereas Schöpf's account shows repeatedly that he recognized the constant transport by streams of sand and mud from the highlands out to the Coastal Plain and the sea, and that the streams do cut down their channels, he was reluctant to think that streams could have carved out the great longitudinal valleys of the mountain region, for reasons that are mentioned farther on, in my account of his interpretation.

The other major geologic entities recognized by Schöpf are the principal rock bodies that underlie the region. Here his results come out in rather broad lines, but actually those of American pioneers a third of a century later, gained with the advantage of Werner's classification, and far more extensive field work, are not a great deal better. Had he been familiar with the works of Lehmann, Füchsel, and Arduino, or had he merely been able to devote more time to the task, Schöpf might well have come out with a more sophisticated picture of stratigraphic sequence, and might even have recognized formations such as the Beekmantown, the Tuscarora, or the Martinsburg. But to have done so with the meager background in actual geology that he brought to the task, and in the short time of his hasty reconnaissance, would indeed have been a feat of genius.

As it was he distinguished clearly the four major kinds of rock in the area—1) the crystallines and related metamorphics; 2) the limestones; 3) the clastics of the mountains; and 4) the unconsolidated sediments of the Coastal Plain, and he laid out the definite belts in which they occur and to which they are largely restricted. Although he fell somewhat short of recognizing the major sequence, yet he did place the crystallines as the oldest, and he strongly suspected that the beds of the Coastal Plain were the youngest. In general his pattern of thinking was not entirely hospitable to the idea of a long stratigraphic sequence laid down through extended eras of time and later uplifted to allow the sculpture of the present surface—but for the matter of that, neither was the conceptual background of such later pioneers as Maclure. This aspect of his treatment will be considered somewhat more fully farther on, in estimate of his interpretations.

In dealing with the strata in the Coastal Plain area Schöpf simplified and generalized, but he did recognize a direct succession of definite units, and he did attempt a correlation. He saw, in downward order, soil, sand, clay, and shell-bearing marine beds, and he concluded that this four-fold assemblage was essentially the same throughout the district. He did not realize the actual complexity of the Cretaceous and Tertiary sequence there, but he did observe and specify variations from place to place. And, considering the scattered and isolated distribution of the actual outcrops, even his mistaken decision that the four units were everywhere the same was an act of correlation, one of the prime goals of the stratigrapher. He was on his way toward truly sound geologic performance and concept. Further, if we allow him the right, in the barely exploratory nature of his venture, to group all the fossiliferous strata in one grand unit, we can say that he was not seriously wrong, that his result needed only the subsequent refinement that is the fate of virtually all investigation in geology.

Schöpf's efforts at interpretation were centered mainly on the origins of the rock bodies and the surface features of the region. The fossil shells in the sandstones and some of the limestones of the mountains convinced him that the terrain concerned must once have been under the sea, but, along with most of the few naturalists of the time who had thought at all about the matter, he pictured the inundation as sweeping in over a surface already elevated, and excepting modifications brought on by the flooding, essentially of the same general sort as that of the present, with sea level far above the heights of the existing mountains, for were not the Andes, with marine shells in the rocks of the highest peaks, also covered by the sea? He saw weaknesses in this theory, however. If the waters, standing over the entire region, deposited sands and muds over the highest mountains, why did they not do so on the lower ridges and in the valleys to the east? After discussing rather fully the facts he knew that bear on this puzzle, he concluded sanely that the disparity must "have other events as its cause"—that is, a history different from anything he could imagine. Here he spoke as a true scientist, ahead of such ideologists as Werner who either failed to see such conflicting evidence or swept it aside as of no consequence.

He not only concluded that the granites could not have been

deposited out of the oceanic waters, but wondered further about the marbles and limestones closely associated with the outer crystalline rocks. He could find in these neither fossils nor any other clear evidence of marine origin, and said that "one cannot flatly claim" them to be aqueous deposits. But he developed no clear idea of any other possible mode of origin.

He concluded correctly that the granite belt must once have stood higher, and have descended to its present position, but for the wrong reason. Generalizing from certain occurrences in the Alps, he thought that the granites normally occupy the highest peaks, flanked below by the sedimentary rocks, and so considered it inevitable that the present Piedmont belts must originally have been higher than the belts of limestone, etc., to the west. As the granite subsided, the bordering lands to the east must also have sunk, and he related this to the withdrawal of the marine waters from the continent (as we shall see shortly) and to the origin of the Coastal Plain sediments.

But although he recognized clearly, in this history of the granite and in his regional view of the surface features, that a vast plain formerly sloping to the west has now become one sloping to the east, he failed to realize the possibility that the sediments now high in the mountains might have been deposited at and near the present level of the sea, and later uplifted to their present position. In this quarter he was reluctant to consider uplift as a factor in the history of the mountains. He recognized that the strata now lying at high angles, and even standing vertical, must have been disturbed from their original attitudes, but he associated subterranean upheaval with volcanic activity and neither in his own experience nor that of American pioneers such as John Bartram could he find any evidence of vulcanism in eastern North America. He thought that the myriads of rock fragments strewn all over the mountains need not have resulted from shattering attendant upon powerful upheaval, but might just as well have been broken out by the freezing and thawing of water in the crevices of the strata—and here, in what might be regarded as an irrelevant context, he recognized one of the important processes in weathering.

So he turned, albeit reluctantly (for he was basically skeptical about the free play of imagination in such venture) to the idea of collapse. He may have been familiar with Steno, but probably not, at least specifically, for he made no reference to him and, again let us recall, was unusually meticulous in general documentation. And here it is important to note that he thought the collapse, or general subsidence, need not have been sudden and violent, but might well have been very slow and long protracted. Here is definitely the germ of uniformitarian idea—he was beginning to think along the lines more fully developed by his great contemporary, James Hutton.

His observations on the tilted strata of the Appalachians, and the nearly horizontal sandstones of the Allegheny Plateau, are about as far as he went toward understanding of the geologic structure in the mountains and its origin. Apparently he never saw a flexural bend, and so was not stimulated to think of folding. But, it was not until more than a third of a century later that a fold was clearly described, when Amos Eaton (see Merrill 1906 p. 253, 1924 p. 78) gave account of one near Danbury, Connecticut, and said "Had some force, applied at the eastern edge, raised these mountain masses from the horizontal toward the vertical position, they would have presented their present inclination." (see Merrill 1906 p. 277, 1924 p. 105.) And it was nearly sixty years later when the Rogers brothers clearly brought out the folded structure of the Appalachians as we know it today (Merrill 1906 p. 493, 1924, 1964 p. 218) .

Schöpf did notice and wonder about the remarkable parallelism of the Atlantic Coast, the several rock belts, and the mountain ridges and valleys, and thought there must be some basic reason for it but concluded that discernment of any causal relation must await further investigation. He suggested, however, that the strong trend of the granite belt may have controlled that of the other rock bodies and land masses, and so evidently must have had some general idea, at least, of tectonic relations and crustal activity.

In his interpretation of the major surface features, whereas he decided correctly that the valleys of the Appalachian-Allegheny region must have been hollowed out of the rock mass whose surface was the great eastward-sloping plain, he did not think the streams alone could have performed this sculpture. He did understand that streams carve out their valleys, even to such dimensions as those of the water-gaps in the Appalachians, but it bothered him that the streams in the mountains, after flowing some distances in the longitudinal valleys, turn abruptly and "veer off in other directions toward the southeast, while the valleys themselves maintain their southwesterly trend." He thought rather that the valleys must have been scooped out by the force of a strong and sudden inrush of the sea from the southwest, and he marshalled some evidence in favor of this theory, including the fact that the valleys dominantly widen out southwestward and narrow down to the northeast. And anent the interpretation of the gaps in the mountains, it is interesting to observe his puzzlement over the wind-gaps, in which he could see no evidence that streams had ever been there, for the loose rock in them was all angular, not water-worn. Yet he did not think that the gaps could have been caused by any rending asunder of the ridges, for the reasons already mentioned that he invoked against the idea of subterranean upheaval.

He observed that the streams of the Coastal Plain flow in narrow channels trenched into the bottoms of much broader valleys, and he thought this meant that the streams were formerly broader and shallower, and because the southwestern banks of the valleys are generally steeper than the northeastern he concluded that the streams must have been narrowed down and forced toward the southwestern valley sides, possibly by the pressure of storms that come dominantly from the northeast. So, although he realized that streams cut down their channels, and that the channels have probably changed with the passage of time, he did not come to the possibility that they might merely have shifted laterally as a natural result of the erosive process.

Now if the sea had flooded completely over the lands, even to such great heights as those of the Andes, he noted, when it withdrew where could such an immense volume of water have gone? To this question, virtually dodged by the Wernerians, Schöpf brought sane reason. He passed sardonically over the notion that the waters might have evaporated, or have been flung out into space, and saw that the only feasible receptacles for them were the present ocean basins, which must then have been profoundly deepened. And as the ocean bottom sank, the bordering lands must have bent downward; this he tied in with his thought that the granite belt had descended from formerly higher altitudes, and that the sea had then extended inward to a shore defined by the granite. His efforts at comprehending the whole picture,

at correlating and logically combining the several features concerned into a reasonable history, despite the false premise from
which he started, are hardly less than praiseworthy.

As a minor element in his interpretation we may note that
one of his reasons for thinking that the Coastal Plain sediments
are the youngest was the fact that they are largely unconsolidated.
Here, without specifying it, he was recognizing the significance
of diagenesis. And he added this bit of evidence to the general
support of his suggestion that when the Coastal Plain sediments
were being deposited the country behind the granites was dry
land.

He thought, indeed, and correctly, that the Coastal Plain may
formerly have been like the banks offshore of the New England
and Canadian coasts. And early in the work, he related the
present outline of the coast to the Gulf Stream, concluding that
the two must be causally interdependent. The fact that the
stream does not now impinge on the coast, he says, does not
necessarily mean that it never has. He is cautious in this specula-
tion, but he favors the influence of the Gulf Stream in the shap-
ing of the present coastal outlines.

He also took a minor fling at the origin of coal, which he
thought might be a deposit of richly carbonaceous matter in the
partly impounded waters of streams behind waterfalls, such as
he had seen on present-day rivers at and near the Fall Line.
Here he was possibly unaware of the lateral extents of the coal
beds, far too great to have been produced by single streams. He
did relate the coal beds to the highly carbonaceous shales that so
commonly accompany them, and he had learned that coal was
thought to have formed from peat, but he did not come out
flatly with any notion of extensive swamp rather than the con-
stricted bed and flood plain of a stream. Further, he toyed with
the belief that coal and petroleum are genetically related, and
suggested that coal beds might be a guide to the discovery of
petroleum.

In his thoughts about the surface features of the Appalachian
region it may well have been a subconsciously restrictive feeling
about time that prevented him from going all the way and visual-
izing gradual uplift of the mountain mass from original positions at and beneath a sea level similar to that of the present,
and exceedingly slow erosional sculpture of the rising mass into

the features we see today. He did take time into account in much of his reasoning (as already observed, he thought that disturbances of the rocks might have been slow, not sudden and violent, and he tried—in vain—to estimate the time required to form the outer layer of soil) and he was obviously aware of historical sequence, for he realized that the events through which the features concerned originated did not take place simultaneously or in rapidly crowded succession. But it is doubtful that he had gone far enough in this line of reasoning to imagine the actually vast stretches of time that we now know to have been involved, and that Hutton was beginning to envision even as Schöpf was engaged in all his studies. However, aside from his greater genius, Hutton spent far more time on the subject than did Schöpf. Considering his general intellectual temperament, it is not at all extravagant to imagine that Schöpf might have advanced to very high historical position in geology had he abandoned medicine and become a geologist.

And actually in certain regard he was already not far behind Hutton. In final remark on his interpretation we might observe that at the end of sec. 45 he says "it is clear enough that more than one cause must be assumed, and effective at very different times" to account for all that is observed. The picture is not simple, nor are the contingent problems. Schöpf was beginning to realize the complexity of geology, an attribute that seems not to be fully appreciated by some geologists of the present day (see Spieker 1965), and to understand time as a basic factor, even if he did not realize its actual dimensions.

By and large, there is much in his thinking that was not to become general for more than fifty years.

Contemplated as an example of field work, Schöpf's accomplishment really shines. First let us consider the time he spent at his task. He left New York on July 22, 1783, and sailed for the Bahamas and England from St. Augustine on March 29, 1784, eight months and ten days later. However, less than half of this period was spent at observations in the field. Details given in the *Reise* enable a fairly close estimate of the time devoted to actual field work, and it comes to a few days less than four months. This is about the normal span of a summer field season for a geologist today, and when we view what Schöpf accomplished in that time, especially considering the prevalent difficulties of travel, we can hardly do less than admire him. Much of what he did is comparable to such present-day field operation as exploration in wilderness areas like northern Canada or Alaska, for the mountain country he crossed was very sparsely inhabited, and so also was a good deal of the southern Coastal Plain. (I may perhaps be permitted to tell the reader, in case he does not already know it, that out of my own career of more than 50 years in the field I have spent periods of more than 18 months on four separate occasions in northwest Canada and Alaska at just such exploratory work, and I feel competent to judge.) And we must also remember that geology was not his only concern; he was constantly observing and recording data on the forests and the general biota of the country, and for populated areas, the agriculture, the people and their ways of life—one might say everything of interest in this new land. His other published works attest unmistakably to his general industry and ability. That he got as much of the regional geology as he did is nothing short of remarkable.

He used well the equipment that has long since become standard for the geologist—hammer, hand lens, compass, acid bottle, steel, magnet, measuring tape, collecting bag, and notebook. That he appreciated strongly the importance of collecting specimens is shown by his bitter disappointment at the loss of a shipment he had confided in Philadelphia to a German merchant from Hamburg.

Further, in sec. 26 of the *Beyträge* he reveals himself as a genuine field man when he mentions not understanding all that he noted at a given locality until he had seen some others farther on, and then, in the interest of testing his enlightened view, wishing he could be back at the first locality. Every good field worker has had this experience time and again, and especially in itinerant exploration, where like Schöpf he can rarely retrace his steps at will. Schöpf here hit upon one facet of an important principle in scientific observation—that what we are able to see in a given situation is strongly conditioned by the background in knowledge and thinking that we bring to the work. I have taken occasion elsewhere (Spieker, 1956) to stress this principle; here let me say that as I read Schöpf's confession it was a pleasure to see this aspect of it recognized so long ago by the young German pioneer.

SCHÖPF'S ITINERARY

The *Beyträge* is organized as a systematic areal treatment. It specifies many of the places Schöpf saw, as well as many that he did not, but only locally does it trace out his actual route of travel. The *Reise,* on the other hand, is based strictly on itinerary, and here we can follow him in detail. In the belief that it will help the reader of the *Beyträge* to identify more effectively the terrain described, and to amplify the general picture of his presence in the new-born United States as well, I present here an abstract of his route as given in the *Reise.* For those parts of the way where it is either obvious or probable that the road he travelled was the forerunner of a modern numbered highway I have specified the route numbers. The map here presented will further help the reader to visualize the extent and outline of his journeys.

On July 22, 1783 he left New York and went through Elizabethtown, Brunswick, Bound Brook, Rocky Hill, Princetown, Trenton and Bristol to Philadelphia, where he arrived July 26 and stayed ten days. On August 6 he left for Bethlehem by way of Germantown, Chestnut Hill, Quaker-town (US 309) and Lehigh. On August 9 he went from Bethlehem to Nazareth, then 8 miles to Heller's House at the base of Kittatinny Mountain, and over the mountain ("3 or 4 miles") to Eckhardt's and on through Pocono Mountain and the Great Swamp (37 miles unpeopled) to Wyoming and Wilkesbarre on the west branch of the Susquehanna, where he stayed five days; then (Aug. 18) he returned to Nazareth by way of Long Meadow and Bear Creek (Penna. 115, approx.). Then, on to Allentown, Kutztown, Reading (US 222), Lebanon, Hummelstown (US 422), and Carlisle. From Carslisle to Shippensburg he was on either US 11 or Penna. 33. From Shippensburg to Fort Loudon, over hilly country in Hamilton Township, he must have followed a route now occupied by backroads, for he speaks of "the other road through Chambers-town to Loudon" and this is now the main route, US 11 and 30. From Fort Loudon he went north up Path Valley, following the west branch of Conococheague Creek, and crossed Tuscarora Mountain, perhaps by way of Fannetsburg, but more likely by a road (now secondary) going directly up the face of the Tuscarora, to Burnt Cabins and then (US 522) to Fort

Littleton. Thence he must have followed the road through Hustontown on southwest to the present locus of US 30, which he apparently followed to Bedford and on through to Pittsburgh, for he speaks of his route as the main road to Ohio; this was wild and sparsely settled country in 1783 and one cannot be sure from his descriptions exactly where the road then lay. This "main road" must have been poorly defined at the time, for he complains of going astray and having trouble finding the proper road again.

He spent a week in Pittsburgh, and left on September 13. For the return journey he retraced his outward route as far as a tavern on the east side of Sideling Hill, where he left his travelling companion, an Englishman named Hare, and went along Licking Creek and over Scrub Ridge to the Cove, the route into which he says "is not so much by highways as narrow 'bridle roads.' " Of this area he says "The Great Cove has the Blue Mountain on the east, the Tuscarora to the north, the Scrub Ridge on the west, and lies between these mountains 16 miles long and 1-3 miles broad." From the Cove he went south through Canalaway Settlement "through fertile valleys and even over a few barren hills . . . to Hancock-town on the Potowmack" and on to Warm Springs,[10] Sheperdstown (probably via W. Va. 9 and 45), Sharpsburg, over South Mountain through Middletown (the exact route uncertain here) and thence somehow to US 140 (the Reisterstown Road) which he followed into Baltimore.

From Baltimore he made a short trip south, to Bladensburgh, George-town, and Alexandria, returning by way of Annapolis. He then went from Baltimore to Philadelphia, by way of Charlestown (just off US 40) "head of Elk,"[11] Christiania (north of US 40) New Castle, Wilmington (he is now on US 40), Marcus Hook, Chester, and Darby, arriving October 31.

Late in November he left Philadelphia for the last more or less continuous span of his journey. He first went to Lancaster by way of Valley Forge, Warwick, and New Holland (Penna. 23), thence to York (US 30) and on to Frederick via Hanover, Pa., and Taneytown, Md. (Penna.-Md. 194). He spent several days in Frederick and then went on southward, with South

[10] Berkeley Springs today.
[11] Probably Elkton.

Mountain on the right, Sugar Loaf on the left, crossing the Potomac at Nowles-Ferry and going on, probably by US 15, to Leesburg, Va. (December 7), Goose Creek, then 30 miles to Red House (he says the road was "more to the east" here). From Leesburg to Fredericksburg he went through a patchwork of roads, frequently losing "the main road," and it seems impossible to recognize his exact route. Then, on to Richmond, through much swampy country, by way of Hanover-town (probably Va. 2). He was detained several days in Richmond by bad weather, and took advantage of this visit to learn much about the government of Virginia. (It might be reiterated here that he made extensive sojourns in Philadelphia, Baltimore, and Charleston, all three of which cities he admired in one way or another and about which he wrote copiously and in detail.)

From Richmond it was a two-day journey, via New Kent Court House (Va. 33 and 30, probably) "mainly through gloomy forest" to Williamsburg. Here he made a side-trip to Yorktown, whose historical importance had already been impressed upon him, and further, where he was probably the first trained natural scientist to enthuse over the fabulous occurrence in the cliffs there of late Miocene fossils. He then continued southward, crossing the James River on a ferry not far above Jamestown, to Surry (Va. 31), Smithfield (Va. 10) and Suffolk (Va. 10 with a detour via Everets). From Suffolk into North Carolina he went through "lonesome country" to Edenton; he says nothing about the route, but it was probably the forerunner of Va.-N.C. 32. Unable to get a ferry across Albemarle Sound, he was detained in Edenton four days, but finally succeeded in crossing on December 31; he says to the south side of the sound, and that it was 48 miles to Washington, so he must have followed the ways of US 64, N.C. 171, and US 17. From Washington to New Bern he was undoubtedly on the predecessor of US 17, but thence southward he went by way of Snead's Ferry, which is east of US 17, and for the route on to Wilmington he speaks of a confusion of roads and paths intercrossing in the forest, but considering the swamps hard by inland, he was probably not far from US 17. It was now January 7.

The final leg of his land journey was from Wilmington to Charleston. He went first by boat "some miles up the Northwest Branch" of Cape Fear River, then made his way somehow, avoiding the swamps, to the present locus of US 17 (he mentions Shallot Bridge), which must have been his route all the way to Charleston. He reached Charleston on January 14 and stayed there until March 9. It was during this sojourn of nearly two months that he worked on his field notes and probably completed, at least in first draft, the manuscript of the *Beyträge*. This should be held in mind as we compare his accomplishment with those of contemporary pioneers across the Atlantic.

On March 9 he set sail in a 25-ton schooner for St. Augustine. He stayed two weeks in this part of Florida, most of which time was spent awaiting favorable conditions for departure—specifically, propitious conjunction of tide and wind for passage over the treacherous outer bars of the harbor. On March 29 he left in a small vessel for the Bahamas, where he arrived April 5. The first opportunity to sail for Europe, he says, did not come for some two months (it was not at all uncommon in these times for passengers to wait such long periods for an Atlantic crossing, but Schöpf, insatiable traveller that he was, did not waste any of this time—he saw all that he could of the Bahamas). At last, however, on June 7, 1784 he boarded the Hero, "a small, light-built, but fast-sailing ship, lying with its cargo deep in the water" and imprudently deck-laden so that it was topheavy and in serious trouble when hit suddenly on June 15 by a fierce squall off Cape Hatteras, but the skill in command and strength at the wheel of Captain Bryan, a Bermudan, pulled the little Hero through despite shredded sails and other damage. After a thenceforth uneventful transatlantic passage the good little ship brought our author safely into the estuary of the Thames on July 9, only eleven days short of a year after his departure from New York. We may justifiably direct an appreciative thought toward the memory of Captain Bryan, without whose masterful seamanship we should probably never have had either the *Reise* or the *Beyträge*.

NOTES ON THE TRANSLATION,
AND ACKNOWLEDGMENTS

The work of translation entailed a few problems over and above those normally expectable in dealing with 18th-century vocabulary and idiom. In some passages Schöpf's German is awkward, in others obscure, and in a few instances even defective. Further, there are a few short sentences that are incomplete— merely terse phrases, some of which look as though they might have been simply transcribed verbatim from field notes. (These may indeed have been so written intentionally, to gain pungency.) It is fair to say, I think, that in places the work was not very well written (there are some rather clear signs of haste), and it might well have stood a bit of attention with blue pencil before going to the printer. Nevertheless I have set aside all temptation to edit, let alone rewrite the text, but have tried consistently to present, in reasonably idiomatic English, as exactly as possible what Schöpf said in the way he said it. The result can hardly be judged to have high literary value, but I trust that this imperfection (if, indeed, it be such) may be counterbalanced by whatever success I may have had in retaining the flavor of Schöpf's prose.

For the benefit of those who may want to compare the translation with the original, and in the interest of sound scholarship as well, I have dealt in brief notes with some obscure passages, uncertain meanings of words, and obvious or probable typesetter's errors not noted in the errata listed at the end of the book.

I have copied exactly all spellings of geographic names that were given by Schöpf in English form (and the reader will notice some inconsistency in his practice) but those that he put in German form (e.g. "Brandtewein") I have changed to the accepted English (here, Brandywine). I have also kept some peculiarities of his punctuation (e.g., his use of dashes) and his use of bold-face type for emphasis of many names. A very few interpolations by the translator are placed within brackets.

In dealing with the problems of translation I have had invaluable help from Professor Wolfgang Fleischhauer, who is not only a specialist in 18th-century and older German, but is also an enthusiastic and well-informed amateur of geology; the reader will appreciate at once my great good fortune in this collaboration. But despite the fact that Dr. Fleischhauer reviewed the entire manuscript with me, and I must candidly and gratefully admit, saved me in one or two spots from defective rendition, he is not to be blamed for any infelicities in the translation, for he left decisions on diction and syntax to my judgment, and I take full responsibility for this aspect of the work.

To Mrs. Corinne Miller Simons of the Lloyd Library at Cincinnati I am deeply indebted for unusually courteous and effective help on many matters respecting Schöpf, including his bibliography, and it is a pleasure to acknowledge this general benefice, with my heartiest thanks.

For the preparation of the index Dr. Aurèle LaRocque generously provided expert guidance and material help, without which the task would have been much more difficult, and for which I find it difficult to render adequate thanks.

In final word of acknowledgement I must pay generous tribute to Professor George W. White, whose suggestions, questions, and actual demands have greatly extended my commentary and notes of all kinds beyond what I originally wrote, and have undoubtedly added considerable value to the work for readers of various persuasions and interests. Professor White's enthusiastic and comprehensive devotion to the history of geology, and especially to that of North America, has scored to excellent advantage.

References for Notes

American Association of Geologists (1843) *Transactions for 1842*, Boston, p. 69.

BROWNING, WILLIAM (1931) The relation of physicians to early American geology, *Annals of Medical History*, n. ser. vol. 3, pp. 547-548.

CUNZ, DIETER (1948) *The Maryland Germans*: Princeton Univ. Press, pp. 100, 108-111, 120-124, 142-144.

DARTON, N. H. (1896) Catalog and index of contributions to North American geology, 1732-1891: *U. S. Geol. Survey Bull. 127*.

DAVIS, W. M. (1889) The rivers and valleys of Pennsylvania: *Nat. Geogr. Mag.*, vol. 1, pp. 183-253.

FERBER, J. J. (1776) *Travels through Italy in the years 1771 and 1773, described in a series of letters to Baron Born on the natural history, particularly the mountains and volcanos of that country, translated from the German, with explanatory notes, and a preface on the present state and future improvement of mineralogy*: L. Davis, London.

FORD, T. D. (1966) Biographical notes of authors on Derbyshire—Johann Jacob Ferber (1743-1790): *Peak District Mines Historical Society, Bull.* vol. 3, part 1, pp. 67-70.

GEIKIE, SIR ARCHIBALD (1905, 1962) *The founders of geology*, p. 201, Macmillan 1905, reprinted Dover, N. Y. 1962.

GOODE, G. B. (1886, 1901) Beginnings of natural history in America: *Biol. Soc. Washington, Proc.* vol. 111, 1886, also *Smithsonian Rept. for 1897*, U. S. Nat. Mus. 1901.

GUETTARD, J.-E. (1752) Mémoire dans laquelle on compare le Canada à la Suisse par rapport à ses minéraux: *Academie des Sciences de Paris*.

HINDLE, BROOKE (1956) *The pursuit of science in Revolutionary America, 1735-1789*: Univ. N. C. Press, pp. 227, 307.

KILLEKELLY, S. H. (1906) *History of Pittsburgh*, Pittsburgh, p. 86.

MACLURE, WILLIAM (1809) Observations on the geology of the United States, explanatory of a geological Map: *Amer. Philos. Soc. Trans.* vol. vi, no. LXII, pp. 411-428.

MERRILL, G. P. (1906) Contributions to the history of American geology: *U. S. Nat. Mus. Rept. for 1904*, Washington, p. 208.

MERRILL, G. P. (1924) *The first hundred years of American geology*: Yale University Press, New Haven, pp. 4-5; reprinted, Hafner, N. Y., 1964.

MORRISON, A. J. (1911) *Travels in the Confederation (1783-1784)*, from the German of Johann David Schoepf, translated and edited by Alfred J. Morrison (2 vols.): William J. Campbell, Philadelphia. Reprinted, Bergman, N. Y. 1968.

MORTON, S. G. (1841) *A memoir of William Maclure, Esq.*, T. K. and P. G. Collins, Philadelphia, p. 11.

NICKLES, J. M. (1923) Geological literature in North America, 1785-1918: *U. S. Geol. Survey Bull. 746*, p. 916.

POWNALL, THOMAS (1776) *A topographical description of such parts of North America as are contained in the (annexed) map of the middle British colonies in North America*: London, J. Almon, pp. 29, 30.

34 *Johann David Schöpf*

RATZEL, FRIEDRICH (1891) biographical notice of Schöpf in the *Allgemeine Deutsche Biographie*, vol. 32, pp. 350-352.

SCHMIDT, C. W. (1928) *Wörterbuch der Geologie, Mineralogie, und Paläontologie*: Walter de Gruyter, Berlin & Leipzig, p. 94.

SCHÖPF, J. D. (1787) *Materia medica Americana, potissimum regni vegetabilis*: Erlangen 1787; also Lloyd Library Reproduction Series no. 3, Cincinnati 1903.

SCHÖPF, J. D. (1788a) Beschreibung einiger nordamerikanischen Fische, vorzüglich aus den neuyorkischen Gewässern: *Schrift der Berliner Gesellschaft Naturforschender Freunde*, no. 3, p. 138 ff.

SCHÖPF, J. D. (1788b) *Reise durch einige der mittlern und südlichen nordamerikanischen Staaten nach Ost-Florida und den Bahama-Inseln unternommen in den Jahren 1783 und 1784. Mit einem Landchärtchen.* Erlangen; J. J. Palm. (For version in English see entry for Morrison).

SCHÖPF, J. D. (1793-1801) *Historia testudinatum*: Erlangen.

SPIEKER, E. M. (1956) Mountain-building chronology and nature of geologic time scale: *Amer. Asso. Petrol. Geol., Bull.* vol. 40, pp. 1770-1771.

SPIEKER,, E. M. (1965) The nature of geology and its place among the natural sciences: *N. Y. Acad. Sci., Trans.* ser. II, vol. 28, pp. 160, 165-168.

SPIEKER, E. M. (1971) Schöpf, Maclure, Werner, and the earliest American geology: *Science* vol. 172, pp. 1333-1334.

STUCKEY, J. L. (1965) *North Carolina, its geology and mineral resources*: N. C. Dept. Conservation and Development, Raleigh, pp. 215-216.

VOLNEY, C. F. (1803) *Tableau du climat et du sol des États Unis d'Amérique, suivi d'éclaircissements sur la Floride, sur la colonie Française au Scioto, sur quelques colonies Canadiennes et sur les sauvages. Enrichi de quatre planches gravées, dont deux cartes géographiques et une coupe figurée de la chute de Niagara.* Paris, 2 vols., xvi, 300, 532 p., 2 maps, 2 plates.

VOLNEY, C. F. (1804, 1968) *A view of the soil and climate of the United States of America, translated with occasional remarks by C. B. Brown.* (Facsimile of the Philadelphia 1804 edition, with plates and maps from the London 1804 edition, and an introduction by George W. White) Hafner, New York, 1968, xvii, xxv, 446 p. 2 pls. 2 maps.

WHITE, G. W. (1951) Lewis Evans' contributions to early American geology: *Illinois Acad. Sci. Trans.* vol. 44, p. 153.

WHITE, G. W. (1952) Thomas Hariot's observations on American Geology in 1588: *Illinois Acad. Sci. Trans.* vol. 45, pp. 118, 120.

WHITE, G. W. (1953a) Early American Geology: *Sci. Monthly* vol. 76, pp. 134-141.

WHITE, G. W. (1953b) Geologic observations of Captain John Smith in 1607-1614: *Illinois Acad. Sci. Trans.* vol. 46, pp. 124-132.

WHITE, G. W., and B. O. SLANKER (1962) *Early geology in the Mississippi Valley*: Univ. of Illinois, Urbana, pp. 8-9.

WHITE, G. W. (1970) William Maclure was a uniformitarian and not a real Wernerian: *J. Geol. Educ.*, vol. 18, p. 127.

WILLIAMS, G. H. (1894) Johann David Schoepf and his contribution to North American geology: *Geol. Soc. America Bull.* vol. 5, pp. 591-593.

Bibliography of Johann David Schöpf

Diss. inaug. de medicamentorum mutatione in corpore humano, praecipue a fluidis. Erlangae, 1776. 4.

Von der Wirkung des Mohnsaftes in der Lustseuche; nebst einigen andern zur Naturlehre und Arzneygelahrheit gehörigen Beobachtungen, Nordamerika betreffend. Mit einer Vorrede von dem geh. HofR. Delius. ebend., 1781. 8.

Materia medica Americana, potissimum regni vegetabilis. ibid., 1787, 8 mai. (Reprinted with introduction as *Bull. No. 6, Reproduction Series No. 3, Lloyd Library,* Cincinnati, 1903, 170 p.)

Beyträge zur mineralogischen Kenntnis des östlichen Theils von Nordamerika und seiner Gebürge. ebend., 1787. *gr.* 8.

Reise durch einige der mittlern und südlichen vereinigten nordamerikanischen Staaten nach Ost-Florida und den Bahama-Inseln, unternommen in den Jahren 1783 und 1784. 2 Theile. *ebend.,* 1788. *gr.* 8.

Historia testudinum, iconibus illustrata. Fasc. I et II contin. textum A-D et praefationem, cum Tabb. pictis I-X. ibid. 1792.—*Fasc. III-IV contin. textum E-K, cum Tabb. XI-XVI et XVIII-XX. ibid.* 1793.— *Fasc. V cont. textum L-O, cum. Tabb. XVII, XXI-XXV, ibid.* 1795.— *Fasc. VI contin. textum P-R cum Tabb. XXVI-XXIX a. b. et XXXI.* Erlangae, 1801, 4 mai. Auch Teutsch unter dem Titel: *Naturgeschichte der Schildkröten, mit Abbildungen erläutert.* Ein unvollendetes Werk.

Catalogus medicamentorum tam simplicium quam compositorum, quae in officinis pharmaceuticis Principatuum Borissicorum in Franconia vi legis praesto esse debent, cum corundem taxatione, inserviens pro norma physicis visitatoribus, pro notitia reliquis medicis atque chirurgis. ibid., 1798. 8. (Der Name steht hinter der Vorrede.)

Ueber den Einfluss des Medicinal wesens auf den Staat und über die Vernachlässigung desselben in den meisten Teutschen Staaten. Hof 1799. 8.

Auch in (K. J. Lange'ns) *Neuesten Staatenkunde B. 1 H. 3. S.* 329-374 (1798). So wie in Scherf's *Beytragen zum Archiv der medic. Policey und Volksarzneykunde B. B. Samml.* 2 Nr. 1 (1799).

Aufsätze in der periodischen Schrift: Der Hessische Arzt.

Ueber Klima, Witterung, Lebensart, Krankheiten u.s.w. in Nordamerika; in Meusel's histor. Litteratur 1781. St. 7 S. 71-87. St. 8 S. 180-198.

Vier Briefe von dem gegenwärtigen Zustand in Nordamerika, aus dem Lande selbst im Jahr 1783; in *Schlözer's Staatsanzeigen H.* 25 (1785).—*Einige Gedanken und ein Brief über den Fichtelberg; ebend.*

Vom amerikansichen Frosche; im *Naturforscher St.* 18.—*Der nordamerikanische Pertsch; der gemeine Hecht in Amerika; der nordamerikanische Haase; ebend., St.* 20 (1784).—*Ueber einige Seewürme; Bemerkungen über eine Art Seeblasen; mineralogische Bemerkungen übereinen Theil der Schweitzergebürge; ebend. St.* 21 (1785)—*Ueber die Temperatur der Pflänzen; ebend, St.* 23.

Beschreibung einiger nordamerikanischen Fische, vorzüglich aus den Neuyorkischen Gewässern; in dem *Schriften der Berlin. Gesellsch. Naturf. Fr. B.* 8, *St.* 3. S. 138 u. ff., (1788).

Obs. circa electricitatis spontaneae in corpore humano indicia; *in Nov. Act. Acad. Nat. Cur. T.* VIII. p. 205-210.

Innere Wirkungen durch aüszere Arzneyen; *in Hufeland's Journal der prakt. Heilkunde B.* 5. *St.* 4 (1798).—Noch ein Beytrag an dem Vorschlage, auch die harthäckigsten Hautkrankheiten blos durch äuszere Mittel zu heilen; *ebend. B.* 15. *St.* 2. S. 41-60. (1802).

Articles in the *Journal von und für Franken* and in other periodicals.

Contributions
to the mineralogical knowledge
of the eastern part
of
NORTH AMERICA
and its mountains[1]

by

D. Johann David Schöpf

Royal Court and Garrison Physician and
District Medical Officer of Brandenburg,
Onolzbach[2] and Culmbach, and member of
the Medical College at Bayreuth

Erlangen
Published by Johann Jacob Palm
1787

———————————————————————

Translated, with commentary, notes, bibliographic addenda, and
route map

by

Edmund M. Spieker

To

His Honor

Court Councillor Schreber

On my departure from Europe in 1777 you gave me the commission "to give attention to the order of the soils and rock strata in America, and to indicate the extent to which those that occur in Europe, according to the observations of Pabst von Ohain and Ferber,[3] are also to be found in the New World. Kalm, you mentioned at that time, did not afford you a sufficiency in the matter." Whether the following observations throw a little more light on the framework and structure of eastern North America, and are worthy of your approval, you may judge from review of the work.

During the war I had no opportunity whatever to undertake anything toward the elucidation of this subject; therefore on my trip through the southern part of the United States of North America in 1783 I also [i.e., in addition to other concerns] made it my objective to travel through the mountains of that region. However, since my time was decidedly limited, and also because I had to use the seasons favorable for land travel in the region as fully as possible, I was unable to sojourn everywhere at pleasure and in measure with the exigencies of the task. In so vast a land merely to visit all instructive regions is impossible, and it was just as difficult at the time to obtain basic and trustworthy information respecting outlying places from the inhabitants thereof. This will excuse me if on the one hand I am not in position here and there to fill in gaps, or have been forced to allow myself one conjecture or another. Under the lack of inland travel by regular vehicles it is further absolutely impossible for a traveller, without exorbitant expense, to gather collections of rock types and to convey them to desired places. I collected and packed up much material that I might have used to produce a fuller report, never to see it again.

No one so far has examined this eastern part of North America with the eye of a natural philosopher, especially in its whole extent, if I except Mr. Evans, who in his Analysis (1) mentions

(1) Geograph. Historic. Polit. et Mechanical Essays; the first, Containing an Analysis of a General Map of the Middle British Colonies in America, &c, by *Lewis Evans*. Philad. 1755, 4to, 32 pages.

41

sundry facts respecting the trend and character of the mountains. Gouverneur Pownall has borrowed these, word for word, in his Topographic Description of North America.[4] Both works have become rare in America, and I was able to come by them only after I had already travelled through the mountains for the second time. To have had them in advance would have been of great help to me; in the meantime it was not merely a matter of unconcern to see my observations for the most part confirmed by theirs. The inner region of mountains, which I have myself examined, lies between the Hudson- and Potomack-Rivers; further, of the outer territory I have become acquainted with the entire stretch from Rhode-Island to St. Augustine in Florida and I have travelled the route from New York to Charleston, Carolina (960 English miles).—I flatter myself, that in the following pages, for which I prepared the outline immediately after ending my trip in Carolina, I have at least pointed out the way which may lead to fuller knowledge of this part of the world, and may guide the attention of other naturalists; and this alone I reckon to my credit. For indeed every single correction of my errors will bring us nearer to the truth. As to the rest, I have the honor, with greatest respect to be

Your most devoted servant

D. Schöpf

Bayreuth, July 31.

The Eastern Coast
Of North America

The major outlines of the present coast of North America bear
off from northeast to southwest. The easternmost part of Newfoundland is about at 52° West Longitude; thence the coast
swings constantly westward until at the point of the Florida
Cape it brings up at about 82°. — This diagonal, evident on any
map, therefore involves about 30° difference in longitude.

This coast is not uniform in character throughout its length,
and the southern part is notably different from the northern.
From the northernmost regions of Labrador, Newfoundland,
etc., etc. on southward it is for the most part steep, rugged, bold
(a bold shore),[5] rocky, as far as the general vicinity of Long Island
Sound and the Hudson River. A few narrow protruding sandy
banks, such as Cape Cod, Cape Ann, etc., constitute no important exception. At about 41° latitude the coast takes on different
character. From the southeastern part of Long Island, along the
sea as far as Florida, there is a uniformly flat, low, sandy shore.
The last highlands in the region are the hills of Neversink, near
Sandy-Huck, in Jersey, and from there on south there is nothing
similar until a few sand hills in Florida, which however seem to
be nothing more than embankments thrown up by the sea itself,
and only a little higher than similar ridges that occur everywhere
on the coasts of Florida, Carolina, and Virginia. I had no opportunity to visit the Neversink, and therefore do not know whether
they are bedrock or merely sandhills, for which they seem to be
too high.[6] Just as the coast is of different character, so also the
inland regions differ in structure. Evans and Pownall observe
that the mountain chains on the east side of the Hudson River,
which strike in part through New York province but also through

43

Connecticut, Rhode Island and Massachusetts, have a different
trend and swing from those on the southwestern side of the
Hudson that run through Jersey, Pennsylvania, etc., and at least
are not their direct continuation. Since I have come to know this
median half of the North American coast better than the northern part, I shall set forth first my observations concerning it, and
add the little that I know or understand respecting the northern
part at the end of this work.

2.

The above-mentioned southern part of the North American
coast, from the mouth of the Hudson on to Florida, has this
throughout in common, that from the strand line toward the
interior and up to the hard rock ridges it rises gently as a shelving
surface; just so, again, the solid ground slopes off gently seawards
from the shore. This last condition is a well-known and important observation for mariners, which teaches them to avoid the
dangers of so inherently low a coast, that cannot be descried
more than 5-6 sea miles away. The sounding lead, in so far as it
shows the depth of the water, informs at the same time as to the
distance of the still invisible land, if not exactly, still in reasonable approximation. And in this extent there seems to be confirmed the general observation made by someone: "that the
eastern coasts of all lands are more gradual and gently shelving
than the western": because of the east-to-west movement of the
water countering the rotation of the earth from west to east;[7]
to which the tides, following the moon in this direction, and the
east trade winds add their assistance. It must not be assumed,
however, that this general movement of the sea from east to west
is the only cause involved.

From the 41st parallel to the 35th, or the vicinity of Cape
Hatteras, according to the information given by all good charts,
the southwesterly slant and bending in of the coast is less notable
than from this cape on, along the coasts of the Carolians, Georgia, and Florida; these latter perhaps owe their deeper embay-
ment to a secondary cause, namely the greater influence of the
Gulf Stream, closer to them.

3.

It has long been observed that North America as well as South America exhibits, as do other lands, three divisions: the plains, the foothills, and the high mountains.

The **plains** (the flats),[5] called Ahkynt by the Indians, constitute the region stretching upward and inward from the seacoast as far as the so-called waterfalls of the several rivers flowing into the Atlantic. They form a flat sandy surface sloping toward the sea, and extend to different distances inland. On the Long Island coast, only a few miles. In the northern part of New Jersey, 15 to 20; in the southern, up to 30 and more, and so increasing through Maryland, Virginia, North and South Carolina, where the greatest breadth to which they extend inland is between 80 and 100 miles. Through Georgia and Florida their width seems, as far as I could get reports, to diminish somewhat again, so that as a whole they are bounded by a curving line. For the most part they form a dreary, gently sloping flat surface; only nearer to the western boundary is there some variation in the form of inconsiderable hills here and there. This is the part of America that has prompted travellers to say that Virginia, Carolina, etc., have no rocks. And in fact, there are none in this district, excepting far back and then only **thin layers** of rounded pebbles (2) buried sundry feet deep beneath sand, or the similarly deep-lying consolidated shell-beds; but no rocks on the surface of this whole region.

4.

The nature and the strata of this outermost stretch of *terra firma* in America are entirely the same from the Jerseys to Florida. At least what I observed here and there in the banks of rivers, in ravines and at springs, in Maryland, Virginia, and Carolina, agrees with the reports given by Kalm (3) for West-Jersey and Stork (4)[8] for East-Florida. The order and succession of the beds is throughout of the same kind; only their thickness varies from place to place, and so also the hardness of the consolidated ma-

(2) Kalm, 2d pt. Philadeph. p. 267. Rounded pebbles 8 feet deep.
(3) Kalm's Travels, 2d pt. p. 499. German edition.
(4) Description of East-Florida, by William Stork. London 1769. 4to. pag. 4.

terials. They appear in the following position: soil, sand, clay, marine sediments.

5.

1.) The **soil,** which everywhere forms the outer layer of the earth, also clothes this clod [Scholle] of sand in a thin layer. For the most part not even pure, but mixed with underlying sand. It is encountered in most places as a rind 1 to 1½ inches thick. In the great expanses of pine forest[9] in North and South Carolina it is so thin that when any of it is broken through by ploughing, or by travel along the roads, it is soon washed away by rain, or carried away as dust by the wind, laying bare the clear white sand. Where trenches have been freshly dug, or where roads have been cut through more deeply than usual in more thickly covered places, there appears this thin blackish rind, which nevertheless is mixed with much sand, or more often is only blackened sand. This is to be understood, however, only for the higher-lying and non-flooded lands; river banks and swampy depressions are excepted, for such have been enriched at the expense of the higher territory.

6.

2.) A bed of sand occupies the most considerable part of the region under discussion. In the hinterlying terrains there are intermixed deposits of small rounded pebbles, but these are neither abundant nor important. Nearer down to the coast and along it, there is only sand. The thickness of this sand bed varies; not so thick away from, and more so closer to the sea; from 2 to 20 or 30 feet and more. Likewise the color, firmness, and composition of this sand bed vary. Bordering the coast near Wilmington, and elsewhere in high river banks, it appears very pure and white, in bright sunlight painfully blinding to sensitive eyes. Farther inland it grades throughout more or less to reddish hues. — The coasts of Florida, Carolina, Virginia, etc., consist either entirely or for the most part of fine shell-sand, in which with the aid of a magnifying glass one can plainly see the tiny crushed remains of organisms. Elsewhere, and more commonly on the banks of transecting rivers, also farther inland, it is more a quartz, or siliceous sand — or mixed with the foregoing. This sand bed is commonly unconsolidated. Here and there an admixture of clay makes it harder. Around Baltimore, Fredericksburg, etc., most of this sand bed has been consolidated to commercially valuable sandstone and freestone, and further at several other places, in parts of this territory far from the sea, the same thing is true.

Not always. and least of all in the shallower beds of this sand deposit, individual layers may be discerned by virtue of either color or hardness. Most frequently it appears as a uniform accumulation of sand; although, as at Baltimore, hard freestone ashlar that the distant eye cannot discern is taken out between over- and underlying loose or soft sand.

7.

3.) Beneath the sand is a **bed of clay,** likewise different in color, thickness, and consistency. Often there occurs, a few feet below, a fairly pure white or gray clay, running horizontally along banks cut through by bodies of water or otherwise. At other places, more blended with the overlying sand, and recognizable rather by sense of touch than by sight. At still other places, in Maryland and Jersey, the clay bed is more fully blended with the shell bed next in succession, and often takes on therefore the properties of imperfect marl. I have seen some specimens of clay taken from this bed in Maryland that contained a large proportion of weathered shells, had to perfection the smell of chalk, but was coarser in grain, and stuck more tenaciously to the tongue. Nearly everywhere through the medial parts of these sand flats the clay layer appears at no great depth beneath the upper sand. Its uppermost layer seemed to me to be always the purest; farther down it is more frequently contaminated with sand. Farther inland it is also often of more reddish hue, but here and there a whiter bed stands out sharply from the overlying sand.

If I am not in error, it seems to me then that this clay deposit must be least considerable near the sea, and is often almost missing; toward the interior on the other hand, seems to increase more and more in thickness; as contrariwise the overlying sand deposit at the western boundary of the territory under discussion seems to be of little consequence, but lies in thicker deposits closer to the sea. The clay farther inland is also more abundantly mixed with sand, and so forms the ground so commonly composed of sand and red clay. Also, the clay deposits seem at some places to thicken irregularly, and concomitantly to fill hollows that have not been occupied by other rock masses.

8.

4.) Finally, the lowermost deposit of the flat foreland is a well-developed **shell bed,** which, as far as I could gather information, seems nowhere to have been completely dug through, and which extends beneath this entire plain from Jersey to Florida, like the sand above. It would be superfluous to mention here all the different places where molluscan shells have been discovered. (I shall perhaps have opportunity to mention them at the close of this work). The banks of all the streams that flow through the lowlands of Virginia, below their so-called lower waterfalls, are full of them. The high banks of the Potowmack, (5) the Rappahannok, the York and James rivers, a large number of smaller streams, millraces, and road cuts afford countless examples, and excite the attention more of the foreigner than of the native. The rivers in North Carolina and Georgia likewise. Less so, the smaller and shallower streams of South Carolina.

At many places on the eastern shore of Maryland, on the Rappahannok, at the cliffs of Yorktown, around New Bern, Wilmington, and farther in North Carolina territory, on the Savannah River and still other places, near and far from the Georgia coast, this shell bed has been consolidated to genuine hard rocks; these show, however, more or less plainly, their foreign constituents, i.e., the shells, whole or crushed, and here and there are dense and hard enough to be worked into millstones. In these rock cliffs, especially in the high ramparts of Yorktown, individual beds and layers may at times be clearly distinguished.

The different kinds of shells are throughout the same as those now found along the seashore, sharks' teeth, whale and other bones included. They are for the most part broken up and

(5) Kalm, 2d pt. p. 247.

jumbled together, although not always in the same proportion. They occur in essentially the same order as that observed for the mollusks at various stations on the coast.[10] Thus, for example, oyster and clam shells commonly occupy the upper layers, and these are likewise found most abundantly farthest inland, near the first rock belt. At the lowest places, between Baltimore and Annapolis, of the so-called War-fields, oysters have been washed out into the open. Oysters and clams are the only shells found in the hinder parts of this district in Jersey (6) in digging, at a depth of 40 feet. Far back on Tar River, near Martinsburg, North Carolina, these species appear in splendid fashion, and similarly about 100 miles farther inland on the Savannah River; they are rarer, on the other hand, in the shell banks nearer to the coast, around Wilmington, etc. Thus the oysters, etc. (7) occupy the shallower parts of the seashore, and therefore lie higher than the other shelled animals.

At sundry places these shells have been preserved more or less entire and unaltered. At some places they can hardly be distinguished from shells freshly taken from the sea; at others they are partly broken, in part half dissolved away, and at still other places they are moulded together to form stone. This is entirely due to the difference in material originally mixed with them; for according to whether this was more or less clay-like, or a sand mixture, or ferruginous earth, at one place they have one, at others another, and at still others all three together as cementing material. Hence some of these shell-rocks resemble an imperfect coarse shell-marble; others to some extent strike fire with steel, and at the same time effervesce with acids.

Farthest back on these flats, near the first hard rock belt, there appear to be found more abundantly still other remains, foreign to the sea and washed up by it on its ancient shore. As marine mud in which trees, branches, reeds, coal, etc. (8) are all tangled up; according to my experience and examination, nothing

---

(6) Kalm, pt. 2, p. 495.

(7) "At low water one sees the muddiest banks of the rivers and creeks covered with endless beds of (living) oysters, for mile after mile. This occurs in some large rivers up to 30-40 miles from the sea. They lie closely packed, with their sharp edges outwards, and form almost a solid reef 1½ to 2 feet thick." Catesby.

(8) Kalm 2d pt. p. 343, 496 ff.

resembling these objects is to be found in the beds situated nearer to the sea, excepting a few individual trees buried in the sand. In the more recent swamps, to be sure, trees are sometimes found submerged, but these were not buried there until later.

In cross section this shell bed is covered by the aforementioned deposits in thicknesses from 10 to 15, commonly however 30 feet and more. On the eastern shore of Maryland and in Carolina diggings have gone more than 40 feet before reaching it. As to how deep the shell beds themselves go, however, we have no evidence, not even conjectural, because for what we can see only the uppermost part of them remains, albeit they are exposed in Virginia on the York River and elsewhere in banks 30 to 40 feet high.

9.

I need not mention, that the deposits of the variously mentioned strata are not always entirely unadulterated, that is to say, never mutually mixed. Often they are; in general, however, the strata remain in the designated order of succession, always clearly distinguishable through the outstanding abundance of their characteristic materials even if some foreign matter be admixed. Out of it all the undeniable fact is clear that they are the deposits of a sea that stood over this region for long years, up to the outer rind of recently-formed soil, and sand spread out by the rivers from the highlands.

10.

This entire low and outer stretch of land, between the ocean and the first line of rocky hills (to be considered farther on) is, as I have already said, a well-developed plain gently sloping toward the sea. Nowhere is it interrupted by relief except along the various watercourses, some quiet, some flowing. All the streams, large and small, have entrenched themselves deeply in the plain, and as one travels across the region one sees plainly that the stream beds in general were at one time unequally broader and consequently shallower, before they were narrowed down to their present channels. Wherever in the midst of the woodland one notices the normally level road beginning to slope down, be it ever so slightly, one may surely expect soon to encounter some river or brook flowing impercéptibly toward the sea, the current hardly noticeable because in part the insignificant gradient and in part the itinerantly inflowing tributaries allow their waters to attain no great velocity. On most of the streams of this belt one observes that the northeastern banks are usually lower and flatter over a greater breadth than are the southwestern. Presumably, since storms come more often and with greater intensity from the former than from the latter direction, they help to wash and blow the loose sand, as well as to drive the current of the water more toward the other bank.

Not until we reach the beaches washed immediately by the sea do we find, at least on those I have seen in the environs of Florida and Carolina, continuous raised embankments parallel to the shore which are the work of the ocean itself, and which it seems to have set as its own boundary. If one travels from Wilmington to Charleston by the lower road, the one along the sea, for 16 English miles the route goes immediately along the edge of the sea, by way of the so-called **Long Bay** — and for the entire length of this route one has on the right, at distances varying from one to 200 paces, a row of embankments running parallel to the sea, from 3 to 10 and up to 16 feet high. The strand rises gently from the sea to the foot of these banks, which at the base may be 10-12 feet broad and on top, 3 to 6 feet. This beach is formed in part of fine quartzose sand and in part of contaminated shells mixed with other things thrown up by the incessant wash of the waves. At some places one finds actual evidence that the shell-sand is already beginning to form almost solid soft rock. The mere wash of the sea water seems to give the sand a definite solidity, even if it does not acquire thereby other cementing elements. If one rides on the wet sand hard by the waves, the horse's hooves leave hardly any tracks, whereas on the other hand the surface of the dry sand is disturbed by the wind alone, and thus contributes to the formation and raising of the above-mentioned embankments. I saw more similar banks of sand later on in the vicinity of Charleston and on the **North Beach** in Florida, and according to reports they occur in the same way pretty well all along the whole coast, wherever local conditions do not inhibit. They appeared to me always to be

broken off almost perpendicularly on the side toward the sea,
but on the opposite side more sloping and covered with vegetation. At times of hurricane, or when extremely strong winds blow
against the coast, the waves reach them, or overwash them entirely, if the billows cannot find ways to surge through the openings that occur here and there, and thus arise countless hills of
loose sand, other sand banks and surficial irregularities, and
behind them, among their hollows, when the waters recede, a
mass of shells, fishes, bones, and other jetsam of the sea remains.

11.

Many of these sand ridges and hills behind the aforementioned
appear, even though broken off and uneven, nevertheless to
maintain a trend essentially parallel to the first ones, (9) and
besides, for distances of half, whole, or several miles inland the
sandy surface continues uneven, cut through into elevations and
depressions, before the broad plains proper described above
begin farther in to appear and continue uninterrupted. Whoever travels this region with some discernment can hardly help
coming to the thought that these hills, now far from the sea,
formerly arose exactly like the present-day sand banks on the
coast, as a deposit from the breaking waves, and that consequently the dry land of this eastern coast is growing in extent,
and that the sea as time goes on is setting narrower limits for
itself.[11] — Nowhere, however, could I gather any evidence on
this based on experience and observation; rather, the consensus
of all the country people living there is that the sea on this coast
rarely causes any sudden or notable change, but rather alternately
and gradually gains and loses. For actual fact in support of this

---

(9) The same kind of banks are encountered at many other places. "When
the strand is low and composed of light sand, the wind reinforces the work
of the waves, and piles the sand higher than the waves can reach. Thus arises
on the border of the sea a roll of sand which is 40 to 50 feet high and here
broader, there narrower. These sand hills are sometimes piled up by the
waves, sometimes torn down, until finally some of them are fixed by vegetation. They are called dunes. They are very abundant in Holland and Fland-
ers, and in many places wind and waves have built whole concentric rows
of them, one after another." De Luc, *History of the Earth*, vol. 1, p. 172.

idea I can only quote the following from Catesby's works: "A dolphin 16 feet long stranded on the north Edisto coast was covered by sand in less than a month. High winds often blow the sand away to depths of 2-3 feet, and lay bare a mass of shells and other things which had long lain buried there. — On Sullivan's Island, which lies on the north side of the entrance to Charleston harbor, the sea has taken so much (although this side was not facing the sea) that in three years it amounted to a quarter of a mile, and in this stretch many spruce and palm trees were uprooted and buried."

If, however, one ventured to conclude from these successions of sand hills that there has been a real increase in the dry land on the east coast of North America, this would refute at the same time the idea that the east coasts of the continents ought to be undercut and reduced by the persistent currents of the ocean as a slowly working cause. However, De Luc, in his History of the Earth, part 1, 24-26th letter, has ably and thoroughly shown the inadequacy of this doctrine, so that I can do no better than to refer my readers to his discussion; for it would be indiscreet as matters stand to pass judgment on the advance or retreat of these coasts before adequate observations are gathered on the subject, and such, in this yet newly populated country, was so far not the state of affairs.

That continual change occurs on the coast is learned by mariners to their grief and disaster. All the entrances into rivers and harbors in the whole stretch from Delaware down to Florida are extremely difficult and often dangerous because of outlying transverse sand bars. — The river waters flowing toward the sea, and the waves meeting them at their mouths, bring about that just there, at the most inopportune places, the sand brought down from above is piled up. Thus arise the bars (obstructions) so greatly feared; these however often shift in heavy storms, filling up a formerly navigable channel with sand and on the other hand opening up a new one at some other place.

Furthermore this coast of the southern half of North America is invested, hard by the mainland, with a line of low, narrow, north-south trending islands, inside of which small craft can make long coastwise runs without being exposed to the dangers of the high seas.

11.[12]

At the very beginning I pointed out that the obliquity of the whole North American coastline, from northeast to southwest, is obvious, without considering it necessary to take note of minor deviations; here, I think, might be the most opportune place to add the observation that this obliquity is considerably stronger and more striking between the 35th and 30th degrees of latitude, or between Cape Hatteras in North Carolina and Saint John in Florida, than along all the rest of the stretch. Even if I do not attempt to explain the trend noted for the major outlines, it seems to me that the noticeably stronger deflection in the minor district is less difficult to account for. Out of the Gulf of Mexico, around the cape of Florida, and along its east coast and the Bahama Islands, there sweeps the so-called **Gulf Stream,** with such strength through the channel, not more than 20 miles wide, that no ship, even with the most favorable wind, can make headway against it. This ocean current, after it has emerged from the constriction of its narrower channel and is past the northernmost of the Bahama Islands, takes up a course parallel to the coast, and stays fairly close to it, so that ships sailing out from North Carolina, often only a few hours after weighing anchor, find themselves in its midst. The stream continues on its way, to be sure, much farther to the north and northeast into the ocean; but as it becomes wider and wider, and farther from the straits which increased its velocity, it loses the force that it seems to have in that area. — If we assume a current running with notable force through any channel, and find a notable obtuse angle, or bay, in the vicinity of the neighboring coast, on which the entire force of the current, if it maintains its original trend, must impinge, it is a reasonable presumption, that this current and that bay must at some time have had some relation to one another. This presumption must take on fresh plausibility if we observe that the altered direction of the current follows the equally altered course of the shore, even if at some distance, and we can convince ourselves further that the soil of that shore can in part be attacked by the force of the water. All of these conditions exist, exactly. Between the east coast of Florida and the Bahama Islands and banks the Gulf Stream takes on a course of **north by west,** on which, all obstacles out of the way, it must impinge with full force on the coast of Florida approximately between St. Augustine and St. Mary; and here we find indeed the most pronounced westward indentation of the whole coast. But **at the present time** the Gulf Stream approaches the shores of this bay by not more than about 60 to 80 miles; it does not maintain its initial direction, but shifts somewhat northerly past the Bahama Islands, and after it is free of the strongest influence of the northeast trade-winds, immediately almost northeast, and the coast of the mainland of St. Mary takes on the same turn, and keeps it in the main as far as Cape Hatteras, where the Gulf Stream still remains constantly not more than, or hardly a day's voyage from the coast. A vessel that find itself in the Gulf Stream in time of calm or of gentle wind will be carried imperceptibly northeastward with the current; be it however between the stream and the mainland, it may steer according to the favor and condition of the wind without losing its true course. The effects of the Gulf Stream thus do not reach the coasts of the mainland, and, it may be objected, can therefore have no relation to its development. Perhaps, however, too hastily. It is true, as I myself have already conceded, that the apparent surficial force of the Gulf Stream does not impinge upon the coast itself **at the present time,** and only occasionally exerts immediate influence on it. During violent storms that commonly strike the North American coast from the northeast with the greatest of fury, the waters of the stream are impeded in their course, and often surge fearfully against the low and frontal coasts of Florida, Georgia, and Carolina, and so, with the combined violence of the wind, have already at different times threatened the destruction, among other cities, of Charleston. But even apart from these accidental occurrences, it does not necessarily follow that what is **now** not the case has never been so; that, specifically, because nowadays the Gulf Stream does not immediately wash the shore, it has never done so. It has not yet been exactly determined, either how wide the stream is after it goes out into the ocean, or what quantity of water its power encompasses and carries on with it in depth. Both of these factors [width and depth] might vary somewhat under different incidental causes. We may allow it, however, a moderate depth of 50-60-80 fathoms, and remember what I have already observed in the second paragraph, that as the dry land gradually slopes

off toward the sea, so the shore drops off only gently into the sea,
and that on ships one **ordinarily** counts the number of fathoms
to the bottom as so many miles of distance from the shore, even
if not exactly. The stream therefore encounters resistance, on the
shallow sloping sea-bottom, at some distance from the mainland,
and changes in direction without coming near the dry land, in
the same degree as this coast and its continuations under the sea
change. I am satisfied that I have shown a probable relation between the Gulf Stream and part of the North American coast.
Whether or not this be applicable to the entire contour of the
coast I do not venture to decide. — The trend of the Gulf Stream
remains constantly northeasterly up to the vicinity of the Newfoundland Banks — for at least that far, and, it is said, even
farther to the north, mariners recognize its effect.

12.

If it can now be assumed as unquestioned from the described
nature of this eastern district of America that the **whole** has been
in the past an arm of the sea bordered by primordial rocks
(which we shall presently be considering) and present to attention the requisite proof in its shell, clay, and sand deposits, then
one can hardly suppress the emerging question that invites the
determination of the time at which the change from sea to land
took place. However, this is not yet the most appropriate place
for me to enter into full answer to that question, because in the
sequel it will be elucidated that not only these plains, but also
the high mountains of North America have once been beneath
the sea. However, whether this change came upon the whole
region all at once, or, after the waters receded from the high
regions they stood for a while over these plains, and these became
dry land in a second and later period, would appear to be another question, and one here more specifically relevant.

The first stimulus toward the conjecture that the withdrawal
of the sea may not have occurred all at one time was afforded
me by the already mentioned report of Mr. Kalm, in the 2d part,
p. 495, that in the vicinity of **Racoon,**[13] that is to say near the
first succeeding rock belt "not only the shells of oysters and
clams, but also **quantities of reeds and fragments of broken
branches,** 40 feet deep" have been found. This is about what one

finds in general cast up all along the **border of the sea.** Somewhat
greater probability was revealed to me when I realized further
that in the vicinity of New York and on to the northward the
rock belt that seems to have served as the border of this great
gulf extends out closer to the sea, often touching it, but that
there, instead of flat dry land before it, at moderate depths are
many and extensive banks. — Eastward from New England here
are the **Nantucket Shoals, Georges Bank, Browns Bank,** and
others known by the name **New Scotland Fishing Banks,** and
then still farther northeastward, the more important **Newfoundland Banks.** — The observation that the great southern dry sand
plains might formerly have been similar banks is not entirely
unfavorable to this hypothesis. And if in suppositions of this
sort the similar opinion of another man might lend greater
weight to my own, I had reason to be pleased when I found later
in Evans' Analysis[14] of his maps of Pennsylvania and Jersey that
he quite frankly takes this first rock belt to be the older shore
of North America, and sees the forelying sand plains as develop-
ing in the course of time. This interpretation remains, however,
no more than conjecture, for I could find no data that would
allow more firmly grounded conclusions.

13.

In vain did I flatter myself that I might be able, as I travelled
through these regions, perhaps to draw some conclusions from the
quantity and thickness of the soil layer lying on the shell and sand
beds. If for example, I thought, one might determine how much
mould the vegetation on these plains would produce in a given
time, one might venture a closer guess as to the actual length of
time they have borne plants, and a comparison with the higher
regions, perhaps longer dry land. But there were more difficulties in the way than a traveller was in position to overcome. I
found often the parts quite close to the sea for miles without a
layer of humus, and still with sundry species growing on it.
Places near streams and exposed to other inundation have a rich
assortment of peat or bog soil, partly grown in place, partly
floated in. The greatest part of the outer sand plain is indeed
covered by somewhat scanty soil, supports, however, mainly
nothing but conifers and meager species of grasses, and is there-

fore generally known by the name of **Pine Barrens** (unproductive
Scotch-pine land). Somewhat farther back oaks and other deciduous trees are mixed in, and still farther in these nearly dominate,
and proportionally one finds the humus increasing in thickness.
Now, however, it ought first be tried and tested, in what relation
conifers and deciduous trees are productive in the creation and
accumulation of humus. At all events it is apparent that in this
regard the conifers are inferior to the leaf-bearers. According to
general observation in the Old World the former everywhere
indicate a lean soil; they produce fewer and smaller leaves and
they drop them more slowly; over and above this, those dropped
are not so easily rotted into humus. — The annual product in
leaves of the deciduous trees, on the other hand, is greater, they
fall more frequently, decay more rapidly, because they are less
resinous; and perhaps in this way they increase the deposit of
vegetable mould around them more rapidly. (10) — I could ac-
cordingly confirm, indeed, that in the past here also these different kinds of trees have grown on soils of different quality, but
nevertheless was not able to draw any conclusions from the
thicknesses of soil at one place or another as to the time at which
vegetation in both began to grow, because it did not seem to me
clearly shown by investigation whether **from the beginning**
deciduous trees grow on better soil than conifers, or whether
both, at least in these American regions, witness different rates
only in the production and enrichment of the soil surrounding
them.[16]

Amidst the sandy barren pine-woods areas are abundant
morasses, swamps, and low-lying places which either have water
flowing through them or retain it. These places are invested to
uneven depths with a layer of black soil and mud. In them,
however, there grow many kinds of deciduous and evergreen
trees and other plants. Now comes the question — has this black
earth, found here in such enormous quantities, been rendered
into these deepened beds of mud by rain, by flood water alone?
Or is it the result of heavier, more potent and richer vegetation,
favored by moisture — or of both causes together? it is still un-

(10) "Rich soil in a beech forest of 52 years' standing, at most places 3
inches deep. In a 105-year damp alder and poplar grove it was 21 inches deep,
and in a very old fir wood in the Harz (only) 13 inches to bedrock." Observations, uncertainties, and questions concerning mineralogy, 1st essay, p. 103.[15]

certain to what extent local conditions, rains, winds, floods, favor or hinder the accretion of the uppermost layer of soil; and that here and there on the leanest sands a lone oak or deciduous tree is found, healthy and strong, shows indeed that they are not always and everywhere restricted to growing in good soil.

14.

In the foregoing account I found need at different times to refer to a rock-belt that surrounds the aforementioned lowlands of the southern part of North America, as a boundary line. This line, and the trend of the rock-belt, are clearly marked by Nature herself in an identically aligned series, on large and small streams alike, of waterfalls. Most of the streams encounter along their courses, on this eastern side of the mountains facing the ocean, various places where they are forced to rush and plunge through and over ledges of rock. Presently, however, I am referring singly and only to the **lowermost falls** going out from the mountains, or the first going up from the sea. A chain of rock ledges, which in the vicinity of New York causes the dangerous passage in the Sound, the Hell-gate, but on the Hudson offers no obstruction, reappears on the other side of the Hudson behind Powles Hook, manifests itself in steep and rugged cliffs behind Brunswick in Jersey, discontinuously at Rocky-Hill, becomes lower here and there at Trenton, Germantown, behind Philadelphia, to Chester, New-Castle, and Wilmington; appears somewhat different, forsooth, around Baltimore and Georgetown in Maryland, resumes its former character around Fredericksburg and Richmond in Virginia, and according to report continues in similar direction through North and South Carolina. It describes, to be sure, a somewhat curved line (or merely appears curved, because it is nowhere exposed in its entire width) but follows a major trend from northeast to southwest. Since on the other hand the general course of the rivers coming out of the mountains is from northwest to southeast, collectively they must surmount this rocky belt at one place or another, and force their passage through it with more or less of difficulty and power. Only the Hudson River has kept its channel free. In the other rivers, however, they follow almost uniformly:

In Pennsylvania	Delaware, at Trenton, 75° west longitude from London, 40° lat. Schuylkill, at Philadelphia, 75.20 Susquehannah, lowest ferry, 76° —
Maryland	Gunpowder Creeck, Potowmack, above Georgetown 77.30 ● — ● ● - 39 -
Virginia	Rappahannock, above Fredericksburg 78. — James-River at Richmond, 78.20 — 37.20 Appomatok, at Petersburg —
North Carolina	Roanoke, at Halifax — — In the Tar and New-River — —

Those here named are the ones generally known, of which
five have become known to me through personal observation. I
have noted the west longitude (11) in order to show immediately
below the probability, if not the certainty, that the continuation
of the rock-chain that causes these falls may be found farther to
the south. I find to wit on a chart of Carolina (12) the following
places indicated:

North Carolina	Ledge of Rocks in Neuse — River, below 79° Rocky-River, a branch of Northwest-River	— — 79.30
South Carolina	Hanging-rock Creeck, a branch of the Pedee-River Rocky-Creek, Rocky-branch, Rocky-Mount, and rock-ridden places in and around the Wateree above Camden, approximately	— 80.30 — — 81 —

These last-mentioned are in fact not indicated as real falls,
rather as notably rocky stretches on the rivers; they belong

(11) According to data on *Governor Pownall's Map of North America,
London 1779.*
(12) *Henry Monzon's Map of South & North Carolina, London 1775.*

nevertheless here. (13) Further, however, on the same map falls are found

In the Congaree, several miles below the junction of the Broad and Saluda Rivers	− − 81°
In the Savannah, northwest of Augusta	82°

The bearing off from 75° west longitude, or the Delaware fall, to 82° on the Savannah is from northeast to southwest. The places named are the first rocky ones going up from the sea, and I do not believe any further or other confirmation is required concerning this rock-belt, which runs from New York **southward.** − We know only its major trend, but not its depth, nor its width. Whether it continues on to the west, forming the foundation of the other superposed mountains and perhaps reappearing somewhere west of the Alleghenies, future investigation will show. Eastward it appears to plunge very rapidly and steeply into the depths, for nowhere has anyone yet encountered it in digging through the overlying shell beds.

This same belt continues on, however, **northward** from New York, is evident along the Connecticut coast, and is still the same in Rhode Island. Farther north I have had no opportunity to see it; no doubt, however, it continues on.

It seems here and there 2-3-4 miles or more broad; rises higher in the more northerly of the aforementioned areas, that is in York, Jersey, Pennsylvania; becomes lower to the south, remains however on the whole always notably elevated above the outlying plain, although nowhere does it form true mountains.

15.

This whole noteworthy rock-belt consists solely of primeval or basement rock types, but principally a **granite,** subjected here and there to certain alterations, and which, at least as far as I have seen on my travels, does not appear farther inland. In and around this belt there are many kinds of clay-like and calcareous rocks, as asbestos, mica, cutstone or ashlar,[17] greenstone, tourmaline, etc.

(13) A line drawn from the fall in the Savannah to that in Roanoke follows this trend fairly closely.

I have seen granite at New York and Richmond, an air-line distance of almost 400 English miles. Consequently it would seem obvious that it appears also in the northern and southern continuations of the rock-belt just described. It should however be noted that this rock-belt, in its extent from north to south, does not everywhere come to light; it is in large part, especially to the south, so low that it is nearly everywhere covered by the ordinary reddish soil of mixed sand and clay, and that in uneven depth. It appears only where cut through by streams or otherwise has been washed clear; and here I shall merely make the preliminary remark that in this part of America the order is exactly the opposite of that found elsewhere; here, that is, the granite occupies the foremost zone in from the sea, whereas contrariwise in other mountain ridges it forms the highest and last peaks that man can climb.

Along this belt are found the mineral components peculiar and incidental to the granite family, (14) but not always in the same mixture, not always in the same quantity and relationship.[18] A coarse-grained quartz, with much intermixed mica, seemed at most places to be the most abundant constituent. Still, in the interest of better order, I shall mention more exactly some of the most outstanding places, from north to south, in this belt. I must however deplore here as in the sequel that I hardly dare express myself throughout in complete certainty, because the larger part of the rock collection I made, which I confided to a Hamburg merchant in Philadelphia for shipment to Germany was lost, — I know not in what manner.

16.

I may be forgiven if I bring in at this opportunity something about Rhode Island, although this part lies outside and to the north of the precincts outlined by me at the beginning, from the Hudson River to the south. Along the Sound the whole coast of Connecticut is elevated and rocky; however, I did not set foot upon it. Farther on lies Rhode Island, grounded in naught but rocks whose bold peaks reminded us in the year 1779 of the Place of the Famine.[19] The principal rock type here is a gray,

(14) Cronst. Miner. p. 268.

simple, fine-grained stone verging in tint on the reddish. It crops out everywhere, and along the seacoast it appears in foliated layers standing perpendicular next to one another. It takes a rough polish, and is worked into tombstones, steps, etc.[20]

In the hollowed-out places from which its rubble has been washed out, a thickly foliated coarse black slate overlies it; this is plainly seen on the bare-washed sea shore.[21] I have found nothing of plant or animal remains in it; it may well belong to the primeval slates. At one place a shaft had erstwhile been sunk into it; I was not able to learn whether the search was for coal or for alum.[22]

Scattered on the shores and on the island are fragments and masses of rock cemented together, or breccia. (15) It contains the common water-worn pebbles in rounded, polished form, in sizes from $\frac{1}{2}$ to 50 lb., which are held together by a fine ferruginous sandy mass.[23] This rock species crops out mainly at the one end of Easton's-Beach and beyond. Where the waves beat freely on it, or have been able to do so, its surface shows many pockets, the containers of the now-lost pebbles. They contain nothing calcareous, for neither on the whole island nor farther on toward Providence has lime yet been found; this must either be imported, or oyster-shell must be used.

This island has many knolls, and everywhere on it are found ponds up to two feet deep, and the most of these are perpetually marshy. A clay layer that lies only about 2-3 feet deep collects the water, which now incidentally becomes sweet either by coming from the atmosphere or from the sea, surrounding the island and finding its own way up. So spare an island remains in any case remarkable for the number of its fresh-water springs. Some of them deposit ochre.

17.

At the outset I designated the New York area as the northern limit of the observations to be discussed in detail.

To the east of New York stretches the stately and fertile Long Island, which extends, strictly speaking, to the east-northeast. The eastern and southeastern parts of this island are flat and

(15) Saxum amnigenum. *Linn. syst. 3, p. 80, n. 38.*

sandy, giving on the sea. The plain of Jamaica or Hampstead is a perfectly barren surface, many miles long and wide, and denuded of all shrubbery. At its northern and northwestern ends, or toward the mainland, it rises in low hills, which in part, as around Huntingdon, consist almost entirely of coarse sand with large pebbles, partly, as around Bokram, etc. of silica and broken fragments of granite, but all worn. The valleys between these hills do not all follow the same direction, but most of them go north-south, and contain more or less of clay, or red soil as around New York, mixed with sand and pebbles. Here and there quicksand mixed with black soil takes over in considerable stretches, as around Tennikot, etc. Elsewhere, around Mosqueto Cove, and opposite York-Island, there are whole hills of loam and blue and white clay, which also lie in thin layers under the surface at various depths, and not infrequenttly appear at the surface.

On Butler's-Island (a smaller one detached from Long-Island) in the sand and other subsurface locations vestiges appear indicating that these areas have undergone recent, purely local changes. Under the upper layer of garden-mould comes clean sand, then again a bed of sand mixed with vegetable mould. —

All the upper layers of this island betray an accumulation of sand washed in and variously shaped by the sea. The true rock basement may well extend fairly deep under the surface; however, the continuation of the rock ledges around Kings-bridge appears as far away as at Hellgate, already much lower and mainly covered by water.[24]

Notwithstanding that at the present time thick deposits of all kinds of shells are accumulating in mud at various places on the shore of this island, yet no case has become known to me where shell beds have been found in digging; it is not easy, however, to dig more than 10-12 feet deep. There is no trace of limestone on the whole island, nor more of fossils from the animal kingdom. However, breccias similar to those of Rhode Island are found everywhere, and in the cultivated hills around Bockram, etc.,[25] also wood petrified into silica, in small and abraded fragments. I found peat in dried out swamps and in some still extant. Coal is said to have been found, but I had no opportunity to see any of it.

New-York-Island[26] itself stretches exactly north-south, rugged

18.

and hilly. In the middle of the island at Blumenthal and along the Hudson River the rocks rise up, all the way to the northern end, where on their heights Fort Knyphausen and other works were laid out.

The general cover of the island is sand and clay. During the construction of the lines around New York in the year 1782 I had opportunity to see it often to depths of 6-8 feet. It was everywhere coarse-grained sand mixed with some clay which gave it a certain firmness. At depths of not more than 1-2 inches, black soil was found mixed with the top soil or overlying it. At this depth lie many and large broken fragments of

> partly decayed mica-schist, with uncommonly much white and yellowish mica,
>
> in part a coarse-grained quartz-rich kind of granite, with large grains of hornblende intermixed, and rarer very small spots of yellowish mica.

Other various but collectively interrelated rock species are found on and around the island, partly in firm-standing ledges and partly in broken fragments. Because their relationship and sequence are not visible beneath the cover overlying them, I am of mind to deal with them in purely arbitrary order.

The high, steep walls standing over the river at the north end consist mainly of a gray kind of rock which is like that of Rhode Island, and likewise here is used for grave-stones, etc.[27] It is a hard, firm stone, that has in groundmass a very fine quartz sand, mixed equally and exactly with likewise very fine black (mica?) powder which however in its midst sparkles in separate extremely tiny points. It will not everywhere strike fire; spalls off in unequal shells, and manifests between them a coating of iron rust; scrapes off white; when breathed upon, however, gives off no odor. It happens that it is this rock, in all presumption, that is related to those later to be mentioned on the Susquehanna and around Baltimore, etc., and presumably is at one with the gray rock that Dr. Kalm described from the highlands to the north of York.

Interspersed (or interstratified) here and there are fragments of a dark green rock — shot through with whiter veins, so that it appears to approximate banded jasper.[28]

On the banks of the East River I found large, loose chunks of dark gray hornstone.[29] Some pieces of this showed incomplete impressions of shells and corals. — Nowhere in the area have I found an actual ledge of this rock, and I am therefore uncertain whether these hornstones are indigenous or accidental.

On the East River, in the vicinity of Kypsies-Bay, cliff-forming rocks crop out which to all appearance are laid out in horizontal layers. They consist of fine sand or quartz fragments, contain much mica, and are not very hard. At least there, where salt water washes and sprays on it, one finds abundant chasms that have been washed out. Veins of pure quartz, an inch or more thick, extend to different distances through it.

Gneiss, that consists of white feldspar, grayish quartz grains, white and yellowish mica, with blackish grains and flecks of hornblende.

Granite, which is made up of pink and white feldspar, whitish quartz, small spots of yellow mica, and black hornblende, comes to light here and there on the sea. — The above mentioned, and fragments dug out on the heights, are the same species, only more foliate.

Beautiful hard granite, composed of white feldspar verging on the yellow, layers of white and partly brownish quartz, rather large plates of transparent mica whose color grades toward the greenish and gray, with a sprinkling of a few small, beautiful red garnets.

In some of these granitic rocks zeolite-like crystals are found. They consist of fine, white, somewhat shiny fibers about half an inch in length, which run concentrically and come together in a raised point. Whole areas of granite locally are overlain with these at the surface, and upon breaking it open one finds that they are distributed through the entire mass as well. In fire, however, they do not behave like zeolites; (16) after several minutes in very hot flames the fibers were still unaltered, rather more brittle; remained so even upon application of borax, sal ammoniac, and strong alkali. Strong oil of vitriol had no effect on it after 24 hours. Therefore they might perhaps rather be called zeolitic (or zeolite-like) crystallized asbestos. (17) And conse-

(16) Cronst. Mineral. 108.
(17) *Amiantus radians* L.

quently, I dare say, the same with that which Dr. Kalm has seen in serpentine rock. (18)

No ores other than bog iron ore have been discovered on York Island and the immediately outlying terrain. Even this island, narrow as it is, and with salt water flowing all around it, is richly supplied with water, and it is an outstanding benefice for the city to have an inexhaustible spring flowing out of the rock, that yields a superb pure water and in the highest heat of summer maintains a temperature of 40-45 Fahrenheit. In the most severe of winter, 45-50. In the vicinity of the spring the island is not half an English mile wide, between the East and North rivers. Presumably it derives its supply from distant regions, through joints in the rock. There is no lime in the neighborhood, nor do I remember having heard of oyster shells dug up in New York. (19)

19.

In Jersey, immediately following, I was not so fortunate, on the short route I took straight through, as to encounter true granite ledges. However, since they reappear immediately beyond in Pennsylvania, and indeed in the principal trend already noted, it is to be supposed that they must lie here for the most part covered up. The bare, low rocks close behind Paulus-Hoock seemed granite-like at a distance; because of unrest resulting from the war I did not dare venture closer. The first high hills and cliffs around Boundbroock, behind Brunswick, are of gray rock like that of New York, and appear, where they are laid bare, in superposed sheets or slabs. **Abbé Robin** (20)[30] claims to have seen granite, and mentions the discovery of isinglass in this

(18) Kalm, Travels, 2d part, p. 437. "Mr. Franklin gave me a piece of a stone that is used in New England to wall up smelting furnaces and black- smiths' forges. It consisted of a mixture of serpentine stone (*ollaris*) and asbestos. The major part of it was a gray serpentine stone, which on handling seemed very greasy and smooth, and lent itself well to cutting and finishing. Here and there however a few little stars twinkled, which formed an asbestos whose little fibers shot out of the center like rays.—*Asbestus fibris e centro radiantibus*. This stone is said not to be quarried out of a solid ledge, rather to be found scattered here and there on the ground."

(19) Kalm, part 2, p. 247.

(20) *New travels through North America.*

stretch. Between Brunswick and Princeton, on Rocky Hill, loose fragments of granite are found, and likewise, although in no great quantity, at the fall of the Delaware at Trenton, where on the other hand one sees a hard bluish fine-grained kind of rock (21) extending across the river.

I had no opportunity to visit the high hills of **Neversink,** which lie close to the sea adjacent to Sandy Hook in Jersey and are the last high land of this region. They seemed to me too high and too broadly based to be mere sand hills. Perhaps granite will be found there.[31]

The route I took through Jersey from Elizabethtown through Brunswick to Trenton belongs otherwise to the elevated and hilly background of the forelying sand plains; here one finds more variation, because it is closer to the true mountain belt. We find sand, sand and clay, gray argillaceous soil; in the valleys, black soil, alternating. However, through Trenton, Princeton, and Brunswick there stretches remarkably a line of hills that consist of red or brown-red stone lying in thin layers.[32] I made no tests with this on the spot, but took samples which, with many others, in the way already mentioned, were lost. Its beds lie partly horizontal, partly inclined; it weathers on exposure, yields a sticky soil but is nevertheless agriculturally usable. Mr. Kalm calls it a red limestone, (22) similar to the one from Kinne-kulle in West Gotland.

20.

Only a few miles from Philadelphia there is a fall on the Schuylkill that is nothing extraordinary, but, in its romantic setting, very pleasant. Here the river rushes over true granite, of quartz, feldspar, and mica; and quartz and mica. In the latter form it shows up in the steep banks of the Schuylkill, at the upper and lower ferries in the city, around Bartram's country-seat, etc. — but only on the high banks, and is covered above by the general soil, so that otherwise one does not get to see it.

At many places in this stretch soapstone (*Saxum talcosum*

(21) Seems related to trap; does not effervesce with acids, and does not strike fire.
(22) Kalm, part 2, pp. 367, 371.

particulis spataceis granatisque inmixtis (23)) is found, and of this the most productive quarries, and the ones that yield the largest plates, are in the vicinity of Chester. This stone is greenish-gray, smooth and rippled; is easy to saw and cut, and is put to many and varied uses.

A talc-bearing slate, with mica and scattered garnets, is found in the neighborhood of the Schuylkill fall.

Asbestos, *Amiantus fibris separabilibus molliusculis,* (24) is encountered at many places in this area, often in big, long pieces.

Isinglass (25) is likewise encountered in abundance and in large pieces, up to half an ell or more. At present I cannot decide whether it is true *Mica membranacea* L., but still I hardly doubt it. A very small piece I brought along from Baltimore, where it is said to be found in this same rock-belt, is transparent gypsumspar, (26) and in fire it reeks strongly of sulphur. However, since white transparent plates of mica occur otherwise in great quantity, this might very well also be *Mica membranacea* L., or Russian glass.

Garnets are found not only in soapstone and the aforementioned talc-slates, but also indeed scattered singly in granite, further also sundered out, in the surface soil in and around Philadelphia. (Garnets are said to be found most abundantly at Germantown on the Schuylkill, in the cliffs on Levering's land.) The sand and the surface soil here and elsewhere often contain much mica weathered out of these granites.

The first genuine limestone beds are encountered no closer to Philadelphia than 15-17 miles, and all limestone used in building must be hauled that far. But loose blocks of a foliate rock "which consists for the most part of black or gray mica running in undulations which here and there, more or less, is mixed with a gray, slack, very fine-grained limestone and containing quartz grains, is found at Germantown (27) and thence toward the Schuylkill." Also white small-grained sand with black small-grained mica and quartz grains, and beneath that, bands of white limestone only, without contamination by mica, or in

(23) Kalm, part 2, p. 437.
(24) Kalm, part 2, p. 441. *Amiantus asbestus L.*
(25) Kalm, part 2, p. 234.
(26) Cronst. 18.
(27) Kalm, part 2, p. 327.

some cases limestone and mica equally mixed. This rock species crops out here and there along the river; it lies in beds about a foot thick; is however covered on the flat lands with 4-6 feet of the common brick-colored soil, mixed of sand and clay. Garnets are found in this rock also.

To all appearances these loose blocks lie on the granite, and have originated later.

21.

The granite of New York, and that on the Schuylkill, which lie opposite one another exactly northeast to southwest, serve us from here on as definite viewpoints from which we shall find its continuation farther southwesterly, everywhere always repeated in the same line, even if it might appear to be interrupted here and there by other intervening rock-species.

The regular post-road from Philadelphia runs in virtually the same direction. After one has passed the Schuylkill flowing between walls of granite at Philadelphia, five miles farther on in a defile at Darby one sees the much-mentioned gray rock-species with some alterations; here coarse slate lies upon it.[33] Twelve miles from Philadelphia we reach Chester, in whose environs the soapstone is quarried. The road now goes over high, mostly flat land, at short distance from the Delaware. At Wilmington we cross the Brandywine, which here makes its way through a rocky gorge toward the Delaware. The rock here is solid, of fine white quartz, with many intermixed black spots which however as far as I can remember, show no mica-glint, and cause the rock to appear gray.[34] But still not like that of York. — Here the Brandywine goes over a litle fall. On the left one has mainly in view the Delaware, flowing in its deeper valley, and here and there in the distance we see the basement rock cropping out. We come through New-Castle, thence to Christianbridge, Elk-river, Northeast-River, or Charleston, and Susquehannah, which at the lowest ferry is a mile wide and has many obscure crags of rock which are continuations of those showing up on both banks, albeit largely covered. Somewhat higher are the actual so-called Susquehannah-Falls. The rocks here are only somewhat lighter and grayer than those next to be mentioned, and on the other hand related to those preceding.

Gunpowder-Creek, 25 miles from the Susquehannah and 16 from Baltimore; in its neighborhood, and especially in the narrow, shallow gorge in which it has its bed and rushes over rocks, appears a blackish, scaly kind of rock, which shall be noticed immediately next at Baltimore, where it is abundant. Here it is different only in the larger proportion of quartz it has in its aggregate. From the manner in which the rock-walls on these banks peel off and fracture it is probable that originally they lay upon one another in layers, or laminae.

In the distance of 110 English miles between Baltimore and Philadelphia the rivers mentioned here are the only places where one has opportunity to look for the underlying rock basement, excepting that here and there one happens upon fragments. The road runs over the reddish sandy soil accumulated above the bedrock.

22.

Around Baltimore, which is almost exactly on a line drawn from New York through Germantown and Schuylkill-Falls, we find again our granite belt with a few related rocks that also accompany it in other parts of the world. Here we encounter the gray quartzose rock mentioned for Wilmington, the Susquehannah, and the Gunpowder, some in the same form, some with certain variation; on that account I have not said much about it there. This city lies at the foot of an eminence, partly also at and on the same, on the Patapsco River, which here forms a spacious basin before it joins Chesapeake Bay. Eastward from the city lies the peninsula, the so-called Eastern Shore, which like all the terrain that lies to the east of the road from Philadelphia here, belongs to the first division, the sand plains. Westward from Baltimore on the heights we have slightly sloping plains, mostly uneven, however, with their foundation cut through by deep stream gorges, its surface mainly a reddish, sandy, clayey soil. Since I had here as little opportunity as elsewhere to seek out the mutual relations of the different kinds of rock I shall mention what I happened upon in purely arbitrary fashion.

Fragments of granite are to be found here and there in ravines; one piece that I have before me consists mainly of coarse, opaque, angular, whitish quartz, and contains much greenish-white mica

in large brittle flakes; but in some places on the surface it has not
only lost its luster but also seems to come loose in fibrous leaves.
Heated red-hot, this mica becomes whiter. In my sample, forsooth,
I see nothing more; from notes written on the scene, however, I
find that other pieces of this rock have shown some sparse feldspar
and several crystals of black tourmaline.

The greater part of the rock basement at this place, however,
is formed of a black, blackish, and blackish-green, even gray rock
species of notable hardness.[35] It consists of a mixture of fine,
thin, slender scales of a truly black hornblende (28) with a not
very considerable portion of a fine-grained whitish quartz, mixed
in various proportions, from which the color arises, now more,
now less, black or gray. The rock species noted in section 21 are
more or less distant relatives of this rock. Its hornblende is dis-
persed in various ways. Now irregular, and in this case it seems
to have no particular luster; again regular, in horizontal layers
overlying one another like tiles (*imbricatim*); and then by re-
flected light it has in part its customary sheen, but in part a play
of colors of the rainbow. This occurs especially at the surface,
for this rock is foliated. One can see this convincingly either on
the rock-faces themselves, or on blocks cut for building stone.
The plates are an inch or more thick, and where they split, which
indeed does not happen at all easily, one finds the uneven surfaces, which fit one another exactly and firmly, coated with a thin
yellow-brown, ocher-like film. Between the black scales one sees
here and there extremely small flakes and spots of a yellow mica.
The black scales of hornblende often occur longer and in the
form of hairs or needles. At some places one sees thin beds of
pure black hornblende and then it maintains a more regularly
drawn-out bed than where it is intermixed with quartz. This
stone does not always strike fire with steel, and does not effervesce
with aquafortis. When pounded it yields a gray powder, which
in a hot flame does not flux either alone or yet with borax, rather
comes out of the crucible as a brownish powder. (29)

These stones are taken in great quantity to Baltimore, and

(28) *Corneus spatosus niger*. Wall. syst. I, p. 360, a.
(29) This kind of stone belongs to *Saxum grandaevum* Linn. syst. p. 79,
n. 35. *Saxum ferreum* Wall. syst. I, p. 420, n. 14. Above all since the contained
quartz is at times so scant that one has trouble recognizing it in some pieces,
or it is totally lacking.

used in foundation walls, cellars, etc., for which purposes they are superb.

Westward from Baltimore I encountered the last traces of this rock, in fragments along the road, 7-10 miles out; but these were already combined and intermixed with the soapstones to be noted farther on. Whether they have been locally dug up, or brought in from farther off, I do not know. Otherwise it seems to serve as foundation for the whole hilly region around Baltimore, and crops out especially abundantly along roads and on the sides of sundry small valleys between the Four-mile-Run and the Fredericktown road, toward the region that I am now about to describe.

23.

On the road from Baltimore to Fredericktown (about 10 miles from Baltimore and half a mile to the right from the road) on the southern and southwestern slope of a hill, are abundant fragments of quartz interbedded with thick layers of superbly beautiful black tourmaline.[36] These fragments are of various sizes, and lie scattered lightly about on and half-buried in the surface soil; the woods in the area have been felled, otherwise they would not be easily discovered; in the neighboring forests there might perhaps be more of them. It was a special pleasure for me, not only to find these tourmalines, but also to be their first discoverer. I had indeed seen earlier, in the little collection of Mr. du Sumetiere[37] in Philadelphia, a water-rounded piece of quartz the size of an egg (30) that contained two or three small, likewise truncated tourmaline crystals that had been taken out of a brook at Charleston in Maryland (some 50 English miles northeast of this place); here, however, they seemed to be right well at home.

The groundmass, on which they lie partly layer-wise, and by which they are partly bound, is a right pure white amorphous quartz, which also occurs thereabout in separate pieces, and then only at times is coated with a red ferruginous rind, or specks of the same, often also has small nests of little sparkling crystals on the surface or in crevices.

(30) Likewise in Switzerland. v. Saussure, Travels through the Alps, part 1, p. 91.

The tourmaline crystals themselves are black and vitreous; because they are tightly and firmly joined together and do not yield to separation without fracture, I cannot estimate the number of their angles with any certainty, but they appear to be hexagonal. They are from 1-2 lines[38] in cross-section, with their faces joined close together and over one another, and they are longer one after another like the pipes of an organ. Still, the individual crystals do not extend far without either showing simple diagonal offsets, which nevertheless fit one another extremely closely, or have their offsets and members joined by thin sutures of quartz. They are partly in parallel and upright columns, but in part also bent to one side or the other, or even running in various directions out from a common point. Further, they do not always maintain these beautifully parallel sets; are often entangled among themselves and with quartz; and beyond that there are places where outside of the simple masses of crude tourmaline and quartz-seams, nothing distinctly crystallized is to be seen. I find small areas where they are interwoven with talc, which is present in large quantities on the same hill, and on closer examination I see that individual small spots here and there between the crystals effervesce with acids.

They have no effect on the magnetic needle, as M. Saussure has noted for that from Geneva; (31) but when heated they become electrified and attract glass threads.

That these American tourmalines are certainly of no volcanic origin I was convinced not only by the general nature of the region, as far as I could perceive it, but also by the pure unaltered quartz with which they are so closely associated. What is more, individual crystals of tourmaline are found interspersed in several other gangue rocks, which betray just as little alteration by heat.

On the same ground with the tourmalines there are likewise abundant fragments of the soapstone mentioned in sec. 20. (32) It shows traces of a slaty texture, the mica-like particles are rather small and its color is mixed, yellow-brownish, greenish, and gray; now and again an interlarded black appears. In this stone there are weathered cubes of pyrite, but no trace of tourmaline,

(31) Saussure, part 1, 90.
(32) Talc-like Schneidestein.[39] Cronst. 263. *Talcum Ollaris* Linn. *Steatites Ollaris* Wall.

for all that they are such close neighbors. It is used here for hearth-stones, and the country people use it for all kinds of casting moulds. The Baltimore area provides different varieties of this kind of stone. It is also found particularly of greenish color, partly with little flakes of mica so abundant that some pieces appear to consist of nothing else. These little mica flakes are smallish in some pieces, in others of reasonable size and curved into wrinkled or wave-like form. Now and then serpentines appear, of whitish, greenish, and yellowish color, and varying hardness, at times so similar to soapstone that one might take it for nothing but hardened soapstone,[40] often with blackish ferruginous specks and coated in its crevices with brown ocher. At some places the greenish and yellowish variety is occasionally translucent. One piece, dense in fabric but strongly jointed so that its texture seems almost slaty, was especially remarkable to me because of its beautiful canary-green color; with reddish and brownish ferruginous spots on the fractured surface, and white as well, which latter are nothing other than asbestos, whose long, soft, and delicate threads one sees plainly where the stone splits lengthwise, less however where it is split crosswise. In its bright red rind especially quartz-grains are interlaced, and consequently on the outside the stone strikes fire here and there; internally, however, it can be shaved. On broken faces I found here and there equiangular three-sided cavities ending in a point, in which some kind of crystals must have been seated — which reminded me of steatite crystals recently found in the soapstone of my fatherland, at Wunsiedel. — These stones, especially the serpentine, are often criss-crossed in all directions with hornblende in now larger, now smaller, straight and curved lamellae, mainly green but in odd fragments more and more of other tints, from blackish all the way to yellowish.

Outside of the white scattered quartz, I found further in the same field a coarse breccia, of small rounded pebbles caked together with sand and ferruginous earth.

In Baltimore I obtained a little piece of so-called isinglass that was said to have been found in the neighborhood and is used as a kind of cement, and for plaster floors, etc. In the flame it gives off a smell of sulphur, and is therefore merely *Spatum fissile* L.

In sec. 6 it has already been pointed out that the beds of sand which lie partly against and before this belt of granite and

partly cover it, here as at other places have hardened into freestone; for the sake of relationship and proximity I note here that
another firm, finely sandy, red-brown ferruginous stone with
much delicate whitish mica intermixed, that breaks out into
pieces which split unevenly but horizontally, occurs abundantly
around Baltimore.[41]

24.

I have brought out the most important features of the Baltimore region, and now I go on in the same direction from northeast to southwest. A few miles above Georgetown in Maryland
is the lower fall of the Potowmack, and around Georgetown as
well as around Alexandria I found the gray rock-species mixed
of fine quartz and black mica that I have already described.[42]

Two miles above Fredericksburg in Virginia the Rapahannock
falls over a rock-bed, that is thus called the Rapahannock-Falls,
and around this city one finds pieces of a perfect, fine granite,
equally mixed of quartz, feldspar and mica, with interspersed
tourmaline crystals; also others that lack one or the other of
these constituents. These fragments come from the rock-zone at
the fall.

From Fredericksburg to Richmond one travels over land of
nothing but sand and clay, and sees no stone, excepting, here
and there on road cuts, thin beds of rounded silica pebbles and
other kinds, covered to various depths with sand, etc. Nevertheless the granite belt must continue under the road in depth, and
in the same direction as the road; and one sees it again as soon
as one descends at Richmond from the high flat sand plain; and
the narrow valley that the James-River has cut here and toward
the sea.[43] Hard by Richmond is the lowest fall of this beautiful,
copious, and navigable river. It does not exactly rush down head-
long over great heights, rather presses with impatient foaming
and raging over and through the low granite belt that extends
across it obliquely from northeast to southwest. This rocky
declivity is said to extend from here 4-5 miles westward, and
yet in all to give the river a vertical drop of only 71 feet.

Here the water has washed the granite[44] bare, and this locality
is especially noteworthy. One encounters all of the principal
constituents of granite, but not always equally and exactly mixed.

Here are clumps of pure granular quartz, there, erratic chunks of beautiful and partly crystallized feldspar, at another place crude masses of finely flaked mica, mainly black — here are mica and quartz, mica and feldspar, feldspar and quartz, now by themselves, now all three mixed together. One sees a hardened dough whose constitutents, when it was still soft and fluid, were not properly kneaded together.

The rocks strike across the river in obvious bands, from northeast to southwest, and make it highly probable that they lie in more or less perpendicular juxtaposed sheets — for in the direction that the sheet-like appearance takes across the river this phenomenon cannot be ascribed to the river. In the same direction white veins or bands of quartz as well as feldspar appear; locally, however, these curve away slightly downward from the line. Where the feldspar is most abundant one can break loose beautiful, large rhombs or crystals over an inch long, (33) and here and there one sees empty cavities where others formerly lay.

On the rock ledges slightly protruding above the water, which at other times are submerged, are many excavated holes, large and small, shallow and deep, so-called giant pots, in which partly sand and partly all kinds of pebbles were encountered. Mr. Kalm (34) mentions that Bartram has also encountered similar occurrences on the streams in other areas of the northern colonies, and explains their origin very cleverly. Only here it seemed to me that liberated chunks of feldspar might have given first instance for the reception of a pebble, etc., through whose whirling action the further hollowing-out occurred.

The constant washing and powerful pressure of the river has worn off all these granite ledges to entirely smooth surfaces. On the sides and between the granites there is a great variety of other small rounded stones which have been dragged in, by force of the water, from other regions.

---

(33) Earlier I saw at Mr. Sumetiere's a large specimen of quartz in which the half of a large empty rhomboid cavity stood out strongly; it had been brought to him by a farmer because of this. Here a feldspar crystal had lain.

(34) Kalm, Tr., pt. 2, p. 269.

25.

According to my observations there is thus true granite around New York and Richmond, which lie more than 500 English miles distant northeast-southwest from one another. — East of them no trace of it is encountered; between both aforesaid places, however, and exactly in the same direction, here and there a true granite peak rises up and appears where sundry streams have washed away its overlying cover. Everywhere further, along the way thus designated by it we find its constituents singly or mingled with other related kinds of rock; we saw foliated gneiss, radiating amiant, Russian glass, asbestos,[45] garnets, hornblende, black tourmaline and potstone in the same stretch, partly alone, partly mixed in various ways among themselves and with quartz, feldspar, and mica. It suffices to have named these different species, to remind my reader that this stretch of rocks thus characterized belongs by all means to the primitive rock groups, and that it remains always the same, except that the mixture changes.

Now, if we find a primeval type of rock following a course of 500 English miles in one unvarying direction, and this course marked out in superb fashion by falls in the streams, and if in the extension of this direction we find several falls indicated on other rivers farther to the southwest, we may well maintain with reasonable assurance that this primitive rock-type must continue on. And so in the course of time the observations of others will confirm my conjectures in sec. 14. If this last be plausible, we have already between New York and Fort Augusta on the Savannah a southwesterly-striking granite belt over about twelve degrees of latitude; and why should one not find continuation from New York northeastward, so abundantly supported by the consistency of the whole picture, just as probable?

The fact that this granite belt is (as far as I know) the only one we find anywhere so close to the sea, so low, and so continuously extensive may induce to special studies in the future. That which lofty Mont Blanc, at altitude of 2426 *Klastern*[46] above the sea, the Büet, the Gotthard, etc., and others contain in their highest peaks, is found here partly at sea level, partly not much higher. What is found in descending from the most accessible summits of these mountains toward the lower lands one observes in America on ascending toward the mountains that rise up stepwise behind the granite belt. Nowhere in or on the mountains have I encountered granite or granite-like rocks, as I shall show in the sequel. Here, therefore, a completely reversed order exists. I am willing to grant that the granite, which indeed seems to form the main basement of our planet, may extend under the mountains loaded upon it; but to the west I have seen it nowhere. (35)[47]

Once again I must point out the trend of the granite belt from northeast to southwest, already many times noted, as remarkable because it is not only faithfully parallel to the main outline of the coast, but also to the western elevated ranges of mountains; and additionally for the reason that various granite belts of the world, in unequally greater elevations, have the same trend.

Ores have not yet been found anywhere in the true granite belt, although they have in the overlying erratic blocks and beds; further, thus far they have been found there only in nests; to that I reckon the traces of copper around Brunswick, Rocky Hill, etc., in Jersey.

26.

Westward from this line of the granite the land rises everywhere, and several ranges of mountains rising higher one after the other look out at varying distances upon a regular alternation of **rock-types** [Felssteinarten] or **rocky mountains** [Felsgebürge] and **limestone flats** which all follow more or less the northeast-southwest direction, and where they locally appear to diverge, one finds on closer examination that these are merely spurs. Several notable valleys form the boundaries between the main ranges, of which there are really three, and which bear no limestone on their ridges.

To designate these in general I admit I use the word "Felssteinarten" or "Felsgebürge," perhaps inappropriately; in order however not to be misunderstood I must explain that under this heading in this treatise I desire merely to denote those more

(35) Nowhere does one have the satisfaction of seeing it in masses sufficiently large to permit any definite judgment as to its disposition in layers.— For the most part, however, it does appear in sheaves; but this upper granite might well be a late-comer.

elevated mountain chains that consist truly of various clayey, quartzose, sandy rock types, etc., but harbor no limestone.

Conversely I call **limestone valleys** the lower grounds that lie between the **rocky ranges,** parallel to them, principally filled with limestone, marble, or even spar-like rocks, and even where they rise into hills, nevertheless remain lower than the ridges of **ledge-forming rocks** [Felssteine] that follow immediately to the westward.

Both form the principal framework of this eastern part of North America, and on account of their outstanding order merit the closer attention of the future American natural scientist, to whom in time it must be easy to show their courses in different colors on the general map.[48] One can neither expect nor demand **complete** description of a yet unknown mountain region from a traveller who was unable to acquire any preparatory knowledge at all for his observation, nor to find the required time and opportunity for it. One must first have seen several parts of a mountain region before he can conceive an outline of its trend, its plan, its subdivision. One may perhaps not find the explanation for what he has seen at a given place until the second or third, far distant; or may there first be led to other fresh observations, for whose confirmation he might wish himself back at the first place. In the meantime, since I have made the trip from the **granite** to Wyoming on the Susquehannah and to Pittsburg on the Ohio, and back again, consequently twice, and have travelled over the mountains and long stretches between and on the mountains through two different regions, I shall allow myself to draw up at least a sketch subject to correction through further observation, but which will afford to other travellers a fore-taste and some facilitation of their observations. My reports refer, then, mainly to the mountain region between Philadelphia and Wyoming, and between Pittsburg and Baltimore, a perspective of about 120 English miles from northeast to southwest. Now if I venture here and there a conjecture as to other regions I have not visited, I rely mainly on general agreement that I have observed at distant places in the same directions, but in part also on reports from people who although certainly not mineralogists, still know enough to distinguish between limestone and other sand and rocks, especially indeed the former, because it is sought out everywhere.

27.

FIRST LIMESTONE BEDS BEYOND THE GRANITE[49]

A bed of limestone seems to join on close behind the granite. At no great distance from Schuylkill Falls a quarry has been opened up on a white, light gray, and bluish marble, partly veined and partly speckled, that is worked in quantity into tombstones, tables, fireplaces, etc. (36); it is soft, and not of the finest, and under the chisel it chips off in thin flakes. At other places it is merely a very uniform, light gray, fine and dense stone and is used for the burning of lime. This zone shows up around the localities of Plymouth, Whitemarsh, Chestnuthill, (37) Seven-Stars, Swedes-Ford. Its breadth at some places reportedly amounts to 1-2 miles or more; here and there it shoots off spurs to both front and rear. At Swedes-Ford a marble quarry is open on a steep hill directly above the river. It breaks into spalls that are nearly vertical, dipping at an angle of about 80 degrees to the east. What I have seen of this belt in outcrop seemed to strike partly east-west, partly west-southwest; its major beds, however, are largely covered over.

A few miles west of Baltimore we find as its southwestern continuation a vein of very beautiful white marble,[50] some speckled with blue flecks, which comes down diagonally across the Susquehannah from northeast to southwest. I have not seen the place, but (I have) the report from a stone-cutter who could not specify its breadth because at that time it was exposed at only one place, and only there, where it is washed off by the river. It is of varying quality and spalls when broken. The pure white is entirely similar to the scaly crystalline marble that is exposed at Wunsiedel, and here as there adjoins the granite and gneiss; locally it contains yellow scales of mica, but not many, and it dissolves completely in acids. The uppermost beds are purer than the lowermost; in depth it loses its brilliant whiteness and becomes yellowish. At the Catholic chapel in Baltimore one sees in several beautiful tombstones that it takes a good polish. There

(36) Kalm, Travels, part 2, p. 234, 235.
(37) These are the nearest places that supply lime in any quantity to Philadelphia, 14 to 18 miles away.

is similar marble in the Pennsylvania belt, but there, because it is softer, it is not so highly esteemed.

This white marble is rightfully to be accounted among the primitive rocks, and is entirely without foreign bodies, (38) here as well as in the Old World.

On the surface of this first calcareous belt are found at several places white, entirely transparent rock-crystals, from the size of a small finger up to the length of a shoe and the thickness of a thigh-bone. (39) In a valley at Swedesford I have seen whole huge druses of these; they are seated in a matrix of quartz and limestone mixed, which effervesces now and then even betwen the crystals. The crystals themselves are hard, strike fire, and cut glass. Often they are only very small crystals contained in crevices of the lime-rock. — Superbly beautiful ones are said to be found in the neighborhood of **Seven-Stars.**

The further extensions of this belt are unknown to me.

28.

SECOND ROCK-BELT[51]

The next following rock- or mountain-belt is not very high, it is true, but rises nevertheless notably behind the land fronting it. Its uppermost beds seem to consist mainly of a greenish, talc-like clayey rock-type, but lower down it contains other kinds of rock. To this belt belongs the **Elk-Ridge** of Maryland, southerly from Fredericktown, which is at least 10-16 miles through in cross-section, but is furrowed by several smallish parallel ravines and valleys. In this Elkridge are Stevenson's copper works. The rock from which the ore is taken at depth of some 60-70 feet is a mixture of reddish effervescing spar and locally quartz, with no mica. For several miles (from 30-39 miles westward from Baltimore) the overlying cover of this region is a dark-gray, thin-leaved but still hard, somewhat shiny clay slate; it does not effervesce, will not strike fire, and scrapes off white; is shot through with dull white veins.

(38) Scaly marble lacks fossils everywhere. Crell, N. Entd. V. 239.
(39) *Crystallus hexagona, pellucida, non colorata.* Waller, min. p. 108, Kalm, part 2, p. 233.

Out of the region from 24-28 miles west of Baltimore on the Conegacheag road I have a gray-greenish kind of clay-slate, dense and hard, dull on fracture; it contains intermixed lime elements which make it effervesce at many places, but which were not to be found with the glass. When wet it is light green; it scrapes off white and exposed to the air takes on a reddish-brown, locally dendritic efflorescence. Splits in the flame. Lies there in sheet-like fragments. (40)

Much commoner on these hills between Fredericktown and Baltimore, for a stretch of 18-24 miles, is a shinier clay slate mixed through with portions of mica and quartz. This is very thinly laminated, greenish, feels greasy and soft, and does not effervesce. (41)

On the eastern slope of a hill 22 miles from Baltimore on the Conegacheag road there appears a pale reddish laminated clay slate, laminated and with unequal or uneven surfaces; it is greasy and talc-like to the touch. Similar slate occurs also in other colors elsewhere.

Between 16-18 miles from Baltimore, in the vicinity of Allen's-Mill, many erratic blocks are found under the topsoil, of thinly foliated whitish highly glossy mica schist, with only very few quartz grains mixed in.

In the same area, 18 miles west of Baltimore, there is another gneissoid kind of stone that is related to the forelying granite belt, of intermixed coarse quartz grains, greenish and black mica, and perhaps feldspar (which however is weathered); it breaks into thin shells. In a low hill which there strikes to northeast and southwest.

This **Elk-Ridge,** in Maryland, goes on southward, fronting the valley in which Fredericktown lies, to the Potomack, shortly before which it ends up in a high rounded hill that is widely visible hereabout and known by the name Sugar-Loaf Hill. I do not know enough to give exact account of the continuation of this second belt beyond the Potomack, but I suspect that the Bull-Run-Mountains, which have a limestone valley between them and the South-Mountain (which thus regarded may be the exten-

(40) It seems to belong to the *Schistus viridus* Linn., although it is somewhat harder than this is described to be.

(41) It could indeed almost be taken for mica-schist. A similar one is found around the Fichtelberg and also in Saxon Voigtland.

sion of the limestone valley at Fredericktown) belong to it; just
as likewise the South-West-Mountain and Green-Mountain, which
appear farther on to the southwest in Virginia, may be connected
with it. Since, as I have already noted, back of Baltimore this
belt has eminently an upper layer of greenish clay slate,[52] the
mere name of this mountain, situated in the same trend and
designated by the name Green Mountain, leads me to believe
that a similar greenish rock has gained this name for it.

In the same trend but disconnected, still some other mountains
are shown on Jeffery's map of Virginia, namely the Long- and
Smith-Mountain, and Mount-Ararat. Whoever visits this region
will be able, from their trends and rocks, from the intervening
limestone valleys, etc., to find out their connection.

If I desire to seek out the northeastern continuation of this
chain of hills from the map alone, I take the aforementioned
Fredericktown limestone valley as its western boundary. I find,
then, that a line of hills, this side of Hannover, Heydelberg and
York extends to the Susquehannah about between Nelson's-Ferry
and Wright's-Ferry, crosses the river, then again on the north
side of the Susquehannah continues this side of Lancaster, under
the name of the **Welsh-Mountains,** approaches somewhat the
Flying-Hills near Reading, but further joins up with **Coventry,**
— **Limerick-** and **Rockyhill** and so (more narrowly hemmed in
between the two adjacent belts, the granite and the South-Mountain) to the Delaware, where it dies out in the vicinity of Hay-
cock.

That this may be approximately the direction taken by this
belt through Pennsylvania, with its breadth of perhaps 10-15-20
miles, with various projections and digressions, with uneven
elevations, etc., is manifest to me in the origin of lesser streams,
as they are shown on the map of Pennsylvania, which coming
down from the higher regions, turn away from this chain, some
to the east and some to the west. There are the Gunpowder,
Deer- and Muddy-Creek; Conewingo- Octaroro- Brandywine-
Pickerings- and Neshameny-Creeks, which arise to the eastward
of the indicated boundary and flow eastward. The Codorus, and
the Saucon go westward out of the same district, the former to the
Susquehannah, the latter to the Delaware.[53]

That I am not entirely wrong in this assertion is manifest
further and principally in the concordance of the rock-types at

different places on this stretch. Thus I found, on the hills behind
Valley-Forge, at Potts-grove and elsewhere, only the types closely
related to the above-mentioned greenish slates; among those that
are still in my possession are the following:

From the hills around Coventry, a dirty-green, clayey stone
with small shiny flakes and nests of calcite; it effervesces only
here and there, scrapes off white, breaks shell-like. — Appears,
however, all around there in prettier and brighter green, and it
is merely a modification of the kind mentioned above on p. 55
from the Conegacheag-road in Maryland (some 100 miles southwest).

Slaty gray stone of clay mixed with sand, with little whitish
mica flakes, and individual little enclosed tourmaline-like ?
crystals. Is hard; fractures shell-like; when wet still gives a play
of greenish color; when breathed upon gives off a smell of clay.
From the east side of Valley Forge-Hill in Pennsylvania.[54]

In this stretch there is a place on the Susquehannah indicated
on Scull's map of Pennsylvania as **Blue Rock;** far northeast of
this, on the road to Bethlehem, at Swamp-Meeting, or Quaker-
town, I have seen a blue, hard trap-like rock, of which however
I have no more.

At other places (westward from Baltimore) there is a kind of
rock (not very hard) mixed of white quartz and feldspar, with
individual little grains of hornblende ? interspersed here and
there. Quartz and feldspar alternate at times in parallel, even
laminae not much thicker than a stout sheet of paper, which
gives it a peculiarly striped appearance. The feldspar weathers
readily, to a porcelain clay ? and then the sheets of quartz remain, standing out alone. Were it harder it would be similar to
the gritstone around Bedford and other places in the mountains;
it breaks into layers a few inches thick or more between which
it has a pale ocher-colored coating.[55]

On the sides of Warwick's Hill in Pennsylvania, and elsewhere,
is another kind of quartzose rock; likewise in layers, a long
stretch; the quartz grains seem externally to be scaly or attenu-
ated, but on fracture appear of average size, white, reddish and
blackish, with iridescent colors, translucent, have no foreign
matter between them, are angular and extremely strongly bound
together.

As this belt approaches the Delaware it comes closer at the

same time to the **Leheigh** hills. I am unable to account for its
course through Jersey on the north side of the Delaware because
I have not seen these regions. Whoever wants to follow it here
will have to give more exact attention, because through Jersey
all the several belts in part crowd together and in part send out
more extensive offshoots as they approach the Hudson, and in
that area they form only narrow valleys. It seems probable to me,
however, that one might find its strike through Alexandria,
Sunburn, Hoffs, Mendum, along Suckasanny-Plains, Rockaway,
Hibernia, Pempton, etc.

This belt contains a great assortment of ores.

Copper is mined at Stevenson's pit in Maryland; (**copper glance
ore** in reddish calc-spar with a talc-like coating. On the waste-
dumps[56] there lies the softer, blackish clay slate, shot through
with mountain-green. — Beautiful malachite with partly heavier,
partly finer, partly unrecognizable rays and threads. —) and the
pits around Limerick and Saalford in Pennsylvania; these last,
as far as I know, are not being worked. — Are there some copper
pits in this stretch in Jersey?

Lead, coarsely cubic in spar, at Pequea Creek in Pennsylvania.

Iron, in masses in several hills, shallow under the topsoil, the
ores washed together as in heaps. — Mines and works are: Mary
Ann-Furnace, at Heydelberg, Marticks, Windsor, Reading, Warwick, and Coventry-Burdsborough, Hopewell, Vincents, Pool-
McCalls, Pottsgrove, and several other works, furnaces, and
mines, which however are not all operable.

To these belong: ironstone mixed with soft soapstone, mica,
and quartz grains, of Jones's mine, in Berks-County, Pennsylvania; lies quite shallow, layer-like, and forms whole hills.

Between the beds of ironstone lie others, of thin-sheeted mild
white-greenish soapstone (42) with ocher-like horizontal seams;
the workers of that place call the "Speckstein" or "Schneidestein"
soapstone or isinglass. It effervesces in some places.

Some miles northeast of the aforementioned mine, in Warwick's mine, likewise shallow beneath the surface, a somewhat
firmer and heavier ironstone is mined, which like the others is
kneaded through with soapstone, and breaks nodule-wise and
nest-wise between layers of it.

(42) The soapstone at Bayreuth is like this, often mingled with iron.

On and around the hills of Valley-Forge, in Pennsylvania, large stretches of **brown iron-earth;** more or less hard stone of clay, quartzose sand and mica mixed with iron earth; in part quite soft, spongy, and greasy.

As far as I have become acquainted with this belt it seems to have in depth a solid basement of spar and quartz, through which copper and other ore-veins run; seems farther upward to be overlain by gneissoid or foliated quartzose solid and softer rock, and in the still higher layers to bear clay-talc slates of more or less greenish color; iron seems dominantly to be deposited only in nests on eminences and in hills. Since nearly throughout traces of talc and soapstone occur in the depths as well as in the heights, one might perhaps not inappropriately call this the **talcose** belt.

In the longitudinal furrows parallel to the ridges, and variously on the ridges themselves, here and there small insignificant streaks of lime are found.

29.

SECOND LIMESTONE LAYER[57]

I have already noted a limestone valley between the foregoing belt and the South-Mountain. Ten or twelve miles from the Potomack is Fredericktown in Maryland, and farther northeastward Tonyton, Peter-Littletown, Mac-Callistertown, York-Town, Lancaster and New-Holland in this valley, which may be followed continuously from hereabouts as far as Jones's-tavern in the Welsh Mountains. Here it appears to be cut off by some high land, of which however I do not even know whether it does not consist of limestone hills. Perhaps it continues also on the other side, but I am not acquainted with it any farther.

It curves following the course of its two neighbors. Just as these send out spurs into the valley, so at other places the valley gives off coves between the mountains. This valley is 3-6 miles wide, fairly even excepting where it is cut through by streams which, when they do not find a convenient opening through the aforementioned rock belt, run along a stretch on the southern and southeastern slope of the valley, so that the valley generally has a greater slope toward this side. The common, uniform, gray thinbedded limestone, of which I shall take opportunity to speak farther on, fills it entirely. I have seen no foreign bodies [i.e. fossils] in it.

On the southwestward side of the Potomack I have followed it in the same trend as far as Leesburg in Virginia; thence, however, since my route turned away to the southeast toward Richmond, I came again across low gneissic hills of the second or preceding rock-belt, and I lost it.

30.

THIRD ROCK BELT. THE SOUTH-MOUNTAIN

The third rock-belt stands out more distinct than the second; it is higher, more compact, and no less rich in ores. Although this one also seems here and there to fade out, nevertheless it soon rises up again, in the same direction from northeast to southwest.

In North Carolina, approximately around the 35th degree of latitude, it begins to form up a distinct range. I could not find out whether it is distinct farther southward from there; perhaps there it becomes lower and less prominent along with the remaining mountains. Through Virginia it runs in a fairly regular, less interrupted chain, under the names of South-Mountain, Blue-Ridge, and Pignut-Mountain (if this last is not perchance a separate parallel branch of it). It goes through Maryland under the same name; but here as there with various branches. As soon as it gets between the 39th and 40th degrees in Pennsylvania, it becomes more broken up, swings somewhat more northerly, and approaches the mountains behind, nevertheless continues along with them in similar direction and there takes on the different names, the **Oley-, Flying-,** and **Leheigh-Hills.** Below Bethlehem it crosses the Delaware, and on the other side in Jersey it forms the high mountains bordering the **Drowned-Lands** on the south that according to Pownall are called the **Mesapetcung,** and go on to the Hudsons-River, where they fall in with the other **Highlands.** (43) Around the Delaware and all the way through Jersey, according to descriptions they are said to be higher and steeper

(43) Kalm, part 3, p. 206.

than anywhere to the south, and at the same time come closer to the **North Mountain.**

As laid out on Jeffery's map of Virginia this South-Mountain is held to be the southern branch of the **Alleghany,** that is, he joins both by a cross-chain; I am not able to contradict him out of my own experience, but it should first be found out, whether this cross-chain, as I suspect, is not limestone ? —

Evans (44) says of it that it does not run in such straight lines as the **Endless Mountains,** but rather stretches out in small inter-rupted steep hills, that in some places it almost disappears for several miles, and elsewhere widens out again to several miles. But he is speaking mainly about its course through Pennsylvania only. He sets the interval between the granite belt and the South-Mountain at 50-70 miles, but again only in the central part of Pennsylvania. From New York out to the first highlands it is about 36-40 miles (45); from Philadelphia out to the Oley and Leheigh Hills 40-45; from Baltimore to Frederickstown at the foot of the South-Mountain about 60. These last two distances I know from my own experience, and I cite them in order to confirm the observation I have already made, that these mountain chains come closer together northwesterly toward the Hudson.

I find it necessary here again to deplore the loss of the rock specimens collected toward Bethlehem in this belt, which pre-vents me from giving more accurate report on it. As a general observation, however, I may say that it is overlain with a foli-ated, quartzose or gneissoid rock. In Maryland, on the road through this belt from **Sharpsburg** to **Fredericktown,** or from one limestone valley to the other, one goes over various low and medium-high parallel hill ridges, which by virtue of beautiful, narrow, well-watered valleys wax agreeable, and both are over-lain for the most part by a reddish kind of soil. Here and there one finds gray thin-bedded sandstone with quartz veins. Broken fragments of coarse ferruginous quartz. At one place along the way I found erratic blocks of gray-reddish porphyry, with small transparent quartz grains kneaded in, and milk-white opaque feldspar. On the eastern slope of this belt a foliated, very hard gneissic stone, of scaly and granular quartz with some fine mica,

(44) *Analysis,* p. 7.
(45) Kalm, part 3, p. 201.

was very abundant; it broke into plates ¼ inch thick and appeared still laminated.[58]

On the other hand upon the west side, between Sharpsburg and Middletown, after one is entirely across the limestone, a gray, likewise foliated gneissic stone appears still more abundant; it has some very fine mica and small brown ferruginous spots mixed in. Breathed upon it gives off an odor of clay, and it scrapes off white, does not effervesce, and is hard.

Along its entire layout South-Mountain contains rich fissures, veins, and nests of ores, especially iron and copper. The iron works at Chamberstown, Carlisle, Middletown, Easton, etc., the almost inexhaustible iron-hill of Colonel **Grubbs,** and many others belong there. It has not been so thoroughly explored, however, as the foregoing chain.

I still have to note for this belt as well as for the foregoing that its eastern slope is gentler and more sloping than on the west side.

31.

THIRD LIMESTONE BED —
THE GREAT LIMESTONE VALLEY

A beautiful valley,[59] remarkable for its situation and fertility, separates the South-Mountain from the North-Mountain. It has no common names, (46) but could rightfully and preferably be called the **Great Limestone Valley,** or indeed, on account of the remarkable number of its German inhabitants, the **German Valley.** From the Delaware to the Potowmack, and even beyond, I have followed it for nearly 120 English miles. It begins at the Hudson-River, and from there on we recognize it through Jersey, Pennsylvania, Maryland, Virginia, down to Carolina, and (as I have been assured) to Georgia, going on in the same trend, of the same character, and directly fronting the next following mountain. The "drowned lands" in York and Jersey are its northeastern continuation, according to Pownall's report. A part of this valley in Pennsylvania between the Schuylkill and the

---

(46) Evans prefers to call it Piemont because it lies at the foot of the principal mountains.

Susquehannah, there called the Tulpehocken-Valley, is widely known as especially productive. In Virginia it is somewhat interrupted at one place only, in the vicinity of Staunton, by mountains jutting out from both sides; to all appearance, however, these mountains consist of limestone. (47) After this, however, it goes on again southwestward in its former aspect, and according to Evans is said to disappear some 200 miles from **Appalachian-Bay.** The width of this valley is changeful, from 6-10-12 up to 20 miles; on the whole, however, so that its width increases toward the south. From the rivers flowing through it it often appears uneven, hilly, and, like the foregoing valley, sloping generally off to the southeast. It also has in common with the foregoing valley the same gray, more or less hard and fine limestone, mostly lying in sheets of various thickness, which for the most part is paler on the outcrop but becomes darker, even blackish deeper in. It often also appears like a thinly foliate gray or black slate. To my knowledge this limestone deposit has not yet been quarried anywhere. Presumably this limestone valley also contains fine marble; at least I have found a beautiful liver-colored one at **Shippensburg.**

A large number of fine-looking caves and grottoes is found in this belt, for example at Easton, at Hummelstown, at Carlisle and elsewhere, which owe their origin to loosened and sunken layers of the limestone deposit, and are embellished by all kinds of dripstone. In the digging of wells crevices are found, larger or

(47) If I am not mistaken it is the Roanoke that has undermined a course through the rocks in this area and thus has formed a natural bridge over itself. This circumstance alone makes it most probable that the aforementioned mountain connecting the South and North mountains must consist of a kind of rock that can be softened and eaten out by water, which no doubt will be the case for the omnipresent limestone of this belt. The disappearance underground of other streams in other parts of the world confirms this further. Thin-bedded limestone gives the Rhone opportunity to go underground. Saussure, part 2, 406. And in just the same measure the Pegnitz, in the Bayreuth area, disappears through soft thin-bedded rocks of the same kind. (My conjecture above is strengthened through what I find about this natural bridge in the *Voyage de M. le Chevalier de Chastellux en Amerique*, p. 107. "Le rocher," it says, "est de nature calcaire, et ses couches sont parallèles à l'horison." M. de Chastellux nevertheless wonders strongly how "le petit ruisseau qui coule sous cette arche immense" could have come through there, for he finds "nulle trace d'un embrasement subit, ou du travail lent et pénible des eaux."[60]—The breadth of the arch is only 40 paces, thus less than that over the Pegnitz.—The height is not given.)

smaller, filled up with calc-spar and druses of spar. On the surface, however, crystals are frequently encountered, and they are excellent as faithful accompaniment and accurate indicator of underlying limestone floor; further if these are not seen, one finds everywhere black silica (flint, silex) and white quartz. The flint almost always has a white rind.

I have not had the luck to find a single trace of fossils in the many and various quarries that I have seen and diligently searched through; according to reports, however, I must believe that here and there, but only on the surface, a few have been found, and those only rarely. My experience permits me to presume for good reason that this limestone must indeed have originated in or under water, but not have derived its substance from comminuted shelled animals; one would then have to suppose that these had first become reduced to a completely uniform mush or pulp, so that not even the smallest trace of an organic body would remain, of which nothing can be discovered even with the best of glass. Its sheet-like beds, from inches up to a foot or more thick, stand out plainly and everywhere. But they rarely lie horizontal; whether this is to be ascribed to the uneven surfaces on which the calcic sediment was deposited, or to subsequent violent alterations, I cannot decide.

32.

THE MAIN MOUNTAIN SYSTEM

At the west side of the foregoing valley we find henceforth the principal mountain system of the eastern part of North America, which consists of several closely-spaced parallel-running ranges (at least the most of them), which individually are designated by different names but taken all together are called merely the Mountains, the Blue Mountains, the Endless Mountains, the **Appalachian Mountains,** the **Alleghany Mountains.** More strictly speaking, however, the Appalachian Mountains are understood to be the southern stretch of these mountains, which lie toward the setting sun from Virginia and the Carolinas, and take their name from an Indian tribe, the Appalaches, as does the Appalachian River, which flows into the bay of Appalache, in the Gulf of Mexico. The northern portion of the mountain system, behind the upper part of Virginia, Pennsylvania, etc., is named, from another tribe, the Alleghany Mountains, which tribe has also provided the name of the Alleghany River, tributary of the Ohio. Because of its ample span and extent the Indians have given it the name **Endless Mountains,** but this is not of course to be taken in literal sense. On the east, in distinction from the foregoing, they are called the **North-Mountain,** which however more properly belongs to the first eastern wall alone, as does also one particular branch of the mountains preferably bear the name Alleghany-Range. According to Evans's description (48) "The Endless Mountains . . . are not confusedly scattered, and in lofty Peaks overtopping one another, but stretch in long uniform Ridges, scarce Half a Mile perpendicular in any Place above the intermediate Vallies. Their Name is expressive of their Extent, though no Doubt, not in a literal Sense. In some Places, as towards the Kaats Kill and the Head of Roanok, one would be induced to imagine that he had found their End, but let him look a little on either Side, and he will find them again spread in new Branches, of no less Extent than what first presented themselves. The *further* Chain, or Allegheny Ridge of Mountains, keeps mostly on a Parallel with the *Isinglassy* Rief, and terminates in a rough stony Piece of Ground at the Head of Roanok and New River. The more Easterly Chains, as they run further southward, trend also more and more Westerly, which is the Reason that the *Upland* and *Piemont* are so much wider in Virginia than farther Northward. This South Westerly trending of the hither Chains brings them to meet the Allegheny Mountain, and in several places to intersect it and form a new Series of Mountains; as is the Case, I believe, of the *Ouasioto,* where the several Chains cross one another or some small *Spurs* (49) spring out from the main Ridges, the Mountains are broken and spread in detached Hills, and generally afford proper Places to conduct Roads through, but not very strait." [Here follows a

(48) Evans, *Analysis*, p. 8.

Translator's note: Schöpf rendered this passage into German, and his translation is very good. I give here the original, exactly as written by Evans, as I have done for all other quotations from his works.

(49) *Spurs* we call little Ridges jutting out from the principal Chain of Mountains, and are of no long Continuation. [Evans note].

passage giving advice on the laying out of roads, omitted by
Schöpf with no indication that anything is missing. It need not
be given here.]

"There are several Chains of the Endless Mountains which
have not come to my knowledge, and had they been so, might
have filled several Places which lie vacant on the Map. But so
far as we are acquainted with them, we observe that each Chain
consists of a particular kind of Stone, and each different from the
rest; and these Differences continue for their whole Extent, as
far as I can learn. When I crost them I was not apprehensive of
this, and omitted enumerating their Species. Some of the Chains
are single narrow Ridges, as the Kittatinni; some spread two or
three Miles broad at the Top; some steep on one Side and extending with a long Slope on the other; and the steeper they
are, the more rocky; but they are everywhere woody where there
is Soil proper and sufficient to support the Trees. Towards the
further Ridges North Eastward the Mountains consist of rich
Land, and in some Places are but as large broad Banks, which
take three or four Miles to cross. In the Way to Ohio by Franks
Town, after you are past the Allegheny Mountain, the Ground
is rough in many Places, and continues so to the River. Hereabouts, the Laurel Hill springs from the Mountains, and continues, though not large, in a very regular Chain, I believe, in
the Ouasioto Mountain. For though the Allegheny Mountain is
the most Westerly, on the West Branch of Susquehanna, it is far
from being so, back of Virginia.

"Except the further Ridges, as just now mentioned, there is
but little good Land in the Mountains; to be sure not one tenth
Part is capable of culture, and what small Matter there is, consists of extream rich Soil, in Lawns, on the River Edges, there
being so much rich Mud subsided there; and commonly gathered
above Falls, formerly in drowned Land, and now drained, by the
Rivers wearing Channels through the Rocks."

I have not hesitated to insert this entire passage, partly because the observations of Evans, who travelled through the mountains as land surveyor, confirm my own, and partly because both
before and after him nobody has taken the plan of the mountains into consideration; for Pownall's reports are merely borrowed from Evans.

33.

THE KITTATINNY

The first and easternmost range of the mountains that presents itself to the traveller coming in from the coast is the **Kittatinny,** which however is equally often called the **North-Mountain,** the **Blue-Mountain.** The route from the sea toward this mountain leads stepwise over the several higher- and higher-disposed areas, but the broad valleys and flats lying between them render the slope less striking and tiring. The distance from the granite to this first wall is from 60-70-100 miles. I saw it for the first time on the way to Wyoming, beyond Nazareth, and I must confess that I found myself disappointed, and did not see the steep, high, and venerable mountain that I had expected from the descriptions that the people in the lower regions give among themselves. However, I was repaid for what it lacks in elevation and awesomeness compared with our Alps and which its inconsiderable altitude and gentler slopes are unable to give it, by the more unanticipated spectacle of its uniform extension and splendid regularity. At the place where I first saw it and at many other localities it presents itself to the eye as an apparently continuous straightline wall, because the spurs and recesses existing here and there are not easily discerned in the distance and under the dense forest that clothes it from base to summit, and consequently do not spoil the impression of the simple and large main-line. Thereafter, on the way between Nazareth and Carlisle, I saw this wall entirely uninterrupted for several miles, and continuous in exactly the same point of the compass; its backbone even stays for considerable distances in the same horizontal position parallel with its base. As a whole, however, the crest of this wall is horizontal, and it drops off stepwise to the south. At times one sees several of these steps or sharp declivities close behind one another, and then again the crest going straight on for a long stretch. Only where the various larger streams and often even the smaller cut straight through, did I notice in the part of these and other ranges I observed that the adjacent and thus transected end of the chain appears again and again in somewhat elevated and often rounded points, and that most of these eminences are on the northern sides of the streams.

This eastern wall, while it follows the dominant northeast-southwest trend, nevertheless makes a few lesser curves here and there. A considerable deflection toward the west appears between the Susquehannah and the Potowmack, or between Carlisle and Shippensburg, which deflection all the other hinter-lying mountain ridges appear to follow more or less. Perhaps a similar turning will be found even in the ranges lying to the fore. It seems at least that the bend the Delaware makes in the Philadelphia area may have some relation to it — ?

At the outcrop the rock of this first escarpment[61] is a solid, fine-grained sandstone, gray, whitish, also verging on the red, some with sparse mica, always very fine, some with no mica at all.[62] On the way to Wyoming, in and around the so-called **Wind-Gape,** one sees an indescribable multitude of fragments, none too large, of this rock along the road, but no large and solid bare ledges, because these are covered by the overlay of soil and trees.[63] It is stratified, but in thick beds.

34.

Since it was impossible for me to follow the full length of this mountain chain from one end to the other, I shall allow myself the liberty of borrowing for further overview some notes appertaining to the next following ranges from the best maps of Jeffery, Scull,[64] Evans, Pownall, which however will receive many improvements and corrections in the future, because their authors neither made the exact number and direction of the various branches of the mountains the principal object of their work, nor could they, in the inaccessible uninhabited wildernesses that obscure them.

Around the 36th or 37th degree of latitude, approximately, the main mountains, which come up from the south under the name of Appalachians, divide into different, more separated and regular branches. The western and more notable arm, which is designated on almost all maps as the more direct extension of the Appalachian Mountains, and farther on under the name of the **Alleghany-Ridge,** draws off at first in this region to the westward, but after that, through Virginia, Maryland, and Pennsylvania, remains for the most part parallel to the eastern arm.

This eastern arm is the Kittatinny, just described. According to the data on the maps, not until these both separate at an acute angle, and the Alleghany by its divergence opens up more space, do several other ridges begin to rise between the two, which, taken as a whole, are represented as running parallel, here and there however broken off, and not extended in a line fitting one another exactly, or even with further intervening branches.[65] Thus the maps show deep down in Virginia 4-5-6, but farther up 7-8-9 of such ranges; the reader must not assume, however, that this is here adduced as sound evidence. According to the same map-information the true Allegany Ridge deviates somewhat more from the Kittatinny through Jersey and New York, although the other ranges appear more compressed and narrowly crowded together.

However, without depending any further on the plan of the mountain ranges on the maps, perhaps more often than not purely arbitrary, I shall adduce my own experience in the matter, inconsiderable though it be. I call attention in advance, however, to the fact that the alternation between lime — and other rock-types occurs in almost as orderly fashion crossing through the mountains as between the coast and the principal mountains. Most of the valleys, or intermediate space between one rock ridge and the next, contain lime, often limestone mountains or limestone hills, which then go likewise in direction parallel to their neighbors on both sides, and on one side or the other, or both, have flowing water, the reason for their hilly form. In many valleys, indeed, no limestone is known, perhaps because it has never yet been sought there, and in the impenetrable swamps and overgrown, mossy, mud-washed areas it is not easy to make discoveries. Perhaps it is entirely lacking in such valleys, which really are only sunken ridges of other rock-types; nevertheless most of them, particularly on the way to the Ohio, do contain it.

35.

Mountain ridges between Heller's House at the foot of the Kittatinny and Wyoming on the east fork of the Susquehannah.

From Nazareth through Schöneck up to a few miles from Heller's House[66] there is mainly hilly limestone floor. A mile back of this house one crosses the Kittatinny; one does not climb over the highest part of it, but passes through a natural gap situated toward its upper part, which may be from half a mile to a mile wide, comes up to half the height of the mountain, and is studded everywhere with rock fragments from the shattered backbone of the mountain. No water flows through this gap, and further, one sees no evidence that a stream ever came through it; because of that, in distinction from others, this opening is called the **Wind-gape.** On the other or northwest side one has a long and gentle descent as far as Eckardts house, 3 miles from Hillers, along which red clayey beds and also nests and nodules of brown umber-like earth are found.[67]

2) Behind Eckardts — a limestone hill of no considerable height; it contains the usual gray limestone but toward the summit is overlain by sandstone, and has many scattered black flints. As far as the eye can view it, it extends in the same direction as the former, but it is not known how far.

3) After this hill, through Brinkers-Mill, as far as Dieters's, there are two or three rows of low sandstone hills which, when one overlooks them from a subsequent height, are in fact all drawn out lengthwise in a north-south line, but are somewhat uneven and broken up. These high grounds are dry and poor, but there is good land here and there in the dales, also limestone and marl soil, and already many inhabitants. On the top of a hill behind Brinkars-Mill there is a lake one mile in circumference, at whose edge I found fragments of a rock composed of rounded, polished, pearl-shaped quartz grains that are not cemented together by any visible binding medium. This lake has indeed no higher land around it on the hill. There are said to be some other mountain lakes in these parts.

4) The Pokono. — From Dieters on one travels through narrow valleys and flats, crosses the strongly meandering Pokono-kriek a few times, and sees along the road nothing but thousands of layered, platy, thicker and thinner sandstone fragments. Six miles from Dieters, nearly always climbing upward, one comes upon **Sebitz's** house; two miles beyond the house one passes through a broad gap, on whose sides its walls still rise high; and over a few small elevations and depressions one has some 4 miles farther to

White-Oak-Run, on the west side of the mountain. — Along the way one sees nothing but platy sandstone in fragments.

From Sebitz's house on the Pokono to Wyoming it is 37½ English miles, through nothing but thick forest, swamp, and wilderness; the road is horrible, only 6 feet wide, hewn out between high trees, and thickly strewn with stones. This whole stretch of the mountains is known partly by the name of **St. Anthony's Wilderness,** partly the **Great Swamp.**

From White-Oak-Run one has in part gentle slope, partly narrow flats and uneven ground, until one comes to the real beginning of the Great Swamp, which is estimated to be 51 miles long. The more outstanding belts that one passes are:

5) A ridge of mainly reddish sandstone, on the other side of Tunkahannok-Kriek;

6) Between this and Tobyhannok-Kriek — another belt of reddish sandstone and much red clay soil.

7) Somewhat smooth land, then a high mountain, the **Locust Hill,** red clayey soil, and reddish shelly sandstone; it has a long steep slope to the west, towards **Leheigh-kriek,** and with the next following mountain forms a narrow, deep valley where beneath the high tree tops cold and darkness prevail, and, on account of its atrocious aspect, is called the **Shades of Death.**

8) From Leheigh on up, a high, steep mountain; the same sandstone, but gray and bluish gray; on the other side, a longer, less sudden descent to the **Bear-Swamp-Kriek.**

9) From the brook on, first steeply upwards, then more gradually, over a ridge of white and finer sandstone; on the other side a long and gentle descent to a mountain valley, or into a high, seemly plain, called **Bullock's-Meadows,** and also the **Long Meadow.**

10) From this mountain valley, a small hillock, but on the west side a deep and steep descent.

Here are found red clay and all kinds of sandstone. But at some steeper places, partly fragments, partly bare standing ledges, of larger or smaller, sharp, white quartz grains closely and exactly fitted together without the admixture of any visible foreign binding medium. Such places occur high up on the mountain; the summit itself, however, is overlain with the platy sandstone.

11) Another ridge — on the east side contains white, on the west side red sandstone; here and there red clay, and fragments of coarse-grained quartz rock.

12) Another ridge; its eastern slope, inconsiderable, has similar quartzose rock, high toward the middle and above lying bare; otherwise however and toward the summit, red and gray sandstone; its western slope toward Laurel-Run, if I am not mistaken, is high and steep; from this creek one has yet

13) and 14) two moderate hills or ridges ahead, before coming to the eastern branch of the Susquehannah, on which Wyoming lies.

However, here one is not yet over the entire mountain, but still has to the westward a few ridges that seem to coincide with the Bald-Eagle-Mountain and farther on with the Alleghany-Ridge.

As far, then, as I can form a conception of the layout of this section of the mountains, restricted as I was to one narrow route and unable to get further information from the inhabitants, it is as follows:

It consists of several ridges, mainly running parallel one behind the other; I have noted only the most distinctly prominent ones.

The foundation of the whole is not granite, rather the aforementioned kind of rock, which consists of sharp, angular, white, translucent quartz grains, now larger, now smaller, fitting closely together and between which no binding material is visible. (50) I have no samples before me, but I remember that I examined the rock thus described often and closely. This kind of rock occurs on the east side and at the foot of the Kittatinny, back of Easton, where it is generally called millstone, because it has been found remarkably good for that purpose, and is transported from there to Philadelphia; however, it appears also on the west side, toward Wyoming, and this justifies me in thinking that it forms the support, the foundation of the mountain and the

---

(50) *An Saxum quartzosum acutangulum albidum—Linn. ? nisi Cos molaris L.—*

following sheet-like rocks piled layer upon layer. Whether this rock itself lies in beds, in sheets, or in large masses, I have had no opportunity to convince myself.[68]

Taken all together the mountain ranges or ridges are only covered or overlain with a sheet-like kind of sandstone, but, to be sure, often in strata piled high. They have as base a more or less fine white sand which because of admixed foreign constituents or even colored sand appears now reddish, now gray, bluish, etc., and thus distinguishes one ridge from another, one side from the other. Breathed upon, most of them give off an odor of clay; on fresh fracture they may be scraped in places, but they have a hard crust. They break into sheets from ½-2 inches thick that seem truly to form a solid piece, but on closer examination one discovers many thin closely spaced laminae. They seem to have only very little mica, very fine and rare, if sparkling sand grains have not deceived me. They belong in general to the family of **whetstones** (*Cos*), of which they provide all kinds, and are generally known and used under the names Grindstone and Whetstone.

Under the outer crust of whetstone there often lies another somewhat solider rock consisting of evenly mixed finer sand that the inhabitants call **Gritstone;** on this route, however, I have seen little of this.

The uppermost layer of whetstone is everywhere split up, and its fragments fill all flat and sloping spots and places.

There are some traces of iron and copper in this region. Around Wyoming there is bog iron ore, and signs of other metals.

36.

MOUNTAIN RIDGES BETWEEN SHIPPENSBURGH AND PITTSBURG ON THE OHIO

Shippensburgh is the last small town one encounters in the great limestone valley on the high road from Philadelphia to the Ohio. The road turns from there to the westward, and goes 4-6 miles farther over limestone ground to the Blue Mountain or

Kittatinny, shortly before which one passes over several hills of loose slate blocks inclined toward it that are overlain with coarse sand and rounded flints. The Blue Mountain as well as the South Mountain in this region appear at a distance steeper and higher than usual, but the latter, which one sees on the left, shortly falls off considerably, and the Kittatinny is also suddenly cut off here, ending up in an elevated rounded summit, called **Parnell's Knob;** however, one is not immediately aware of it, but while travelling on an oft-winding road between high woods all at once one perceives, with no small astonishment, the aforementioned Parnell's Knob behind him, which he had at first thought it necessary to climb over. For here the front of the Kittatinny is much interrupted over several miles; does not rise up again until farther to the south, and thus facilitates entry into the mountains. An unimportant stream, the Greater Conecacheague-Kriek, issues here from the mountains. On the road that leads around this mountain extremity (51) are fragments of medium fine-grained quartzose rock that people here call freestone, but use their own also for mill stones; whetstones are also found, and in the valley that stretches up to the right and northeast-ward behind the Kittatinny, called **Path-Valley,** limestone as well. On the summits of the mountain there is good farming land, and some of them are inhabited.

The road starts out somewhat northerly before it crosses and goes along the base of the next following mountain, which here at first is called the **Cove-Ridge,** but farther on the **Tuskarora.** The Cove Ridge, with a few other interrupted ridges, surrounds two fertile inhabited valleys, the **Big Cove** and the **Little Cove.**

The **Tuskarora,** the second ridge, has at its base as well as farther up reddish sandstone[69] and reddish quartz in whose crevices small crystals are abundant. It is fairly high, but the road, after several windings through the valleys, goes all at once steeply up its side.

On its top are large fragments of a jasper-like rock. It is dark red-brown, very hard; strikes fire strongly; on fracture is slightly convex; of not very fine, often scaly grain, dull with little sparkling specks; gives no odor when breathed upon; on closer exam-

(51) On Scull's map the Conecacheague-Ridge and the Kittatinny come together here from the northeast in Parnell's Knob, and leave between them the Horse-Vallay and other vales.

ination, however, and especially when wetted, it reveals plainly that it consists of thin superposed laminae, which are however extremely firm and most intimately united, and that betray themselves by so many paler streaks. When struck together the pieces give a bright ringing bell-like tone.[70]

On and around the Tuskarora were found also small pieces of the aforementioned quartzose pearl-like rounded rock. But it is covered most abundantly by a gray sandstone which here, however, does not exhibit such regular bedding. The western slope of the mountain is long and easy; from the heights down to Fort Littleton it is 10 miles, over low hills and through various valleys; one finds alternating red soil, white sand and sandstone, clays, and marly soil. Limestone exists in the neighboring valleys, in Cove-Aughwick and Shirley-Valley. Fort Littleton lies in a rather low area, but before one is completely there, to the right two mountain ridges, i.e. the **Shade-Mountain-Ridge** and the **Black-Log-Ridge** are seen to be cut off in the area, so to speak leaving space for the accommodation of the highway; to the left, however, a few mountains that belong to the Cove Mountains. When one reaches the fort he has therefore really 4 mountain ridges behind him, without having had to climb over all of them. And from there on one has still farther for 9 miles a fairly good, mainly level road, over red clayey ground, and here and there clay deposits in low hills up to the base of the next main ridge. Iron and beautiful crystals are found in these parts.

Sideling-Hill-Ridge forms by this time the fifth mountain that one sees on this route, and it still extends, like the foregoing ones, from southwest and south to north and northeast. This ridge is one of the more stately mountains, and is rather steep and stony to climb, but on its broad back it has various wide and level flats, or less broken land. It contains most of the rock types already noted. On its sides and on the summit are fine- and coarse-grained pieces of quartz with sharp grains, coarse whetstone in thick layers and of different colors; here and there somewhat finer whetstone; at the very top are long stretches of loose sand, fine and quartzose; the grit-stone also occurs; here it consists of small quartz grains with fine sand, rare and small blende and some black (tourmaline?) grains. Its western slope does not amount to much, but in the direction taken by the road one does not go entirely down into the valley that separates it from the next slope, rather follows a few spurs through which it is connected with

Rayshill, which farther south is also called the **Ragged-hill,** and farther north the **River-hill,** in other respects, however, of the same constitution and structure as the foregoing ridge, and perhaps making up with it only one broad-based mountain. The western slope of Rayshill is considerable and long. Between its foot and the eastern foot of Sidelinghill one has at least 10 English miles, and more. After this one goes a few miles farther over small foothills of red sandstone or whetstone, and reddish clays, and yet has still a short but steep slope over **Crossing-hill,** at whose base, which I consider really to be the foot of Rays-hill, one comes for the first time to the Juniata River. This last slope, on the water side, exhibits throughout inch-thick (more or less) beds of dark red whetstone, with layers of gray partly between the red, partly above it, on the summit.[71]

In the red whetstone, as in the other further occurrences of this species, nothing can be distinguished; they have finely pulverized sand as basis, give an odor of clay when breathed upon, scrape off pale, do not strike fire; like others of this whetstone, it has little shimmering specks, which however are hardly mica.

On the other side of the Juniata (which here comes at first straight from west to east, bends sharply around a jutting hill and on its other side takes up a course in the opposite direction until finally it is flowing northeastward) the highway goes for almost 4 miles along the top of a narrow and low eminence on both of whose sides one sees the Juniata to the left and right, flowing here to the east, there to the west, at some places hardly half a mile apart. This salient is entirely covered by red sandstones, in sheets, whose fragments here as well as elsewhere are seen very abundantly in almost perfect rectangles. This salient leads, rising almost imperceptibly, to the seventh main ridge, which is the

Allequippy-Ridge; albeit one does not go over its highest top but rather through a hollow, nevertheless one has again on the west side a considerable slope ahead; and still always the same bedded sandstones, which in this area appear in especially regular beds, of various colors and different fineness. As they lay on the road the fragments often had coarse dendritic patterns on their surfaces. After one is down again and has reached the north bank of the Juniata, the road leads along this river, mainly level, to the little town of Bedford; before this, however, one passes the high, stately faces, separated or cleft by the river, of

Evits-Mountain, if I am not mistaken also called Great-Warriors-Mountain; its open, ever rolling sides are steep, and end off on both sides of the river in high, arched profile. The rock fragments lying below are a kind of gritstone;[72] fine quartzose gritty sand, firm and hard, mostly white, here and there somewhat reddish or with reddish streaks; the entire mountain-sides appear mainly white, and one sees no strata, unless they are covered and rendered imperceptible by the loose blocks.[73]

Farther on and closer to Bedford the mountains become somewhat lower, and the river goes through a more open, hilly landscape; by this time, however, one encounters limestone,[74] partly gray, partly blackish, which fills up for the most part the space intervening between the last mountain and the Alleghany, and which rises here and there in moderately high, massive ridges parallel to the foregoing ridges; among others this is most plainly seen on

Wills-Mountain, which extends southward toward **Fort Cumberland** on the Potomack and northward toward **Frankstown,** and has fertile valleys around it. On the road fragments of the limestone appeared that partly had white veins, partly small empty cavities in which presumably crystals of spar had been seated. In the country around Bedford these limestone hills appear indeed to be irregular and confused; however, one must consider that the rivers and waters make more impression on them, cut through them and hollow them out in different directions, and so produce fronts of various appearance. Many of them are also overlain by sandy blocks.

For 6-7 miles from Bedford the highway goes on still in valleys, and on the roadside we have now limestone, coarse silica and flint (*Silices*), now sandstone and gritstone. After this, however, the road rises, and goes for 12-13 miles over a narrow projecting branch of the next mountain, long and sharply ascending; above, however, one finds partly level, partly gentle-rolling top, and sees nothing but the aforementioned red whetstone, in small, very abundant rectangular plates. This whole spur is called the **Dry-Ridge,** because no water is found on its narrow top; it goes principally southwest, and on both sides we see others like it; they form the foothills of the Alleghany, or one could take them for branches of it. At the end of the 12 miles we have a considerable drop toward the west, and come then to **Irelands-Run;** and some two miles farther, over another low hill, finally to the foot of the

Alleghany-Mountain itself — which there, where the highway approaches it, presents a straight wall, as far as the eye can reach. We have about a mile on a winding road to the top, and then a gentle slope for a few miles, over nothing but shelly fragments of grindstone,[75] which covers both sides of the mountain: whitish with intermixed red, gray, reddish, blackish; this last has a few fine sparkling spots (mica?); the others seem to have none; they vary in hardness; on the steep roadside we see them lying over one another in plates of ½-1-2-4 inches, or projecting out of the soil. I have been assured that this ridge goes as far as South Carolina, maintaining the same rock composition and structure. Traces of quartzose and granular stone also appear.

This mountain top and ridge is held to be one of the highest, or even the highest, which we are warranted in believing by both its position and by the direction of the many streams flowing out from it on the east and west sides of the whole mountain system. The mountain itself does not seem high, and it does not stand out much above the others, but its base is already high. On down from it we come to the so-called **Glades,** (52) under which designation we mean here a mountain valley, or lower, more open and broad areas between the mountains. These **Glades,** which in distinction from others in the mountains are called the long or the great, are from 8-10-12 miles wide between the two bordering mountain ridges, and they are known for 40-60 miles in length; they contain much good land and already have numerous inhabitants. Taken in the large, it is an elevated valley, cut through variously, however, by smaller and lower hills; it contains much limestone; its western boundary is the

Laurel-Hill, toward whose top from the Glades one has just as moderate a way up as from the Alleghany down into the Glades. Its top is broad, and here and there has good land, but occasionally large stretches strewn with fragments of platy whet-

(52) In literal sense, an opening, a long clear space in a forest.

stone lying thickly one over another; and still more so along its western slope, which is several miles long and often precipitous. One counts 14 miles from the foot of the mountain in the Glades to its other foot, and finds no dwelling on this road. Its structure and rock-types are the same as the preceding.

It is said of Laurelhill that in these regions it begins to branch out from the Alleghany; or to express myself more plainly, that somewhat to the north of here its outstanding ridge, that comes up from the southwest, joins up with the Alleghany or fades out. After it we have still the

Chesnut-Ridge to climb over, which in truth is of no great note, but still of similar structure. It is the eleventh of the most particularly distinctive mountain ridges that I have observed on this route, and the westernmost of the true mountain ridges. From here on it is still about 35 miles to the Ohio, and this interval is filled with several low hills, on which however one finds all the way through nothing but reddish or gray platy whet-stone. As a whole, however, they are covered with much better, richer, brown-black soil, and from here on one misses entirely the pale red sandy-clayey surface of the landscape on the auroral side of the mountains. Nearer on to the Ohio, and in a few other valleys, limestone is found. The breadth of the mountains be-tween the east side of the Kittatinny and the west side of Chesnut-ridge may come to some 120 English miles, measured along the highway; less, however, in straight cross-section.

The main arrangement of the mountains of this side is thus entirely similar to that noted in the preceding section. That is to say, they have a foundation of quartzose rock; are without exception overlain, sides and summit, with stratified rocks; all strike more or less southwest-northeast, and have limestone in their valleys only.

Here and there they contain traces of various ores, but these are still little investigated, discovered, and known. Iron is found in quantity; showings of copper, and lead in abundance; they have further zinc, vitriol, alum, sulphur, saltpeter, and salt.

37.

Beyond the rock-types noted in the foregoing sections there is a multitude of other and different kinds of soil and stone, on and beneath the surface of these American mountains and their foothills. Data are still too few, however, to say anything about their disposition.

Taken on the whole, however, the commonest uppermost cover of the rock- or silica-ridges, as well as the limestone beds, along the more elevated drier places, is a reddish soil of sand and clay varying in depth which, just as we understand things for the dry lands, has only a thin cover of black garden-soil. And everywhere one finds iron-earth, iron-mould, or on the whole iron particles in many forms richly distributed over this entire surface and mixed with the others.

Clay deposits of various kinds, quality, color and hardness are encountered abundantly here and there in the lower regions, valleys, and at the bases and sides of low hills. I was not able to notice that they followed anywhere a particular trend or position, but it seems rather that they have been swashed together by chance at one place or another and have occupied spaces not filled with other materials. There is fairly fine porcelain clay, potter's clay, kinds of ocher, and others that approach the Spanish brown, or otherwise can be used for painting.

Walls and beds of **shale**[76] are very common in the valleys of the principal mountains and the foothills, and along the rivers (53) there. They are always found on the sloping sides of the other heights, hills, or mountains, different likewise in fineness, color, and hardness. The shales lie just as often on the quartzose rocks as on the limestone; also quartz-rocks, limestone, and shale one above the other. I have found impressions of fern fronds on the rocks of shale at Wyoming, on the Susquehannah.

Marcasite or pyrite, yellow and white, are found abundantly in nodules and laminae on and between the shale layers in the mountains.

Eastward from the mountains, however, in contrast to the main mountains and their western parts, few shale beds are found, and those not thick. The most of it this side of the mountains occurs along certain banks of the rivers, around Nelson's Ferry on the Susquehannah, on the Schuylkill, on Slate-River in Virginia, etc., etc., and this is not everywhere of the best.

With the shale, and under it or interbedded with it, mineral

(53) Kalm, part 2, p. 469.

coals are commonly found in the mountains if the stream bed is deep enough. At several places, especially where the coals crop out on the steep river-sides, as at Wyoming and at Pittsburg, etc., it appears undeniable that coal and shale must have had common origin. At such places coarse, sandy, thick-bedded shale lies wholly above; deeper down, however, increases more and more in fineness of bedding and blackness, on the whole, however, still remaining softer and more friable than pure clay-shale until it gradually merges into a vein of dense, shiny, unevenly crumbly coal; to be sure these veins are only inconsiderably thin and are merely coal-like shale (richly carbonaceous shale), often, however, very thick, like those on the Ohio, which are also laid down in layers throughout. The coals around Wyoming and elsewhere had coarse shale again as substratum; those on the Ohio have marble beneath them,[77] but whether directly so I do not know. That these coals have originated from former accumulations of peat, or peaty soil, through fermentation and compression, (54) I daresay will admit of no doubt. The aforementioned plant-impressions are found in the shale roof of the Wyoming-coal. The coals occur only in the valleys of the mountains, and there at various depths. Where they crop out it happens entirely by occasion of the rivers or creeks, which cut their courses through them and thus leave them bare on the banks, often high above the water. The hill opposite Pittsburgh is forsooth over 100 feet high, and fairly steep toward the Monangahela; the very thick coal bed[78] may be about at the middle of the hill, so that it is little trouble to send the lump coal in chutes straight down into the boats lying below; the entire hill nevertheless is made up exclusively of coal measures.

It is noteworthy in this regard that most of the loose shale blocks,[79] or at least many of them, occur at such places on the rivers where at short distances before them there are so-called falls, i.e. where the rivers go over a shallow rock-ledge. This is the case at Nelson's-Ferry, and at Wyoming, etc. But just so does the only considerable coal bed thus far discovered on the east side of the mountains occur, behind the fall of the James River in Virginia, and thus in other regions, in similar situation, black, loose vegetable mould is found behind waterfalls, accumulated

(54) v. Beroldingen, Beobacht. die Mineral. betr. p. 106.

to thicknesses of 6-8-10 feet, where still in latter days the same thing has come to pass as that which long ago may have given occasion there for the origin of the shales and coals, that is, damming up of the rivers, or at least diminution of their velocity.

The aforementioned comparatively rare shale deposits on the east side of the mountains may therefore have origin in common with the coal equally rare on this side. Outside of that just mentioned on the James River, so far coal has been found only not far from Reading and on the Susquehannah (20 miles from Lancaster at Elizabeth-Furnace). Some is said to have been found on Long Island, and this is possible, for in its swampy places it has considerable supplies of peat, although it is not dug; this however would not be of as great age as the former. (Farther to the north there are rich coal mines in Nova Scotia and Newfoundland.)

In the neighborhood of some coal measures one encounters partly springs, partly flowing water on which petroleum is floating; this is the case at Wyoming. Elsewhere, however, petroleum is found, or traces of it, where up to the present time no coal has yet been found; however, since the petroleums are apparently the offspring of coals, (55) in the future man may thus be led to discover them.

38.

They do not belong directly with the survey of the mountains, to be sure, but a few observations concerning the later alterations that rain, rivers, and floods have worked on North America do stand in fairly close relation to the contents of the foregoing section.[80] The American farmer calls all soils infertile and poor that will not produce rich crops for 20-30 years hand running without manuring, and soil of this blessed quality is abundant along the larger and smaller streams, in and fronting the mountains, and at the other lower-lying places, swamps, and morasses. Here we find again all that which rain and flowing waters, from their well-springs on, have removed from the higher soils. To be sure, this is nothing more than what happens everywhere, but one cause more than any other seems to bring it about in

(55) v. Beroldingen, Beobacht. die Mineral betr. p. 139.

America. On their way toward the Atlantic Ocean all of the waters coming from the east side of the mountains have their courses through the northeast-southwest trending rock belts already described, and lines drawn straight from the sources of most of the rivers (perhaps all?) to their mouths fall in exactly opposed position from northwest to southeast. Thus we have the many so-called falls, which are such a hindrance to inland navigation, for those that I noted at the granite belt as the first up from the sea are not the only ones. The obstacles that the streams find in their courses, especially at low water, give the earth, mud, and sand washed down from the higher regions occasion to settle out. This will happen mostly where the obstacles are most notable, and on that account we find the most productive and richest landed estates mainly above these falls, where it is not uncommon to encounter tracts that are indeed narrow but that amount to many acres, with absolutely black soil 6-8-10 feet deep and more of inexhaustible fertility. The same condition has frequently been caused, where there were no falls in the vicinity, by the bending of the river beds, for many rivers, especially in the mountains, have to curve and turn aplenty before they find their way through the ridges. Considering the lengths of the rivers from source to mouth, with all their branches, it is easy to conjecture that these rich lands must be multifarious, and in fact they are found everywhere where the streams do not absolutely have to force their way between rock walls. The spring and fall rains, which cause the so-called **floods** (freshes)[81] help always to maintain the supply, and to restore what is removed from the lower regions.

Where the rain-water pouring down over the higher regions and waters otherwise gathering find no channels, morasses and swamps collect in the valleys and rather flat places; this happens even on the mountain sides where trees and stones thrown over one another form accidental dams. All such places, which likewise occupy a not inconsiderable part of the surface, are extraordinarily fertile; it is only through lack of industry, money, and workers that their utilization through the necessary preparation has not yet become sufficiently general.

The roots of the trees that clothe the mountains prevent the summits from being washed bare, and with their leaves, branches, and trunks increase or at least maintain the upper layer of fertile soil, and so a supply always remains to replace that which in any event the streams tear off from the ground and carry to the sea. Contrariwise, where roads are cut out across the mountains, or the outer crust is otherwise disturbed, the bare rocks soon make their appearance. The most notable rivers between the Hudson and Florida are those from the Delaware down to the Roanoke. The mountains lying behind this stretch are higher, and spread out in more branches than the ridges back of North and South Carolina and Georgia. Virginia has this condition to thank for the important advantage she derives from her many rivers that are navigable up to the granite belt.

After the streams have overcome all the various obstacles of the mountains lying athwart them, they come out on the more gently sloping sand-flats, where consequently a slower current affords their waters time to deposit the foreign matter brought down from above. This is still further favored by the high and low tide that generally penetrates up to the granite belt, since between the cessation of the one and the onset of the other the waters are entirely motionless (Slack Water.)[82] — On that account the lower banks of the rivers and creeks in Maryland, Virginia, Carolina, Georgia, etc. consist in major part of a black, rich garden mould with fine sand intermixed, and banks of this type lie deeper than the sandy flats through which they cut, or form islands in the middle of the rivers that barely rise above the water surface and are full of beautiful plants. Similar banks, now wider, again narrower, form in particular the rice-lands that are so valuable in Carolina and Georgia. Other low places in the sand-flats that do not communicate with flowing water collect the rains, etc. from the surrounding areas and contain likewise the same rich earth to considerable depth, are decked out with the most beautiful evergreens, and a wealth of plant growth. These morasses, artificially or naturally drained, become thereafter the most productive peat-pits.

39.

Thus far I have drawn up a sketch of the plan of the middle and eastern parts of North America. I did not dare to venture more than to draw these outlines, because further observations are necessary to yield a more nearly complete whole. However, since the foregoing remarks show plainly enough that this sketch of the earth and its mountains belong to the sedimentary rock-groups, or at least in all are covered over by strata and sedimentary deposits, one has no reason to doubt, according to generally accepted hypothesis, that it has gained its present structure and constitution through some inundation. It might seem almost unnecessary to bring forth evidence that the higher parts of these mountains have formerly lain under water, after this has been amply shown for the disproportionally higher Cordillera of South America,[83] and the height of the column of water standing over that permits the presumption, as a necessary consequence, that these lower mountains in northern America must also have been covered by water.

However, more definite evidence on the point is not lacking. In the platy sandstone that covers the various ridges of the Endless Mountains impressions of sea-shells are found, not within the rock itself, but between its layers. On the Alleghany and at the Warm-Springs in Virginia I had the satisfaction of collecting impressions of little pectinids in platy whetstone, and joints of crinoid stems, but at both places only in the lower parts of the mountains. Whether anyone has seen them on the tops of one or the other mountains I could not find out by asking. They appear indeed not to occur in any overly large numbers, at least the astonishment over the few I found was guaranty of their rarity, but at the same time thoroughly sufficient proof as to the matter itself. Perhaps it is only for lack of attention that they have not been found more abundantly, and according to Evans's testimony they must be numerous in some parts of the mountains; however, all my attention notwithstanding, I was not as lucky as he who assures us that "The Stones in all Parts of these Mountains are full of Sea Shells: It is not in the loose Stones scattered through the Vales that these Shells abound only, but they are found at the Tops of the Mountains also. I saw some" (says Evans) "mixed with the rocky Base of a high Mountain; in Wishoôchon Creek I found a soft Stone Five or Six Feet long, as full of all Sorts of Shells as if they were kneaded into a lump of brown Clay: There was all the Variety that could be imagined, and many that had

never before come under my Observation, many that I could not
imagine to exist in Nature as the Shells of an Animal, particularly a large Escolop with Corbels, as fine as those of Cockles."[84]

Many fossils are found on Waldon's-Ridge, a branch of the
Alligheny-Mountains between Virginia and Kentucke, where
the entire upper part of the mountain comprises a bed of shells
a foot thick, but I have never had any in hand, to determine
whether the matrix is sand or something else.

Near Huntingdon on the Juniata people admire the so-called
standing Stone, which likewise is said to be entirely full of shells.

The limestone strata and hills in the valleys are said likewise
to afford examples of them here and there, but rarely and only
on the surface. I received some incomplete reports on them at
Bedford, but my informants could no longer show me the place
where they remembered having seen shells in limestone several
years earlier.

40.

Of the landscapes on the other side of the mountains I admit
I know nothing out of my own experience, but various oral reports from other travellers agree closely with the short and general description that Evans has given. "To the North Westward
of the Endless Mountains is a Country of vast Extent, and in a
manner as high as the Mountains themselves. To look at the
abrupt Termination of it, near the Sea Level, as is the Case on
the west side of Hudson's River, below Albany, it looks as a vast
high Mountain; for the Kaats Kills, through of more lofty Stature
than any other Mountains in these Parts of America, are but the
Continuation of the Plains on the Top; and the Cliffs of them,
in the Front they present towards the Kinderhook. These UPPER
PLAINS are of extraordinary rich level Land, and extend from
the Mohocks River, through the Country of the Confederates.
Their Termination Northward is at a little Distance from Lake
Ontario; but what is Westward is not known, for those most
extensive Plains of Ohio are Part of them; which continue to
widen as they extend further Westward, even far beyond the

Mississippi, (56) and its boundary southward is a little Chain of broken Hills, about 10 or 15 miles South of the Ohio River. 'Tis an odd Phenomenon to observe how near the Tide comes up Hudson's River to the Heads of Delaware and Susquehanna; when these two Rivers are obliged to go so far to meet in their own Channels. The Reason is, Delaware and Susquehanna have their Heads in the Plains, and Hudson's River the Tide and the Foot of them."[86]

Various travellers who have wandered through the regions between Fort Pitt and Detroit, Sandusky, Niagara describe them as great expanses of plain which at most places are overgrown with grass as tall as a man. The apparent unevennesses arise principally from the deepening of the river-beds only; true mountains are said not to be found there. According to the sources and distribution of the many waters that betake themselves out of these areas in the neighborhood of the Canadian lakes, westerly to the Illinois and Mississippi, southward to the Ohio, northward into the lakes and the St. Lawrence River, they belong indeed to the more elevated portion of this zone; the most elevated above sea level would then fall, according to Carver's observation, still farther northwesterly, and westward from the sea, in the province of the Assinipoils and the Naudowessies, where in a district of some 30 miles 3-4 of the most important rivers of North America arise, each one of which travels nearly 2000 English miles to the different seas into which they flow; (57) these are the Laurence, the Mississippi, the Bourbon, and the Oregon or the West River, of which the first flows into Lorenzo-Bay, the second into Hudson's-Bay, the third into Mexico-Bay, and the fourth to the west into the sea.[87]

The pronounced elevation of the areas around the Canadian lakes, and of the lakes themselves, becomes apparent from various other circumstances. Many creeks and rivers rise closely

---

(56) "The great plains beyond the mountains across Kentucke are called the Great and Little Barrens. The former extend far beyond the Mississippi and are more than 500 miles long and up to 40 miles wide, all flat, no trees, no shrubs, but only the most beautiful and longest of grass. The ground, otherwise good, the water does not run far. On blasting there is said to be no reverberation, and when one excavates, huge trees are found everywhere, flat in the soil."—[85]

(57) *Carver's Travels, p. 71,* English edition.

neighboring the lakes, but turn away from them westward or southward. The extraordinary fall of Niagara alone plunges the waters of Lake **Erie** 170 feet vertically into Lake **Ontario;** from there out on the Lorenzo there is a longer gradient until its waters meet the ocean-tide at Trois-Rivieres.

For all that, however, there is really no considerable river, if we except the Hudson, that separates the afore-described mountain ranges, through which these hinterlands are divided from those lying to the southward, and one could conjecture without hesitation that precisely these mountains have at some time formed dams to the waters standing over the hinterland, and that the Canadian lakes have taken up, in their deeper basins, the remainder of those waters.[88]

41.

Among the more noteworthy objects in the mountains of this country the openings in their ridges deserve at least some mention. They are known by the name of *Gapes* (an open passage, a notch, a breach in a hedge or a dam) and differentiated into those where rivers and streams flow through (Water-Gapes) and those that are dry (Wind-Gapes). The former are certainly nothing peculiar, since their origin and gradual widening are easily understood as the result of the water still flowing through them. On the other hand, here and there the volume and strength of the water now flowing through seems by far disproportionate to the existing opening. It seems therefore apparent that some rivers must in former times have been stronger and more voluminous, and presumably later on have flowed into other channels. Of less obvious origin, however, are the various dry *Gapes*, i.e. where in a straight continuous mountainside a more or less notable cleft suddenly appears, and hospitably relieves the traveller of the trouble of climbing over the whole ridge of the mountain. The opening in the Blue Mountain back of Nazareth, generally known by the name of the *Wind-Gape,* is of this kind. Not only does no water flow through here, but there is no clear evidence to be found that a river bed ever existed; at least the rock fragments scattered along the road are not of that nature. Further and closer observations may perhaps afford a conclusion as to this.

42.

As to the origin of such transected mountain sides, one might perhaps cast a remote suspicion on subterranean convulsion. For several reasons and circumstances, however, it becomes most improbable that either fire or earthquakes resulting from it have contributed anything to the formation of the surface of this part of North America. It contradicts the major and thus far generally observed order of sequence in the strata, and trends of the mountains, which nowhere give notice of confusion so marked as to require that we fall back on such powerfully effective causes. The heaps of scattered broken fragments of the platy whetstones that are met with on the mountains and in the mountain valleys and which if need be might permit the conjecture of a mighty rending of the outer crust are not sufficiently convincing, because in rocks of this sort, laid on in sheets, separation of the layers can occur just as easily through freezing of the water that seeps in between them. (58) It is further contradicted by the total lack of observation, so far, of traces or remains of volcanic products. Nothing has come to my notice that had the remotest similarity to such, because the aforementioned tourmalines in quartz are not so to be reckoned. Many years ago the French Royal Academy of Sciences posed several questions to the Philadelphia Academy, the object of which was to verify reports as to volcanic remains in the American mountains. There was nobody who was more intimately acquainted with the mountains than Bartram, and his answer was that in all his many trips through the mountains nothing of all that was asked about had come to his notice.

And still beyond this, as long as North America has been inhabited by Europeans earthquakes have been exceedingly rare in occurrence; only some two or three of these are recalled in the fore-lying regions, but their effect was never noticed back of the granite belt — rather they were strictly limited to the provinces near the sea.

(58) I mention this advisedly, because some of the country people in America really cherish the delusion that their mountains are growing, and explain this quite obviously by a ruptured outer crust just as the splitting of the bark of a tree is caused by the expansion of the trunk. They have thus the same idea of upheaval of mountains from the depths as has the Ecclesiastical Councillor Silberschlag.[89]

The supposition, formerly very plausibly held, that in all the places where mineral bitumen or rock-oil is found, mountains still actually burning, or obvious remains of mountains already burnt out (59) would be found nearby, now indeed does not fit in for this part of North America. Among the evidences of rock-oil and coal that occur so abundantly in the mountains and beyond them, neither has actual discovery been made, nor permissible conjecture, of the presence of burning coal measures, from whose chemical disintegration by subterranean fire petroleum is said to originate. (60) But I certainly must confess that most of these coal beds are perhaps too inconsiderable and thin to make any traces of their internal burning evident at the surface, or to produce phenomena similar to those of volcanoes, and the cited author of the Mineral Notes shows indeed from other examples that this does not always happen. As the only indication of subterranean heat in these parts of America I know merely the so-called **Warm-Springs** in the neighborhood of the Potomack in Virginia, which however I found only 74° by Fahrenheit thermometer; and they have their origin in the shales and marcasites quite nearby.

However, hotter water is encountered at the Augusta-Springs, likewise in Virginia, which are said to have 120° Fahrenh., but these I did not see. According to oral report from a resident of the region around the Ohio, a place was once found by woodsmen in the forest that seemed especially warm to their feet; they convinced themselves further of this with their hands, and dug several feet down into the soil without finding anything of note.

However, no mountain in North America is known to be truly volcanic except the one recently discovered by Cook on the west coast,[90] on the Pacific Ocean; this, however, can have no connection with these eastern regions.

43.

If we now cast further a general glance over this whole eastern part of North America thus far under discussion, that is between the Hudson River and Florida-Bay, and between the principal mountains and the Atlantic Ocean, we can regard it in the large

(59) v. Beroldingen, Beobacht. die Mineral. betr. p. 166.
(60) idem. p. 147, 155.

as a simple plain sloping in general to the southeast and cut through lengthwise from northeast to southwest by great furrows or deep hollows, which narrow to the north as the prominences or mountain ridges that characterize it, taken as a whole, appear higher toward the north and become lower to the south.

This slope that I note is explained and attested by the general direction and flow of the rivers in these regions. "As long as they flow in a valley their direction is southwest, and wherever they can find a way toward the east through openings and uninterrupted ridges of the mountains they take these and plunge and rush to the southeastward over rock ledges and precipices in continuous cataracts and falls, and so their course along the various ridges and from one to the next is in large zigzags of southwest and southeast courses. This is the general direction of the Delaware, the Susquehannah, the Potomack, etc. (which rise in the mountains or beyond them); but the shorter streams, which arise from the eastern slope only of the mountains, as the Rappahannok, the James-River, the Roanoke and the remaining rivers of Carolina, make their ways in diverse directions (according to the nature of the ground) southeastward toward the sea." (61)

A glance at any one of the maps of the North American continent will convince the reader, by the plan and direction of almost all the streams, of the truth of this observation.

This slope will indeed be found entirely natural and inevitable; but yet it stands out by its arrangement in a remarkable manner. Of old, waters have stood over the higher and rearmost mountains, or over the principal mountains, and these mountains have been covered by the deposit of sediment from the waters. This might have happened, if it wanted to, so under condition of the noted slope toward the sea the lower and fore-lying mountains must have been covered by water at the same time with the higher mountains to the rear.[91] If these higher ridges of the principal mountains were now to receive a notable accretion through the sand and clay deposited on their groundmass of quartzose rock out of the sea covering them, which deposit now appears as whetstone (§ 35, 36) and contains remains and impressions of marine animals (§ 39), then the question indeed

(61) Pownall, p. 3.

arises, why did not the same thing happen on the fore-lying lower mountain ridges? But on the granite, on the second and third rock-belts, not only are no similar beds of whetstone found at all, but no signs at all of marine animals known to me, or perhaps only fortuitous ones, just as is the case in the limestone valleys lying between them (§ 31). And although the rock-types of the outer belts are likewise mainly laid on in sheets, yet they are made up for the most part of constituents that one cannot flatly claim to be the direct deposit of waters long standing over them, as (one can for) the upper strata of the rearward mountains.

Had the sea covered the whole sloping surface here defined at the same time and for the same length of time with a quiet over-flooding between the Alleghany and the granite belt, anyone would be inclined to believe that the sedimentary deposit from this sea, in regard to constituents as well as quantity, in a space of only 100 English miles, could hardly be seriously different. It is with surprise, then, that we see in the lower parts of the slope granites and gneisses, which are themselves no products of water, but yet are not overlain by other deposits that are found first on the higher main ridges. In every precipitation out of a quiet fluid the solid particles fall universally to the bottom in such manner that they cover all parts of the bottom receiving them to equal thickness. Be the bottom level, then the surface of the deposit will be the same; if uneven, then the surface of the deposit will certainly be likewise, but still under most conditions so that the material of the deposit will nevertheless cover the unevennesses of the bottom to equal height. Therefore under a long-sustained and quiet inundation a similar deposit would have had to accumulate proportionally on the lower foothills just as on the principal mountains, even if the original floor of the former were itself already lower and more sloping than that of the latter, and even if the former were not brought by the same quantity of deposit to the same height as the other. However, since there is no agreement of the kind between the upper rocks of the forward and hinder regions, and also since we cannot assume that the waters standing over the forward and lower ridges were possibly loaded with less solid particles and matter otherwise constituted, or their deposition hindered by other causes, so must this striking difference, the presence of marine organisms in the principal mountains and their absence in the forward and medial ridges, have other events as its cause.

The known and highest mountain chains in all the rest of the world consist of granite peaks and ridges which are accompanied by the other rock-types commonly reckoned with the primitive, talc, garnets, mica, tourmaline, white marble, etc., and left elevated above sea level during a former inundation or long-continued higher stand of the sea. Lower than these and surrounding them lie the stratified rocks of the second order, sandstones or limestones invested with sea-shells. — One may climb up from any of the European lakes to any mountain and always come first upon the stratified rocks, that contain sea-shells, and only last upon the granite and its investiture. Although the granite rather often occurs in lower positions in other parts of the world, and perhaps forms the greatest part of the ocean bottom itself, and the substratum of the other rock-types, so in the case before us we must ever consider that behind it stratified rock-types of the second order are piled up, without its being overlain itself by them, and without its coming to outcrop again in still higher mountains situated farther back.

From this reversed order, and from the reverse of the normal plan of most high mountain chains, in this part of America, I might almost believe that this American granite belt formerly stood higher, that just as other granite belts are elevated above their neighboring rocks of the second order, it too was once higher than the Endless Mountains.[92] If we accept this, then all those primitive rock-types are found in their normal places, and one will never take it into his head to search for traces of marine productions on mountain ridges that earlier stood higher than the formerly lower, but now higher mountains, on which they still can be perceived.

It is frankly audacious to dispose at pleasure with the arrangement of worlds, to have belts of the earth sink here and elsewhere to bring others to light, in order to explain what we observe. This poor clod of earth has been so extensively raked through, and raked over again, uplifted, sunken, rent asunder, melted and made over again in all manner of way with all kinds of hypothesis, that everything of the kind that is said comes out in the end to the gist that each one tells us how he would have set out about it in order to produce the phenomena he has observed.

I confess that I find myself in the same situation. In order to cede nothing from the granite and its retinue of the rank it maintains on the most elevated summits in the rest of the world, I should like to think that in the past a mountain or part of the earth's crust bordering on it immediately to the east must have sunk into the depths, in order to take up the waters that stood behind the American granite and gneiss belts, and over the End-less Mountains; that on the occasion of this important change the foundation of the granite and the other adjoining belts have themselves sunk in such manner, that from a plain formerly sloping to the west the entire present eastern part of North America between the granite and the principal mountains has now become one sloping to the east.

Almost all known dry lands stood at one time, up to a certain height in the primitive mountains, under water. These waters, if one only does not have them utterly evaporate, must have drawn back into deeper basins which before this change were not there. The origin of these basins presumes deepening through subsidence of a large part of the ancient ocean-bottom in order to make space for the reception of so many thousands of square miles of water (62) that earlier stood over the earth surfaces that are now dry land. In the event of so momentous a change it could indeed hardly fail that in addition to the sinking of a part of the former ocean bottom itself, a part also of the former dry land that was next to the area where the subsidence occurred must have sunk in part along with it, and the bordering land must have bent down. Now since the Atlantic Ocean must have taken up a part of the water formerly standing over America, and in order to take this up must itself have become deepened, it is not entirely impossible that the eastward-sloping part of North America bent downward from a formerly considerable height, and that the granite belt became that which it was not before, namely the border of the receded sea.

Almost all the rocks that occur in the forelying areas and behind the granite of North America dip to greater or lesser degree to the southeast. So far the same has been observed at depth; the veins of ore in Jersey strike on the whole northeast-

---

(62) Buffon calculates that the waters covered the now-inhabited earth-sphere up to a height of 2000 fathoms; this amounts at least to 300 million cubic miles of water.

southwest and all dip to the east, and become thicker in this direction; and the underlying barren follows the same dip.

Immediately behind the granite belt in Pennsylvania at Swedesford and variously elsewhere there are foliated marble and limestone strata that stand almost vertical, and a similar nearly vertical attitude was noted by Mr. Kalm (63) for the black calcareous slates at Quebec and other places in Canada. The observations of M. de **Saussure** in Switzerland, to be sure, are unfavorable to the opinion that similar vertical-standing stratifications of sedimentary rocks have come into this attitude by a kind of collapse; he prefers to explain it by a kind of confused crystallization. I am just as little inclined to assert the contrary, but I could not prevent it, that on frequent sight of such vertical or strongly east-dipping strata the idea of a collapse pressed ever upon me. And that so much the more, in that occurrences of the kind came to my notice in the middle belts only, that is between the granite and the principal mountains. The whetstone, etc., piled up in strata on the tops of the principal mountains mostly maintain a horizontal attitude, and so also the sand, clay, and shell beds lying between the granite and the sea, wherever one finds them, occupy a horizontal position.

This subsidence of the forelands could indeed have taken place so gradually that the effects of a violent collapse might remain less noticeable, and the waters receding from the hinterland toward the ocean might have been afforded opportunity to effect still further changes in this surface, and to wash sand and clay over it; this, in order not to be too long-winded, I pass over.

44.

If it be found plausible that a deepening, a downsinking of the eastern part of North America has caused its present slope and has brought the granite belt trending adjacent to the sea (perhaps the only one of several striking parallel with it now remaining visible above water level) from a former higher position nearer to the center of the earth, there follows then from this what was apparent at the outset (§ 12) namely that all of the land fronting the present granite belt is of more recent

(63) Kalm, Travels, part 3, p. 551.

origin. The foreland from York down to Florida (§ 4 and following) now belongs to this. Its constitution and plan leave no
doubt that it was not produced by the sea,[93] and that it can be
of no great age is shown by the total softness and unconsolidated
nature of its beds, which have attained a hardness greater than
the general only here and there, perhaps because of local conditions.

The middle regions, between the granite and the principal
mountains, may therefore have long been dry land, as the sea
bordered them directly and the broad plains of Virginia and
Carolina still really stood under water. And restricting to these
forelands, I am at one with the opinion of those who view America as a rather young land. But if the Abbé Raynal[94] and others
think that the ocean did not leave America until long after our
part of the world was populated, I find it impossible to agree
with him. According to the general law of gravitation the sea
cannot stand notably higher at any place on the east coast of
America than it does at the same parallel on the opposing west
coast of Europe, even if one desired to ascribe a greater piling
up of the waters toward the west to the rotation of the earth
toward the east. Hence if the continent of America were to have
remained longer under the sea than the European, the sea must
have stood many fathoms higher there than the lowest areas of
already dry and, in Raynal's opinion, inhabited Europe, to assume which, however, would be absurd. America may have been
populated later than Europe, but the sea must have left it at the
same time as that when it withdrew from the other lands, if the
laws of equilibrium are to be observed, by virtue of which the
surface of the ocean (leaving out of account any causes affecting
it externally) must maintain everywhere the same distance from
the center of the earth.

That the continent of America is at the same time dispropor-
tionately cooler and warmer than Europe does not stem from the
moisture left behind after the withdrawal of the sea, rather is
caused partly by the slope to the southeast, which allows the sun
more influence, and by the extension toward the north and the
northwestern lakes, which cool off the winds coming thence.
That a land is a wilderness full of swamps and morasses shows
only that no inhabitants have applied their industry to it, but
not that Nature herself be in infancy, who yet brings forth her

indigenous products to the same completeness as other lands do theirs.

Over and above this, the depths of the river channels, especially in the mountains and where they have cut through the mountains to make their way southeastward, bear witness to the age of America. Appearance shows that they must have spent no less time at this than have the rivers in the rest of the world at the deepening of their channels. America could be considered younger only if the dry land had been raised up out of the depths;[95] however, since this cannot be assumed for the areas between the granite and the mountains, because they do not have the character of a sea-bottom as do the higher lying mountains and the lower-lying plains, this further cannot be the case. Therefore America certainly must be as old as Europe, or at least much older than it has been assumed to be.

45.

Withou being bound to the supposition of subsidence in the middle regions of America, one might well explain the same phenomena by other hypotheses. One could assume, with Mr. Silberschlag, that the principal mountains had been upheaved by subterranean or central fire; then to be sure the forelying ridges, by the same process, must have been proportionally lowered. Or one could concede that the middle ridges, like the principal mountains, may have been formerly overlain by stratified sandstones, which have been stripped off in violent manner on withdrawal of the sea. I do not wish to contend further for one interpretation or the other; still further observations must first be gathered in the matter before one may venture to decide with somewhat greater certainty. But whatever interpretation one may assume about it, there still remains an important question. What cause has bestowed upon the granite belt, presumably the oldest, and all the other mountain ranges, their remarkable parallel trend from northeast to southwest, which stands out especially in this part of America through its great, almost uninterrupted length? In regard to this trend, this low American granite belt agrees with the plan of other elevated granite chains in southern Europe; with the central chain of the Swiss Alps,

the Fichtelberg, the Riesengebürge, and many others. Taken as
a whole the highest mountains of the earth approach a north-
south direction, and the most northerly mountains of Europe,
such as the Norwegian, (64) strike more exactly in this direction.
But in this the northerly ones in America also agree, as will be
clarified in the sequel. — According to **Buffon** (65) a continuous
range of high mountains runs from north to south through the
center of Africa, and the high chain in southern America strikes
in the same direction.

Since all these highest mountains consist of primitive rock-
types, among which the granite takes first place, it is to be supposed that the trend of the granite belts at all places controls
the others to certain extent, even if no one is ever able to specify
the cause that determines the course of the granite.[96]

It becomes indeed probable, from the agreement and similarity
of several lands, that at one time a mighty inundation or current
of the waters from the southwest must have taken place, and
this interpretation is favored by many natural philosophers, and
each one concludes it from different observations that have presented themselves to him. From contemplation of the many large
headlands that are deflected to the south **Buffon** (66) supposes
that the water came in greater quantity from the South Pole
than from the North Pole, and Mr. **Forster** confirms this interpretation in his observations on his travels around the world.
(67) From his observations on the mountains of the Russian
Empire (68) **Pallas** judges that the inundation that befell them
must have come from the south. From the fern fronds and other
Indian plants that are found impressed on the European shales
Jussieu infers an inundation from the south, or from the seas
around India. From the constitution of the peat pits of Holland,
Friesland, and others, and the fallen trees that occur not rarely
in them, always in the same position, their crowns or tops in
direction between east and north and their roots toward the

(64) *Buffon,* Supplém. à l'hist. nat., vol. IX, p. 440.
(65) idem.
(66) *Supplém. à l'hist. natur. Tom. IX.*
(67) Joh. Reinh. Forster's Observ. on a trip around the world, Berlin
1783, p. 3.
(68) Pallas, Observ. on the Mountains, etc. Collection for Physics and
Natural History, Leipzig, vol. 1 part 2, no. 1.

southwest, a strong overflooding from the southwest may be conjectured. (69) The trend of the mountain ranges and valleys in America here described gives these interpretations still further much apparent plausibility. For that the long valleys of these regions cannot be regarded as channels scoured out by streams alone is shown by the fact that the streams carry on for a certain distance in them but then veer off in other directions toward the southeast, while the valleys themselves maintain their southwesterly trend. I have noted as to the great limestone valley that it becomes broader to the south; whether this proves also to be true of the others I do not know, and just as little could I learn whether the other valleys, and especially the narrower ones of the principal mountains, can be followed so far and so continuously as this great limestone valley, so that one might ascribe their origin with some certainty to waters streaming in from the south and southwest. One would also first have to set himself right as to their true slope toward this region,[97] which however might be more difficult, because in subsequent times the valleys could have become washed over with the materials of the higher regions, cut off and unequally filled up, so that one might be able to discern their original course unaltered. But however much agreement one might now find between the overflooding from the south here advertised and now generally assumed and the trend of the American mountains, there are several other conditions that stand in the way of accepting it as settled. And many objections would first need to be answered; yes, one could ask here with just as much of justice, whether the waters did not rather withdraw in southwesterly direction, to the Gulf of Mexico? — At least it seems to me further improbable from other considerations that the structure of the mountain ranges has any relation to that inundation from the south. This I cannot and therefore will not deny. But presumably it took place later, after the mountains were ordered in their present form. As an outstanding evidence on the direction of this inundation from the south Mr. **Pallas** accepts the remains of land animals that live only in the tropics and which are yet found buried abundantly far into the northern lands. (70) As is well known, these remains

(69) v. Beroldingen Beobacht. die Mineral. betr. p. 14.
(70) Pallas on Mountains. Leipz. coll. p. 188.

are now found also in America, (71) but only so shallow beneath
the surface that one cannot believe that the waters that washed
them into these regions could have had great effect on the mountains, for it seems to have been a brief, transitory, and extraordinary inundation, which no doubt presumed an already populated world in America, and there can just as surely be assumed
a certain ordering of the surface of the inundated floor that permitted the waters to flow northward. For if they had found a
high mountain striking east-west they would perhaps have broken
through it here and there but would not have altered its trend.

If we assume that earlier than this a long protracted inundation deposited the layered sandstones, with impressions of sea
shells, on the Endless Mountains, then the question arises, why
this happened only in ridges, on narrow mountain backbones,
and why the limestone valleys lying before and between these
were not covered by the same bottom deposit? And why do these
limestone valleys show so few remains of marine animals similar
to those in the principal mountains, if they show any at all? This
enhances the conjecture of a land sunken to the east, and makes
it likewise still further probable that the limestone adjacent to
the granite and between the following gneiss and quartzose
ridges be true primitive limestone (§ 31) and not formed of
shellfish; and from this it follows in my opinion that from the
very beginning these quartzose ridges, with the primitive limestone beds lying on and between them, were ordered separate
and laid up in direct succession. On this point nobody to my
knowledge has given us the reason why the primitive limestone,
which contains no traces of marine organisms, nevertheless is
always laid out on other high mountains lower than the peaks
of basement rock, uniform and parallel with them, as **Saussure**
notes it on the Buet and other Swiss Alps, and as it also occurs
elsewhere, among which occurrences the white marble is especially to be reckoned. However, that this, and the other valleys

(71) Until a few years ago only one place was known, on the Ohio,[98] where
a large accumulation of such bones was found; recently, however, individual
but similar bones have been found also on the east side of the mountains, in
North Carolina, in Pennsylvania, and in New York. They are also found
in Canada. Therefore this inundation must have affected the entire continent,
and must have flowed, if not over, at least around the mountains from all
sides.

filled with primitive limestone as well, lie higher than the granite in America leads back again to the hypothesis that this belt has been depressed. Should the great American limestone valleys be the bottom deposit of a sea that long stood over them, why did this sea not deposit lime over the middle mountains, the South Mountain, which are lower than the principal mountains? If the limestone of these valleys be a product of a sea that did not attain the heights of the surrounding mountains, then the gneiss and quartzose ridges must already have had valleys between them in which to receive this sea, and to be filled up with its calcareous bottom deposit, and that at a time when this sea still contained no shellfish, or at least extremely few. But if this part of America was beforehand an elevated land originally slopping toward the west which in later alteration of the earth's crust plunged eastward, then the limestone belts, which are adjacent to the granite belt and between the middle mountains, must indeed have had their origin along with them and at the same time, and, for important and general reasons unknown to me, have gained their trend, so remarkably concordant with the other mountains.

One still might perhaps assume the effect of various ocean currents coming from the south and southwest that could have arisen during the protracted inundation and have hollowed out the valleys in their present trend, and one might be supported in this regard by the presence of an ocean current still manifesting itself in this direction (§ 11). One might indeed be able thus to explain certain occurrences, but, again, at the same time stir up other doubts.

Out of it all, however, it is clear enough that more than one cause must be assumed, and effective at very different times, in order to consider point by point the plan and structure of this eastern part of North America, with all of the phenomena occurring on it. Whole regions, and all parts of the mountains must yet be attentively investigated before this can be done.

46.

As I specified at the outset, I have so far limited myself entirely to the southern part of North America, because I knew only that part lying south of the Hudson. The mountains on the east side of this river, between New York and Canada, run like the others, mainly parallel with the sea. According to Evans they consist of two levels. "This series consists of two stages; and (supposing you travel across it westward from Boston) the first begins about Water Town and continues a rough hilly ground until you are past *Western;* thence to within twenty miles of Hudson's River the second Stage is for a great Part covered with small Mountains, running here in small Chains and Ridges; which extend Southerly to the Sound dividing Long Island from the Main, and form those Cliffs, Ridges, and broken stony Ground which you observe in travelling along the Connecticut Colony shore, and prevent the possibility of making a better Road in that Direction further within Land. The greater part of Connecticut is of this second Stage, and is enriched by the fine interval Lands between the Chains, the greatest being along the Connecticut River, and near 20 miles wide. 'Tis the courses of these Chains of Mountains and Hills that give Direction to the several Creeks and Rivers. To the eastward of the first Stage, some Land is made by an Accumulation of Sand from the Ocean, heaped together by the Meeting of the Recoil of the Flood Tide from the North Eastward with another from the South Eastward; and forms near all the Land of Cape Cod to the eastward of the bottom of Massachusetts Bay." (72)

These mountains therefore continue further for some distance more or less in a northerly direction, begin at some distance from the Hudson and extend along Lakes St. George and Champlain to the St. Lawrence River; still, the White Mountains, from which the Connecticut, the Kennebec, etc. arise, appear again to veer somewhat toward the northeast, in the same measure as does the shore run from Cape Cod, first northerly and then from Cape Cod Bay again northeasterly to the Bay of Fundy. Nearly all the rivers of this section, the Connecticut, Thames, Sagadahock, Kennebec, Penobscot, St. Croix, St. John, etc., have their main direction from north to south.

We still have no information on the arrangement and diversity of the mountain ranges in this region, and to what extent they correspond to the southern ranges. **Evans** complains that he could

(72) Evans, Analysis, p. 6.

not learn anything about them excepting that a mountain (73) which forms the continuation of the high mountains around Lake St. Sacrament, after passing Wood Creek and Otter Creek, goes on northeastward until 15 miles below Quebec on the St. Lawrence it becomes lower. In agreement with this are the reports of Mr. **Kalm,** who saw some of the mountains around Fort Frederick, along Wood Creek, striking from south-southwest to north-northeast, (74) that contained various species of granite, gneiss, (75) and norrke (76) .[99] Between them were the hills on which Fort Frederick stands, of coal black slaty limestone, the upper beds however of dense gray limestone. The first black limy slate contained a quantity of fossils. (77) Lake Champlain is surrounded closely on both sides by high mountain walls that run from north to south and consist of unstratified rocks of gray quartz and dark mica, on which fossiliferous gray or black limestone is laid. (78) Farther on, around Quebec, Mr. **Kalm** found limy slates still very abundant but entirely devoid of fossils, and from other circumstances it is clear that these limestone beds might be different in origin from the first-mentioned, and of different age. ". . . on the southeast side of that river [the St. Lawrence] appeared a long chain of high mountains running generally parallel to it, though many miles distant from it. To the west again, at some distance from the rising lands where we were, the hills changed into a long chain of very high mountains, lying very close to each other and running parallel likewise to the river, that is, nearly from north to south. These high mountains consisted of grey rock composed of several kinds of stones which I shall mention later. These mountains seemed to prove that the lime slate strata were of as ancient a date as the gray rock and not formed in later times; for the amazingly large rocks lay on the top of the mountains, which consisted of black slate" (79) .[100] He mentions repeatedly, however, that fossils have never been encountered in this black lime-slate (80) , and that here and

(73) Analysis, p. 9.
(74) Kalm's Travels, part 3, p. 290.
(75) idem p. 311.
(76) idem p. 316.
(77) idem p. 312.
(78) idem p. 322.
(79) Kalm, part 3, p. 450.—Region between Quebec and Lorette.
(80) *idem* p. 532, 552.

there its layers are indeed encountered horizontal, but still more often lying at steep angles, so that they approached the vertical, with the upper end inclined to the northwest, with the lower, however, leaning to the southeast (81). At some places, however, beds occur that dipped to the north, although they were close to the perpendicular (82); again elsewhere the strata stood, so to speak, stacked up against one another, almost entirely vertical, except that they inclined a bit toward the west-southwest (83). Wherever these black lime-slates were further encountered, on Bay St. Paul, on Orleans Island, around Montreal, etc., he found them disturbed,[101] and never any fossils, with which on the other hand the abundant gray limestone lying around and next to it in horizontal attitude was richly endowed. The rocks in the other high Canadian mountains around the St. Lawrence were gray calcareous stones with intermixed mica and quartz which seem to belong to the mountains of the second order "for a large part of these gray rocks in Canada stands on those black lime-slates (84) and even at times contains fossil impressions" (85). All these regions, however, already slope westward, in the trend maintained by the principal mountains, to whose mainstem I reckon the **White Mountains;** and the determination of the arrangement and relationship of these northern mountain regions remains yet to be settled. However, in reference to the arrangement of the strata in general it is said to have been found long ago that they are in the same position in Canada as in Switzerland (86).

(81) *idem* p. 551, 509.
(82) *idem* p. 552.
(83) *idem* p. 514.
(84) *idem* p. 527.
(85) *idem* p. 532.
(86) "La nature après avoir produit, dans le nouveau monde, tant de végétaux et d'animaux absolument inconnus dans l'ancien, n'a rien changé au regne minéral: plus on fait des recherches, plus on decouvre, que les métaux et l'arrangement des couches terrestres sont les mêmes en Amérique que dans notre continent sous les mêmes latitudes; *au point que Mr. Guettard* (*) *a prouvé que, dans le Canada, la disposition intérieure de la terre est precisement comme en Suisse.*" Defense des Recherches philosoph. sur les Américains Tom. III. Chap. XXI.[102]
(*) Voyez les Memoir. de l'Academie des Scienc. de Paris, l'an 1752.

48.

In former times the mainland of America may possibly have extended much farther to the east, whether it has been there as dry land or as inundated. The easternmost part of Newfoundland falls almost on the same line as the easternmost of the Windward Islands, in the West Indies, and in the middle of this line — so to speak as remains of a more solid land[103] — between these northern and southern islands lie the Bermudas. That which has thus far been sought in vain on the present mainland of eastern North America, namely traces of volcanoes, is found in these broken-up southern regions. — The Sulphur Mountain on Guadeloupe, which still smokes continuously, contains sulphur pits and hot springs, and Mount-Misery on St. Christopher, which like the former has sulphur and boiling hot water, are still existing evidence of the possibility that subterranean fire may formerly have wrought considerable devastation in these regions, whose effects might quite as well have extended still farther northward, as this group of islands appears to have gained its existence in present form mainly with matter from there.[104] Lava and related stones are found in almost all of these Caribbean islands, and if I have been correctly informed, also on the Bermudas.

If we consider further, beyond the traces of extinct volcanoes and those still remaining on this west side of the ocean, the still frequent and destructive earthquakes, and often terrible hurricanes that convulse these latitudes so frequently from the ground up, that besides these, on the west side of the ocean as well, among the Cape Verde Islands on Fogo, among the Canaries on Teneriffe, volcanoes are actually present, that these islands, and still farther north and almost in the middle of the ocean, the Azores, are not at all rarely afflicted by subterranean convulsions, then the conjecture that the present floor of the Atlantic Ocean formerly may have stood higher but latterly has sunk becomes more and more probable. — We do not know whether a number of other volcanoes, when this happened, have not collapsed along with it and become extinct. Further, the bottom of the Atlantic Ocean is by no means everywhere of extraordinary and equal depth. On the sea charts of the West Indian pilots there are many places indicated in the middle of the ocean where sunken rocks are said to have been observed, and I have several times heard it told that once an English frigate on the homeward voyage from the West Indies lay to as often as possible on the open ocean to make soundings, and at many places unexpectedly encountered such sunken rocks. If we now assume the possibility of a collapse, it is not at all difficult to perceive that the line along which this happened must have depended strongly on the trend of primitive mountain ranges. — And since these are so generally found running from north to south, it might be possible therefrom to reach some conclusion toward the explanation of the slanting-off of the American coast in the direction mentioned in the introduction.

In so far as the oldest of traditions are always founded on actual events, which however in the passage of time become distorted, I might, at least in passing, remind my reader of the ancient saga of the lost continent Atlantis.

In his discussion of South America Mr. Forster observes that there is a striking similarity between the southern promontory of this continent and all the southern promontories of other continents. With limitations this observation may be applied also to North America. Still more, however, do both halves of America agree as regards their entire outlines. The mainland of North America, like the former, is of imposing breadth in the north, between · Berings-Strait and the Labrador coast, and narrows down, like the former, toward the south. Moreover, the mountains of North America have no relation in trend to the Cordilleras of South America. If one projects the line in which they run southward through the Gulf of Mexico, it strikes exactly on the Yucatan province of New Mexico, which in a narrow strip of land projecting far into the Mexican gulf seems to go toward the mountains of the northern half. However, since I know nothing further about these regions, I abstain from pursuing mere probabilities any farther, and rest content with the little I have noted that I know out of my own experience. The incompleteness of the foregoing observations notwithstanding, they will still be of some use if they lead other travellers to further observation, and through correction or confirmation of my own, advance the knowledge of this continent.

Notes on the Translation

by

EDMUND M. SPIEKER

1. Schöpf's word here is "Gebürge," interpretation of which in some 18th-century geologic literature may be uncertain. Normally it means simply "mountains" or, more commonly, a "mountain chain," but some 18th-century writers, including Werner, used it in the old-time miners' sense to specify or denote rock units (see Schmidt 1928 p. 94) and even for geologic structures and other features. Schöpf, however, used it strictly in its fundamental sense, and at one point (Section 26) even explained his practice, — with some misgiving — showing that he was aware of the looseness in usage that prevailed in his time.

2. "Onolzbach" is an archaic form of Ansbach; it was originally Onoldisbach.

3. Pabst von Ohain was Werner's teacher, and his sponsor at Freiberg. He was generally recognized as the leading mineralogist of his time in Germany. Johann Jacob Ferber was a Swedish mineralogist who travelled widely in Europe and taught for a while in Berlin. See pp. 8-9 of the Introduction to this translation.

4. Here Schöpf is not quite fair to Pownall, who gave credit to Evans for all that he "borrowed" (see White, G. W., Lewis Evans' early American notice of isostasy: *Science,* vol. 114, p. 302, 1951) . Schöpf may not have appreciated this. Or, he may have merely wanted, with no intended aspersion, to indicate Pownall's source; but if this be the case we can only say that his wording was unfortunate. It is probably worthy of note that this forthright statement would seem to be a clear indication of Schöpf's attitude toward plagiarism.

5. In English in the original.

6. The hills at Navesink are composed of Cretaceous and Tertiary beds.

7. It seems impossible to find out where Schöpf got this idea. In any case it is evidently an early suggestion of the Coriolis force.

8. Stork's work is very rare. Schöpf exhibits here his thorough knowledge of reference sources. See the entry for Stork in the annotated list of authors cited by Schöpf.

9. "Fohrenwaldungen" is what Schöpf wrote. "Föhrenwald" now means fir-forest, but "Föhre" means Scotch pine, and this is undoubtedly what he intended.

10. Schöpf evidently meant here that the lateral distribution is the same as that of occurrences on the coast.

11. This must be the earliest mention of the Atlantic coastal plain terraces, such as the Pamlico. Schöpf interpreted them all as marine in origin, and in

modern times so did Cooke until the Brandywine was clearly shown to be the deltaic deposit of a stream—but the others still are thought to be marine (see Thornbury, W. D., *Regional geomorphology of the United States,* pp. 33-34, Wiley, N.Y., 1965). Schöpf was a real pioneer almost everywhere you strike him.

12. In the original text this section number is repeated.

13. Raccoon was the early name for Swedesboro, New Jersey.

14. In English in the original, as transcribed here.

15. The author of this quotation, not named here, is von Beroldingen.

16. The original of this last phrase reads "oder beyde, wenigstens in diesen Amerikanischen Gegenden, nur in der Erzeugung und Verbesserung der Erde um sich, verschiedene Geschwindigkeit beobachtet." There is evidently a printer's error here, easily made in uncritical type-setting from Schöpf's German script; the last word should be "beobachten."

17. Schöpf's word is "Schneidestein," which is apparently not used nowadays. In the 18th century it was used to mean stone that could be cut, and in modern terms this might be either cut stone or ashlar. It should be noted, however, that elsewhere Schöpf refers to "Schneidestein" where he specifically names soapstone, and that is what he may have meant here, but if so it seems peculiar that he did not say "Seifenstein" outright, as he did later on.

It might be noted further that Schöpf was apparently a bit careless in his classification here, for the only ones of the minerals and rocks he mentions that could be considered argillaceous or calcareous is the "Schneidestein."

18. The word here is "Verhältnis," use and meaning of which were evolving in the 18th century (see Sperber, Hans, The semantic development of *Verhältnis: Language,* vol. 14, pp. 167-177, 1938) so that in context such as the present, translation is problematic and one has no way of knowing exactly what Schöpf meant. In the 17th century the word meant only ratio or proportion in strictly mathematical sense, and this may be what Schöpf meant here, but by 1780 its meaning had broadened considerably, including the sense of relationship so common today, and it is also possible that this is what Schöpf had in mind. Forced to choice, I should guess at the translation here offered. (I am indebted to Dr. Fleischhauer for discussion of this problem and the reference to Sperber.)

19. Schöpf wrote "an den Sitz des Hungers." This may well be some classical allusion, but whatever it is I have been unable to place it.

20. This gray rock should be the Rhode Island formation, of Pennsylvanian age, which is phyllite. There is considerable variety of rocks on this part of the coast, and one cannot be certain just what Schöpf is describing.

21. This sentence is somewhat puzzling. Here is the original: "In den Vertiefungen, die seine Geschiebe hie und da lassen, steht ein dickblättrichter, grober, schwarzer Schiefer auf ihm auf; man siehet ihn an den nacktgewaschenen Seeufer deutlich." In modern usage "Geschiebe" almost always means some kind of glacial erratic, but has occasionally been used for flattened stones transported by streams. In the 18th century it seems to have been used for any pebbles or cobbles washed out of some resting place, and that is probably Schöpf's meaning here; hence the somewhat free translation here offered. Further, the sentence is ambiguous in that the "Geschiebe" might be of either the younger or the older body of rock, but considering the total sense of the statement, this is of no great importance.

22. This was undoubtedly a prospect hole for the famous Rhode Island "anthracite."

23. This rock is not breccia in the modern sense—rather conglomerate, and probably from the Purgatory formation, of Pennsylvanian age. (I am indebted to Dr. George E. Moore for first-hand information on all these rocks of the Rhode Island coast.)

24. This passage is somewhat obscure. Here is the original: "Der eigentliche felsichte Grund mag wohl ziemlich tief unter der Oberfläche wegstreichen; von den Felsen um Kings-bridge aber, ist doch die Fortsetzung in denen schon weit niedrigern, meist vom Wasser bdeckten, noch in der Hellgate zu entdecken." A strict translation of this is not only awkward, but uncertain in meaning, and I believe that the rendition here given, itself none too clear, comes as close as possible to what Schöpf wanted to say.

25. I have been unable to identify Bockram.

26. Here begins the very earliest description of the geology of New York City, and it is remarkably thorough and accurate. What a shame it is that this did not serve as foundation for later work, such as that of Mitchill! (Mitchill, S. L., A sketch of the mineralogical and geological history of the State of New York . . . Medical Repository, vol. 1, 1798, pp. 293-318; 445-452. For biography of Mitchill see Hall, R. C., A scientist in the early republic, Samuel Lathan Mitchill: N. Y., 1934.)

27. The rocks at the north end of the island are the Inwood marble and the Manhattan gneiss. There is nothing on the Rhode Island coast like the Manhattan, so it seems impossible to guess that Schöpf is describing here. Farther on, he names and describes gneiss very well. The "gray rock" may be one of the phyllites in the Manhattan complex, but even this does not fit Schöpf's description very well.

28. In the original this sentence is both corrupt and unclear. It reads "Eingesprengt hie und da, und Bruchstücke von einen dunkelgrünen Felsart —mit weissern Adern durchzogen, die sich dem Bänderjaspis zu nähern scheint." The second "und" is evidently a typesetter's error for "sind," easy to make from rapidly written German script, but even when this is corrected the sentence is somewhat puzzling because of the relation between "einge-sprengt" and "Bruchstücke" in terms of the rock Schöpf was describing. "Eingesprengt" has several meanings, but only two of them apply realistic-ally here. In geologic parlance it commonly means insterstratified, as a synonym of "eingeschichtet," and it may also mean interspersed as applied to small clusters of crystals in a rock matrix or little flecks of native metal in gangue, as for example gold ore. But neither of these meanings is thoroughly consistent with "Bruchstücke," etc. Schöpf is evidently still talking here about the gray rock at the north end of the island, which is almost certainly the Manhattan gneiss, possibly the Fordham (which, however, is across the river) and hardly the Inwood marble. There would be no rock fragments either interstratified or interspersed in such rock. There are some lentil-shaped rock masses interlarded in the foliation of the gneiss, and I think it likely that Schöpf simply used "Bruchstücke" in rather free sense so, I have settled upon the alternative translations here presented.

29. Chert. According to the Oxford Dictionary first used in 1679; hornstone in 1668. An 18th-century writer might have used either. Schöpf wrote "Hornstein."

The fossiliferous chert here described must have been in glacial erratics, and therefore "accidental," as Schöpf alternatively surmised. This is a very early observation of glacial erratics (even if they were not identified as such) ; Kalm had noted them earlier.

30. George W. White notes that the geological observations of the Abbé Robin seem so far not to have been noticed in the literature. Here we have Schöpf to thank for the lead toward a new discovery in the history of American geology. See the entry in the list of works referred to by Schöpf.

31. See note 4. There is no granite here.

32. This is Triassic sandstone of the Newark group.

33. There is no bedrock at Darby, but Schöpf must mean here the hills to the northwest, in which the Wissahickon schist is exposed; it contains the Octaroro phyllite, which is probably the "coarse slate" mentioned here. The Wissahickon is evidently the "much-mentioned gray rock species"; see note 27.

34. The bedrock at Wilmington is gabbro, and this hardly fits Schöpf's description. About five miles up the Brandywine from its mouth, however, we encounter the Wissahickon oligoclase schist, and this may be the rock concerned.

35. This is the Baltimore gabbro, and the description of it that was admired by Williams.

36. This location, about 10 miles out of Baltimore, would be in the vicinity of Ellicott City. The rock there is the Ellicott City granodiorite, which is rich in wallrock inclusions and is foliated, locally porphyritic, but not reported to contain tourmaline (see Maryland Geological Survey, *The geology of Howard and Montgomery Counties,* 1964, pp. 168-175) . Half a mile north of the road, however, the rock is locally Wissahickon oligoclase mica schist, and this does contain some tourmaline (see *ibid.,* p. 76) ; furthermore, its texture corresponds well to what Schöpf describes.

37. See the mention of M. du Simitière in the Introduction, p. xiii.

38. A "line" is an old unit of length, about one-twelfth of an inch.

39. See note no. 17, in sec. 15.

40. In both of these cases the word in the original is "Schneidestein."

41. These sandstones are all in the Lower Cretaceous Patuxent formation.

42. At Georgetown and Alexandria the rock is granite; at the Great Falls it is the Peters Creek mica schist with quartzite layers, and this is undoubtedly the rock he mentions here. He recognized granite at so many places that he would certainly have used that term if he meant the rock at Georgetown.

43. It is not at all clear what Schöpf meant by this hanging phrase, which I have rendered literally. With the foregoing part of the sentence (which needs to be held in view) the original is . . . "und man hat sie auch wieder, so bald man bey Richmond von der hohen ebenen Sandfläche herabsteiget; und das enge Thal, welches der James-River sich hier und weiter Seewärts gegraben hat." Evidently something is missing in the phrase following the semicolon, but considering the grammatical problems involved in any attempt to fill in something that would make sense, I have not succeeded at reaching any helpful suggestion or interpretation.

44. Here Schöpf definitely uses the term "granite" in good sense, and gives a vivid description of the Petersburg granite, which has pink porphyritic facies and is cut by pegmatites.

45. In this sentence Schöpf used both "Amiant" and "Berglein," indicating that he was differentiating between two kinds of asbestos; amiant (amianth) is the spinnable variety. The "Russian glass" was probably leaf mica (muscovite) , and the "potstone" the variety of talc also called soapstone.

46. An old unit equal to about six feet.

47. The extension westward of the crystalline basement under the Paleozoic strata of the mountains was not to be noted again for more than half a century. Here once more we have a fine example of Schöpf's original and perspicaceous geologic thinking.

48. This is the first known suggestion by a worker on the ground that a colored geologic map of America might be made. Schöpf here anticipated Maclure, and had he enjoyed adequate time and facility, would undoubtedly have preceded him.

49. This is in the marble belt.

50. A fine description of the Cockeysville marble, which lies in a big sinuous belt north of Baltimore. We may wonder what Schöpf would have thought and said, could he have returned to the Baltimore of the late 19th and early 20th centuries, with its miles of red brick row houses, every one punctuated at the portal by a rise of gleaming white marble steps (gleaming, that is, thanks to daily scrubbing by itinerant black boys and girls eager to earn a nickel) .

51. The rocks described in the next six paragraphs are in a complex succession of crystallines and metamorphics that may as well be identified in general here; the reader can spot the ones described by Schöpf with little difficulty. Schöpf goes through this belt from west to east, between the Martic overthrust and the country some six miles west of Ellicott City. In this belt the rocks are as follows, going westward: Setters quartzite, serpentine, Peters Creek formation (biotite-chlorite schist, quartz gneiss) Sykesville granite, Marburg schist (blue and green muscovite-chlorite schist and chloritoid schist, with quartz injection parallel to the layers) , Ijamsville phyllite (soft blue, purple, and green phyllitic slate with quartz injections) , Urbana phyllite (green ferruginous quartzose chloritic phyllite with green slaty layers, thin calcareous layers, many massive white quartzite beds, thinner purple, green quartzite) then, one mile to Martic overthrust, the Ijamsville phyllite again. Most of the rock types described by Schöpf are readily recognizable in this succession.

52. This is the Urbana phyllite.

53. Here we have certainly an early, perhaps the earliest analysis of stream patterns in relation to bedrock geology. In this instance Schöpf takes one of his several valid steps toward geomorphology; but it all had to be done over again, and much later.

54. This slate is undoubtedly from the Harpers formation, of Cambrian age.

55. Probably one of the pegmatites associated with the granitic rocks of the region.

56. The word as printed here is "Halten," which might possibly be what Schöpf wrote, to mean some kind of mine support, but I think it more likely a misprint for "Halden."

57. The rocks here are limestones of the Frederick Valley, the Frederick

limestone of Upper Cambrian age, and the Grove limestone of the lower Ordovician.

58. Most of the stretch between the limestone valley of Sharpsburg and the Frederick Valley is underlain by the Catoctin metabasalt, and this must be Schöpf's porphyry. The "sandstone" and the fragments of ferruginous quartz undoubtedly came from the Weverton formation of lower Cambrian age. But what the "foliated, very hard gneissic stone" might be is not so easy to say; it might have been from the thin-bedded part of the Loudoun quartzite, also of the lower Cambrian.

59. Although the Great Limestone Valley, as indicated by Schöpf's notes, was observed earlier by Evans, this is a fine description of it, actually the first of its kind. The limestones in this belt are the Tomstown, Elbrook, and Conococheague formations of Lower, Middle, and Upper Cambrian age.

60. Schöpf used the "surreptitious" (commonly called the "pirated") edition of Chastellux printed at Cassel in 1785. See the entry in the list of works referred to by Schöpf. Chastellux wrote fully about the Natural Bridge and illustrated his account, but this was in the 1786 edition, not the one cited by Schöpf.

61. The word Schöpf used here, and at a number of other places to designate this kind of feature, is "Wand." I have translated it variously as wall, front, or escarpment, as best seems to fit the individual situation.

62. This sandstone probably came from the Shawangunk formation, or the Tuscarora, which forms the mountain front for many miles across eastern Pennsylvania.

63. This is a "block field" similar to the ones described by H. T. U. Smith (The Hickory Run boulder field, Carbon Co., Pa.: *Am. J. Sci.,* vol. 251, pp. 625-642, 1953) and by Noel Potter and J. H. Moss (Origin of the Blue Rocks block field and adjacent deposits, Berks Co., Pa.: *Geol. Soc. Amer. Bull.* vol. 79, pp. 255-262, 1968).

64. According to Morrison (1911, vol. 1, p. 412) Jeffery's map of Pennsylvania, 1782, was taken from a 1770 map by W. Scull.

65. What Schöpf evidently means in this rather involved sentence is that the subsidiary, intervening ranges lie *en echelon.*

66. Heller's House was eight miles north of Nazareth.

67. The rocks mentioned under headings 1 to 12 here are as follows:
The red clayey beds are probably of the Silurian Bloomsburg formation.
2. The limestone in the hill behind Eckardt's is probably Helderberg (Devonian) with associated sandstones.
3. The low sandstone hills are possibly of the Hamilton group.
The sandstones noted under nos. 4 to 8 are Catskill, as are also nos. 10 and 11; those under 9, possibly Pocono, and no. 12, certainly Pocono.

68. This standstone is the Tuscarora (Shawangunk to the northeast) of Silurian age. The reference to Easton is somewhat puzzling, for the rocks around Easton are mainly limestone.

69. Tuscarora Mountain is flanked by the Tuscarora sandstone, which is not normally red.

70. This is probably red sandstone from the Juniata formation.

71. The rocks around this locality (where Brush Creek flows into the Juniata) and on Allequippy Ridge are of the Catskill formation.

72. Tuscarora quartzitic sandstone.

73. This is exactly what Schöpf wrote. What he must have meant was "there appear to be no strata, but they must be covered" etc.

74. Schöpf's description here fits the Onondaga limestone very well. The limestone does not, however, fill up the space between these low hills and the Allegheny front.

75. The sandstone on the top of Allegheny Mountain is the Pocono.

76. The words here are "Schieferwände und Betten," by which Schöpf probably meant shales standing at high angles as well as lying horizontal, and if so, "Faces and beds of shale" might be a better version.

77. The coals on the Ohio mentioned here are of the Monongahela formation. They are locally associated with freshwater limestone that is very dense and fine-grained, and somewhat like marble in appearance.

78. Schöpf gave a somewhat fuller account of this coal, the Pittsburgh, and its mining, on pp. 252-253 of the *Travels* (Morrison 1911, vol. 1). This mention, incidentally, was noted by Eavenson, H. N., *The Pittsburgh Coal bed— Its early history and development*: A. I. M. E., N.Y., 55 p., 1938 (pp. 12-13).

79. Schöpf wrote "Schiefergeschiebe." Despite the fact that in the context it is somewhat puzzling, no other translation than the one here offered seems possible.

80. George White points out (personal communication) that sec. 38 is "the earliest description of American stream regimen, deposits, and characteristics in such detail."

81. In English (as here given) in the original.

82. In English in the original.

83. This is almost certainly a reference to Antonio de Ulloa (1716-1795) who was governor of Louisiana in 1766 and who wrote abundantly on South America—*Relation historique du voyage fait à l'Amérique méridionale, par ordre du roi, pour mésurer quelques degrés du meridien et connaître la véritable figure et grandeur de la terre, avec diverses observations astronomoiques et physiques, etc.*: Madrid, 1748, 2 vols.; also *Noticias Americanas, Entretimientos physico-historicos sobre la America Meridiona, y la septentrional-oriental*: Madrid 1772.—Thomas Jefferson mentioned and quoted Ulloa in reference to this matter.

84. This passage does not occur in Evans's *Analysis*, and originally I simply translated the German given by Schöpf, but later on George White discovered the original, in Pownall's 1776 *Topographical description . . .* (see entry on Pownall in following list of works referred to by Schöpf), Mulkearn edition, pp. 112-113, and here again we see that Schöpf translated Evans very well. Following my general rule, I give here an exact copy of Evans's original.

85. Although Schöpf put this footnote between quotation marks, as shown here, it does not occur in Evans, and is therefore either Schöpf's own addendum or a passage taken from some other unacknowledged source.

86. Schöpf gave no specific reference for this passage; it is on page 9 of the *Analysis*. His translation here is very free; he rewrote one sentence entirely and added a parenthesis of his own without so indicating it. To follow my general intention of presenting exactly what Schöpf said I should probably offer a translation of his version, but the differences are really not serious,

and in consistency with my treatment of Evans elsewhere I give here an exact copy of the English original.

87. Here Schöpf has obviously transposed the Mississippi and the Bourbon. Oregon was an early name for the Columbia River, and the Bourbon is therefore the Nelson River, which flows into Hudson's Bay.

The Oregon, or the "River of the West" was first brought into the literature on our then unexplored northwestern terrain by Carver (first edition, 1778) and it enjoyed a long fictional history. George White (personal communication) has a microfilm of the *Beyträge* from an unidentified German library with a map at its end that shows these rivers and betrays Schöpf's source—the 1778 edition and not that of 1781. The "River of the West" was thought to rise as Carver described it, and to flow into the Pacific. Lewis and Clark looked for it, largely in vain, as a possible path to the Pacific.

88. *cf.* Merrill 1924, pp. 50, 51.

89. There were two Silberschlags of note at this time: Johann Esaias (1716-1791) and Georg Christoph (1731-1790) and the idea mentioned by Schöpf might have come from either (the latter looks a bit more likely), but see the entry for Silberschlag in the list of works cited by Schöpf.

90. Probably Mt. Fairweather.

91. The first part of this sentence is obscure; the syntax is disturbed, and something must be missing, but what it might be I am unable to guess. The original reads "Dieses mochte sich ereignen, wenn es wollte, so muszten unter Bedingung des erwähnten Abhangs nach der See zu, die niederen und vorderen Bergreihen, zu gleicher Zeit mit den hintern und höhern vom Wasser bedeckt gewesen seyn."

92. Here we have another example of Schöpf's prescience. George White has this to say (personal communication) : "America was not to see another such penetrating analysis of the now low-lying ancient Piedmont crystalline rocks for almost a century! As far as I know Maclure in 1809 and 1817 and Eaton, in 1818, · 1820 and later, never even recognized the anomalous low position of the 'granite'—anomalous in Wernerian terms of Primitive rock being in mountain cores."

93. This ambiguous phrase is exactly what Schöpf wrote. He must have meant to say that we cannot suspect it to be of nonmarine origin, because in his discussion of the coastal plain sediments (sec. 9) he concludes positively that the shell-bearing beds were deposited by the sea.

94. See the reference to the Abbé Raynal in the list of authors cited by Schöpf.

95. In attempt to be emphatic Schöpf produced here a rather poorly written sentence, difficult to translate with equal emphasis into good English. The original is "Anders nicht, als wenn das feste Land aus der Tiefe wäre heraufgehoben worden, könnte Amerika jünger seyn." It would be closer to the German to say "In no other way than if the dry land had been lifted out of the depths, could America be younger"; and even in this more accurate but awkward form, what Schöpf had in mind is not at all clear.

96. The latter part of this sentence is grammatically defective. It reads "so ist zu vermuthen, dasz die Richtung der Granitreihen aller Orten, die der übrigen gewissermassen bestimmen, ungeachtet nemand wird die Ursache angeben können, die dem Granit seinen Weg vorgezeichnet." The translation here offered overlooks grammatical error and is mainly a guess at what Schöpf wanted to say.

97. "Nach dieser Gegend" is what Schöpf said, and he may have meant toward the southwest; "in this direction" might be a better translation.

98. Here Schöpf refers to the Big Bone Lick of Kentucky, near the Ohio River, which was discovered in 1739 by Captain Charles Lemoyne de Longuell. Between that time and the period of Schöpf's work the locality was visited and specimens were taken by many travellers, some of whose reports were not published until after Schöpf might have learned about the locality but the most likely are the report of Pownall, a paper by Peter Collinson on some specimens sent in 1766 by Captain Harry Gordon to Benjamin Franklin (Collinson, Peter, Of some very large fossil teeth found in America: *Phil. Trans. Royal Soc. London*, vol. xii, pp. 476-478, 1767), and one by Thomas Hutchins, *A topographical description of the eastern parts o fVirginia, Pennsylvania, Maryland, and North Carolina*: London 1778, pp. 82, 83. (See Simpson, G. G., The beginnings of vertebrate paleontology in North America: *the early history of science and learning in America*, Am. Phil. Soc., 1942, pp. 130-188, esp. pp. 135-149; also, Jillson, W. R., *The extinct vertebrata of the Pleistocene in Kentucky*: Frankfort 1968, esp. pp. 87-90.) It is most likely, however, that Schöpf got his information in conversation with some of the many well-informed men he met and visited during his stay.

99. What this is I have been unable to find out, even by trying several possibilities of typographical error, and consulting Kalm. The passage referred to by Schöpf, on page 316 of the German edition, deals with garnet sand.

100. Schöpf took this passage from the German translation of Kalm. The version in English by Benson (Benson, A. B., *Peter Kalm's travels in America*, vol. 2, pp. 457-458: Wilson-Erickson Inc., New York, 1937; Dover, New York 1966), although based on Forster's translation (Warrington, England, 1770-1771) which in turn was taken from the German translation, was carefully revised by Benson from the original Swedish, and is preferable in general to a translation of the German given by Schöpf. I have therefore given Benson's rendition here, even though this be a minor deviation from my intent to present what Schöpf said as strictly as possible. Incidentally, Schöpf omitted Kalm's promise (at the end of the third sentence) to mention later on the stones in the gray conglomerate, possibly because he did not want to introduce any such involvement, but rather probably because Kalm apparently never got around to the later mention.

101. The verb here is "stürzen," and Schöpf may have wanted to connote collapse.

102. The author of this work, not specified by Schöpf, was Cornelius de Pauw; see the entry under his name in the annotated list of works referred to by Schöpf. I am indebted to Richard A. Gray, Reference Librarian of the William Oxley Thompson Memorial Library of the Ohio State University for locating the work and identifying de Pauw as the author.

103. The original is "gleichsam als Ueberbleibsel eines festeren Bodens." Schöpf must have been thinking of a former continent.

104. Schöpf wrote "als diese Gruppe von Inseln ihr Daseyn in gegenwärtiger Gestalt vorzüglich mit von daher erhalten zu haben scheint." Perhaps he was merely trying for terse effect, but strictly considered a word is missing, and I have inserted "matter" as probably what he had in mind.

Annotated List of Works and Authors
REFERRED TO BY SCHÖPF IN THE *BEYTRÄGE*

BEROLDINGEN, FRANZ COLESTIN FREIHERR VON, *Beobachtungen, Zweifel, und Fragen der Mineralogie betreffend*: Hanover 1778.

von Beroldingen was born October 11, 1740 at St. Gallen, and died March 8, 1798 at Walshausen.

In this work he favored the authochthonous vegetal origin of coal, and explained gneiss as "regenerated" granite. He dealt also with the Jura of the Bavarian Palatinate. He tried to reconcile the Vulcanist and Neptunist interpretations of basalt by proposing that basalt owes its origin to fire and its form to water — basaltic lava poured into the sea. He fell into error indeed here, however; he cited ammonites, belemnites, and Gryphea in basalt!

Schopf cited von Beroldingen on the origin of soil and coal, and petroleum from coal; also in reference to burning mountains and other features of peat and coal.

BUFFON, GEORGES LOUIS LECLERC, COMTE DE, *Supplément à l'histoire naturelle*, vol. IX. The full title of this work is *Histoire naturelle générale et particuliere avec la description du Cabinet du roy* . . . Paris, de l'imprimerie royale, 1779-1804. Supplément, t. 1-15, 1774-1789.

CARVER'S TRAVELS — English edition. Carver, Jonathan, *Travels through the interior parts of North America, in the years* 1766, 1767 and 1768: London, 1778 (many other editions).

Jonathan Carver (1732-1780) was born in Connecticut, became an army officer at 18, and fought in the French and Indian War in 1763. In his travels that the book describes he reached the headwaters of the Mississippi in northern Minnesota. He passed most of the rest of his life in straitened circumstances in London, deriving little profit from his book, which passed through several editions in English and several other languages. From Schöpf's reference to the rivers on his map it is clear that the 1778 edition was used, rather than one of the later ones.

CATESBY, MARK. *Natural History of Carolina, Florida, and the Bahama Islands*: London, 1731-1743, two volumes. (Several later editions).

Catesby (born March 3, 1683, died Dec. 23, 1749, London) was in America from 1722 to 1726. His studies were made possible by financial support of Sir Hans Sloane and other members of an English circle interested in natural history. He studied both the flora and the fauna, and especially ornithology. His work is distinguished by the first professional identification of a vertebrate fossil, a Mammoth, in America, about 1724. For the definitive work on Catesby, including a chapter on his geology, see Frick, G. F., and Stearns, R. P., *Mark Catesby, the Colonial Audubon*: University of Illinois Press, Urbana, 1961.

CHASTELLUX, *Voyage de M. le Chevalier de Chastellux en Amérique*. Schöpf was quoting from a "surreptitious"—i.e., pirated—edition, printed in Cassel in 1785 from extracts of Chastellux' journal first published in a Gotha periodical. The complete authorized edition, Chastellux, Francois Jean, Marquis de, *Voyages de M. le Marquis de Chastellux dans l'Amérique septentrionale dans les années 1780, 1781, et 1782*: Paris: Prault, 1786, was followed by later editions and translations. A recent revised translation with biographic and bibliographical material is *Travels in North America in the Years 1780, 1781, and 1782 by the Marquis de Chastellux, a Revised Translation with Introduction and Notes* by H. C. Rice, Jr:, 2 vols.: Univ. of N. Carolina Press, Chapel Hill, 1963.

Member of a noble family, Chastellux (1734-1788) entered the army at the age of 15, and by 1780, when he went to America, he was a major general in Rochambeau's army. He was here three years and during that time was closely associated with George Washington. Accounts have come down to us of his high courage and sustained activity. The *Voyage* contains many interesting accounts of the natural history of America. Chastellux was a prolific writer in general.

CRELL, LORENZ FLORENZ FRIEDRICH VON, *Die neuesten Entdeckungen in der Chemie*. Gesamlet von D. L. Crell, 1781 etc., Leipzig.

Although this work professes to report the most recent discoveries in chemistry, Crell (1744-1816) was a devoted adherent of the phlogiston theory. From 1778 to 1803 he edited *Crells Annalen, Journal, Archiv und Entdeckungen*. He was a chemist, "of influence less through original investigation than through his great journalistic and literary activity" (*Allg. Deutsch. Biog.*). He was interested in mineralogy and mining. He translated Kirwan's writings, Black's lectures on chemistry and other English tracts of the time into German.

CRONSTEDT, *Miner*. CRONSTEDT, AXEL FREDRIK, *Försök til Mineralogie, eller Mineral-rikets upstellning*, Stockholm,, 1758, is the original Swedish; Schöpf used the German translation by G. Widenmann, *Versuch einer neuen Mineralogie*, Copenhagen, 1760.

Cronstedt (1722-1765) was chemist, mining geologist, metallurgist, and mineralogist. He was discoverer of nickel and of the zeolite group of minerals. He wrote on the chemical classification of minerals, and distinguished between minerals and rocks. His work on mineralogy was translated into many languages; the German translation by Werner in 1780 led to Werner's interest in rocks and to his work on "geognosy," which makes him the real scientific founder of petrology.

DE LUC, see LUC, JEAN ANDRE DE.

EVANS, LEWIS, *Analysis.* The full title is *Geographical, historical, political, philosophical, and mechanical essays, the first introducing an analysis of a general map of the middle British Colonies in America, and of the country of the Confederate Indians: a description of the face of the country; the boundaries of the Confederates; and the maritime and inland navigation of the several rivers and lakes contained therein.* By Lewis Evans. Philadelphia: printed by B. Franklin and D. Hall. MDCCLV. and sold by R. and J. Dodsley, in Pall-Mall, London.

For fuller information on Evans see Gipson, L. H., 1939, *Lewis Evans*: Philadelphia, Historical Society of Pennsylvania; White, G. W., 1951, Lewis Evans' contributions to early American geology 1743-1755: *Illinois Acad. Sci., Trans.,* vol. 44, pp. 152-158; and White, G. W., 1956, Lewis Evans (1700-56): a scientist in colonial America: *Nature,* vol. 177, pp. 1055-1056.

Evans was a gifted, highly versatile and well-rounded naturalist. He travelled widely in eastern North America and is probably best remembered for his geographic and geologic observations and the maps he made. His importance in this category is clearly evident in the remarks Schöpf offered about his work, and the quotations from the *Analysis* that he incorporated (translated into German but taken by me for this text from Evans's original) in the *Beyträge.* These quotations speak for themselves.

FORSTER, JOHANN REINHOLD, *Bemerkungen auf einer Reise um die Welt*: Berlin 1783.

The full title of this work is *Observations made on a trip around the world on the physical geography, natural history, and moral philosophy,* written in English by Forster's son George and published first in London, 1783; German version written also by George from data furnished by his father and published in Berlin, 1783; a Dutch version, Haarlem, 1788; Swedish, 1785; French, vol. 5 of Cook's second voyage.

Forster (1729-1798) was appointed naturalist on Cook's second voyage around the world, in 1772. He was a difficult character, said to have quarreled with everybody and to have been constantly in trouble despite Cook's generosity. He was created Councillor by Frederick II of Prussia, and was Professor of Natural History at Halle from 1781 to his death.

GUETTARD, JEAN ÉTIENNE, Memories dans laquelle on compare le Canada à la Suisse par rapport à ses minéraux: *Mem. Acad. Royale des Sciences de Paris, 1752,* pp. 189-220, 323-360, 524-533, 1756. Schöpf cited Guettard's work in his footnote on the "Recherches philosophiques . . ." for which he failed to name the author — it was de Pauw (see the entry on de Pauw in this list).

Guettard (1715-1786) was the French "mineralogist" (actually a first-rate geologist — see Geikie, *The Founders of Geology,* Macmillan 1905, Dover 1962, pp. 105-139 for a fine account and appreciation of this remarkable man) who is remembered mainly for his geologic map of France, the first of its kind anywhere. As Geikie has aptly put it, Guettard was the "father of all the national Geological Surveys which have been instituted by the various civilized nations of the Old and the New Worlds." (Geikie, *op. cit.,* p. 115.) We remember him also because of his assistant in the arduous labor of mapping, who was none other than the great founder of true chemistry, Antoine Laurent Lavoisier.

Schöpf does not seem to have been aware of Guettard's total output (and few are the scientists who *have* read it all, not even Sir Archibald Geikie, who devoted a 35-page chapter to Guettard — see p. 109 of the *Founders*), and especially, I am inclined to believe, of his geologic map. I have touched on this question in my comparison of Schöpf's work with that of William Maclure.

JUSSIEU. The reference is to one or both of the papers by Jussieu, Antoine de, Sur des empreintes de plantes dans des pierres; *Histoire de Academie Royale des Sciences Année 1718,* Amsterdam edition, 1723, pp. 3-6; Recherches physiques sur les pétrifications qui se trouvent en France, de diverses parties de plantes et d'animaux étrangers, avec le supplement: *Mem. Acad. Roy. des Sciences de la Année 1721,* Amsterdam ed., 1725, pp. 89-98.

KALM, PETER, *Travels in North America* (orig. *En Resa Norra Amerika,* 3 vols. 1753-1761). This work was translated into several languages and appeared in several editions. Schöpf's first reference, concerning rounded pebbles found in beds of the Coastal Plain, is to the 1770-71 or 1772 English edition, then, immediately thereafter, dealing in general with the Tertiary strata of the Coastal Plain, he refers to the German edition (1754-1761), part 2. Later references are all to this same edition. (Also see note 100).

Kalm (1716-1779) was a Swedish naturalist, especially in botany, entomology, and ornithology, who was sent to North America by the Swedish Academy of Sciences to study and collect plants, 1747-1751. In 1752 he became Professor at the University of Abo. His account of the insects, the plantations, and the agriculture in general of North America is the first ever written.

LINNAEUS (LINNÉ), CARL, *Systema Naturae,* 1735.

Schöpf refers five times to Linnaeus (1707-1778), in each case concerning identification of a rock or mineral, and it is without much question the *Systema* of 1735 that he invokes. Linnaeus also wrote later (1768) concerning the succession of strata (see A. G. Nathorst, *Carl von Linné als Geolog*: Jena 1909, pp. 61, 62) and it seems strange that Schöpf was not acquainted with this, having almost certainly been briefed on Linnaeus by Schreber. He might well have done better in ordering the rocks of the Appalachians. But, Schreber went to Linnaeus in 1760, and he may never have grasped (if indeed he had the opportunity) his teacher's ideas on the rock succession, either then or after the publication of 1768.

LUC, JEAN ANDRÉ DE, *Geschichte der Erde.* The work cited by Schöpf is *Lettres physiques et morales sur l'histoire de la Terre et de l'homme* — 5 vols., the Hague and Paris, 1779.

de Luc (b. Geneva 1727, d. Windsor 1817) was a prolific writer, on a wide variety of subjects — meteorology, physics, cosmology, chemistry, philosophy, theology, "socialpolitik," geography, geology. He went to England in 1773. He became a Fellow of the Royal Society, and was elected to the French Academy, and the Royal Society of Dublin. In 1798 he was appointed Honorary Professor of Geology at Göttingen.

With de Saussure, he was the first to use the term geology in its present sense, in 1779. He labored to uphold the Mosaic account of the creation, and, with Kirwan, the Irish reactionary, was a bitter opponent of Hutton. He held "that the original surface of the earth had sunk down, leaving the Alpine peaks as upstanding remnants of the original crust" (F. D. Adams, *The Birth and Development of the Geological Sciences,* Williams & Wilkins, Baltimore 1938; Dover, N. Y., 1954, p. 392). But, he made several valid discoveries in physics, including the fact that water reaches its maximum density at 4° C.

MONZON, HENRY, misprint for
MOUZON, HENRY, *An accurate map of North & South Carolina.*: London, R. Sayer & J. Bennett, 1775, one sheet 40 x 56¼ inches. Also reproduced in Faden, W., *The North American atlas. . . .*: London, 1777, map 29-30; Jeffreys, T. and others, *The American atlas. . . .*: London, 1778, map 23-24. Later editions of each and later printings, see U. S. Library of Congress, Division of Maps and Charts, *List of maps of America by P. L. Phillips*: Washington, 1901, p. 819.

PALLAS, PIERRE SIMON, *Beobacht. über die Gebürge &c., Sammlung zur Physik und Naturgeschichte*: Leipzig, 1ster Band, 2tes Stück, nr. 1. The full title of this work, which is a collection of essays on various subjects, is *"Neuen Nordischen Beiträge" pour servir à la "Geographie, Ethnographie, Naturgeschichte, und l'économie domestique,"* St. Petersburg and Leipzig, 1781-1783.

Pallas (1741-1811) was called to Russia in 1768 by the Empress Catherine II on the occasion of the 1769 transit of Venus. The great lady had been severely annoyed by sharp criticism offered by a French astronomer at the time of the earlier transit (1763) and was determined to do without foreign assistance for the 1769 transit and to ensure the best job possible. The expedition, which covered almost every conceivable aspect of Russia's vast territory, was put in charge of Pallas, who for six years did a stupendous job (see Geikie, *op. cit.,* p. 178) and whose report, *Observations sur la formation des montagnes et les changements arrivés au globe, particulièrement de l'Empire Russe* (3 vols.), St. Petersburg 1777, is the work for which he is most generally known, and it seems peculiar that Schöpf did not consult it (a German version came out in St. Petersburg in 1777), but his reference, despite the lack of a date, certainly specifies the later work, for he gives Leipzig as the place of publication, and the *Observations*, both the French and the German, was published in St. Petersburg only. Furthermore, in the *Observations* Pallas vigorously opposed the idea that the mountains were covered by the sea, and Schöpf could hardly have known of this, for he accepted the idea the while he realized its difficulties (see my comment in the evaluation of Schöpf's work).

DE PAUW, CORNEILLE, *Recherches philosophiques sur les Américains, ou, Mémoires interessants pour servir à l'histoire de l'espèce humaine. Par mr. de P. . . . Studio disposta fidele Lucret.* Berlin 1768; vol. 2, 1769; vol. 3, *Defense des recherches, etc.,* Berlin 1770. Later edition,s Berlin 1771, London 1771, Berlin 1777. A translation into German appeared at Berlin in 1769, but Schöpf obviously used the French version.

de Pauw (1739-1799) was canon of Xantu, in the duchy of Cleves, Germany, on the lower Rhine some 15 miles above the Dutch border. He was a liberal. Attracted to the study of science when young, he was aided by his theologic mentors and he published the *Recherches philos. sur les Américains* before the age of 30. The work fell prey to a storm of criticism; de Pauw's attack on ideas widely accepted from the accounts of travellers were considered unacceptable. However, Diderot and d'Alembert thought otherwise and engaged him to write for the *Encyclopédie*, to which he contributed several articles. When the first two volumes of the *Recherches philos. sur les Américains* came out (Berlin 1768, 1769) the Abbé Pernetty published a "dissertation" in strong dissent; this came out independently at Berlin in 1770. The third volume of de Pauw's work, the *Défenses,* is a response to Pernetty in particular and to other critics in general.

POWNALL, THOMAS, 1776. *A topographical description of such parts of North America as are contained in the (annexed) map of the middle British colonies in North America*: J. Almon, London. See also Mulkearn, Lois, ed., 1949, Pownall, T., *A topographical description of the United States of America (being a revised and enlarged edition)*: Pittsburgh, University of Pittsburgh Press; also White, G. W., *op. cit., (Science,* 1951, p. 302). Pownall's book was a revision and amplification of Evans' earlier book; he gives Evans full credit.

RAYNAL, ABBÉ GUILLAUME-THOMAS-FRANÇOIS, was born at St.-Géniez in the south of France in either 1713 (*Encyclopedia Britannica*) or 1711 (*Dictionnaire générale de biographie*). The later date is the one most often given. There is a biography of him by B. Lunet (*Biographie de l'abbé Raynal,* Rodez, 1866) and an incomplete account in the Geneva edition (1780) of his own *Histoire philosophique et politique des deux Indes.*

The celebrated abbé was so pungent a character that a few words about his career, beyond any specific relevance to Schöpf's concern with him, are virtually unavoidable.

His private life was not exactly exemplary. He studied with the Jesuits, took holy orders and joined the Jesuits but left them in 1747 and went to Paris, where he was a *prêtre desservant* until he was thrown out (for simony!) in that same year. After that he lived by his pen and his cleverness at flattering important and highly placed personages. He became editor of the *Mercure de France,* and compiled a number of works, some of which he bought from hack writers; others he pilfered without permission. He worked up a reputation as a philosopher, and mainly on the strength of his friendship with Voltaire and other philosophers, frequented the best salons. He was condemned for plagiarism before the Revolution and lived for a while merely from hand to mouth. During the Revolution he was elected a deputy of the *tiers-état* from Marseille, but his *Letter to the National Assembly* brought on such a furore that he barely escaped the guillotine. He lived quietly at Montlhéry for a while and died at Paris (Chaillot) while visiting a friend there in 1796.

The ideas to which Schöpf takes exception are probably those expressed in his *Philosophical and Political History of the Settlements and Trade of the Europeans in the East and West Indies* (translated from the French by J. Justamond, M. A., 3d Ed., Dublin 1779) vol. 3, pp. 1-4.

Here he discusses occurrences of marine organisms (fossils) found far inland and concludes that "the ocean has broken its natural limits, or perhaps, that its limits have never been insurmountable; and that varying the surface of the globe, according to the irregularity of its own motions, it hath alternately taken the earth from its inhabitants, and restored it to them again. Hence those successive though never universal deluges that have covered the face of the earth, but not rendered it totally invisible to us at once . . ."

This may be interpreted, as Schöpf evidently did, to mean that man has witnessed such changes, including the withdrawal of the sea that left the evidences of former marine occupation observed by Schöpf. There may well, however, have been other ideas attributed to Raynal that Schöpf obtained through hearsay.

ROBIN, ABBÉ CHARLES-CÉSAR, *New Travels through America.* Schöpf gives simply this English title. The full original title is *"Nouveau voyage dans l'Amérique septentrionale en l'année 1781 et campagne de l'armée de M. le Comte de Rochambeau,* par M. l'abbé Robin — Philadelphie; Paris, Moutard, 1782. Translated into English by Philip Freneau, Robert Bell, 1783. For various editions of Robin see Monaghan, F., *French Travellers in the United States,* N.Y. 1933, p. 81.

The Abbé Robin was one of the chaplains in the French Army commanded by the Count de Rochambeau that collaborated with General Washington during the Revolutionary War. He made many observations, especially of the American people, as he travelled with the army from Rhode Island to Yorktown, and gave account also of the various happenings and conditions that invested the war.

SAUSSURE, HORACE BÉNÉDICTE DE, *Voyages dans les Alpes,* 4 vols., Geneva and Neuchâtel, 1779-1796.

de Saussure (1740-1799) was a great pioneer of Alpine geology and Alpinism, and one of the founders of geology as well. His life and work have been fully reviewed by Geikie *(Founders of geology,* pp. 182-191), Adams *(The birth and development of the geological sciences,* pp. 387-392) and Freshfield *(The life of Horace Benedicte de Saussure,* London, Arnold, 1920) as well as in other biographies listed by Wells and White *(Ohio Jour. Sci.,* vol. 58, p. 296, 1958) and are well enough known to require here only two comments that concern Schöpf's work and his use of de Saussure, plus perhaps a reminder that the term "geology," although it was apparently first used in 1661 (see Adams, *op. cit.,* p. 165) was effectively introduced in essentially its present significance by de Saussure in 1779. We might also note that it was de Saussure, among the great founders of geology, who more prominently and effectively than any of the others emphasized the importance of actual field work, as opposed to the arm-chair theorizing that had so fatuously and boringly prevailed through the 18th century.

In 1786 de Saussure showed clearly that streams carve out their valleys and ridiculed the notion that the sea could have done it. It is almost certain that Schöpf did not see this, at least not before the *Beyträge* had gone to press. He refers to the 1779 issue only, the first part of the *Voyages.* We may recall that Schöpf realized the work of streams in cutting their channels but was unwilling to think that the prominent Appalachian valleys could thus have been fashioned and so invoked powerful inrush of the sea as the cause. This would seem to be the only outstanding case in which Schöpf fell into somewhat unscientific ambiguity.

In 1779, however, de Saussure did attribute granite to precipitation from water, and here Schöpf was ahead of him. But, seventeen years later (see Adams p. 390) de Saussure realized that this must be impossible. At the same time he concluded that the rocks in the Alps must have been folded. We may readily speculate that if Schöpf had brought out, say in 1797 or 1798, a revised edition of the *Beyträge,* his account might well have anticipated those of Eaton and the Rogers brothers.

SCULL'S MAP. Two Sculls made maps of Pennsylvania; it is possible that Schöpf referred to Scull, Nicholas, *Map of . . . Pennsylvania . . .:* Philadelphia, 1759, 1770; but much more likely he referred to Scull, William, . . . *Map of . . . Pennsylvania:* Philadelphia, 1770; London,

1775, also in various atlases, see U. S. Library of Congress, Division of Maps and Charts, *List of maps of America by P. L. Phillips*: Washington, 1901, pp. 673-674; also see Note 64.

SILBERSCHLAG, JOHANN ESAIAS (1716-1791) was born at Aschersleben. His early schooling was at Magdeburg, and at the University of Halle he specialized in theology and "natural history" (science). He became Oberconsistorialrath of the Realschule at Berlin. The bibliography given with his autobiography and in Meusel, *Lexikon der vom Jahren 1750-1800 verstorbenen teutschen Schriftsteller*, Bd. XIII, 1813, p. 168 ff. does not list any work on the earth, but his title agrees with that cited by Schöpf.

Silberschlag, Georg Christoph (1731-1790) was also born at Aschersleben, studied at Magdeburg and Halle, and specialized in theology and natural science. He became a clergyman and devoted much effort at reconciling science and scripture. He became General Superintendent "der Altmark und Preignitz" at Stendal. He wrote *Neue Theorie der Erde oder ausführliche Untersuchung der ursprünglichen Bildung der Erde*, published at Berlin in 1764, and this is probably the source of Schöpf's remark (it is strange that he gave no specific reference, considering his bibliographic habits otherwise). Silberschlag also wrote a three-volume work on principles of physics and mathematics, published at Berlin in 1780, and *Geogonie: oder Erklärung der Mosaischen Erdbeschaffung nach physikalischen und mathematischen Grundsätzen* (3 vols., Berlin 1780-1783) and if Schöpf gave much serious attention to the *Beyträge* after his return to Germany he may have derived from this.

STORK, WILLIAM, may perhaps most aptly be called a shadowy character. Information about him has proved to be most difficult to ferret out, and I am indebted to George White for the following information.

Dr. William Stork wrote a book, *Description of East Florida . . .* which went through several editions, 1766, 1766, and a third in 1769, which includes John Bartram's "Journal . . . for the Floridas." The third is the best edition, with an excellent map by Thomas Jeffreys covering Florida and the adjacent islands. Chapter II, "Soil," contains a brief but perceptive account of the topography and the underlying "four strata or beds of earth found in East Florida." Bartram's "Journal" contains some scattered brief references to the geology.

According to C. L. Mowat *(East Florida as a British Province 1763-1784.* Facsimile reprint of 1943 edition, Gainesville, University of Florida Press, 1964), "Dr. Stork, a botanist and member of the Royal Society, visited East Florida as agent for various land grantees" (p. 50). He had considered bringing Germans to settle on some of the grants (p. 61). He was a physician who lived in St. Augustine for a time, but whether he practiced is not clear. He was primarily a planter, for in 1774 William Bartram *(Travels through North and South Carolina,*

Georgia, and East and West Florida . . . Philadelphia 1791, p. 253) saw the "deserted plantation, the property of Dr. Stork where he once resided," on St. John's River.

WALLERIUS, JOHAN GOTTSCHALK, syst. I. The book referred to is *Mineralsystem, worin die Fossilien nach Klassen* . . . *beschreiben* . . .: translated by Leske, N. G., and Bebenstreit, E. B. G., 2 vols., 1781-1783. The original edition was *Systema mineralogicum, quo corpora mineralia in classes, ordines* . . .: 2 vols., Stockholm, 1772-1775.

Wallerius (1709-1785) introduced the system of natural classification for minerals. He studied mathematics, philosophy, and medicine, attaining the M. D. at Uppsala in 1735. He travelled widely in the Scandinavian countries. For a short time he taught physics, physiology, and mathematics at Lund, but then went to Uppsala, where he taught and practiced medicine. Later he lectured on chemistry, metallurgy, and materia medica. He was elected to the Royal Swedish Academy of Science, and became President in 1783.

In addition to his pioneering work on classification of minerals (which included a good deal on rocks) he did research on the composition of both mineral and organic substances. He was further noted for his application of chemistry to agriculture, and his research on artificial fertilizers.

Index

Beyträge

zur mineralogischen Kenntniß

des östlichen Theils

von

Nordamerika

und seiner Gebürge

von

D. Johann David Schöpf

Hochfürstl. Brandenb. Onolzb. und Culmb. Hof- und Garnisonmedicus, auch Landphysikus und des med. Collegiums zu Bayreuth Beysizer.

Erlangen,

verlegt von Joh. Jakob Palm. 1787.

Un

den Herrn

Hofrath Schreber.

Bey meiner Abreise von Europa im Jahr 1777.
ertheilten Sie mir den Auftrag: ,, auf die Ord-
,, nung der Erd - und Steinschichten in Ame-
,, rika Acht zu haben, und anzuzeichnen, in wie
,, fern diejenigen, die nach Papsts von Ohain und
,, Ferbers Beobachtungen in Europa statt haben,
,, auch in der neuen Welt gefunden werde. Kalm,

erin-

„erinnerten Sie dabey, leiste Ihnen hier nicht
„Genüge.„ Ob folgende Anmerkungen etwas
mehr Licht über die Anlage und Bauart des östlichen Nordamerika geben, und Ihres Beyfalls
würdiger sind, werden Sie aus der Uebersicht
urtheilen.

Während des Krieges hatte ich ganz keine
Gelegenheit, etwas zur Erläuterung dieses Gegen-
standes zu unternehmen; ich machte mir es daher,
bey meiner Reise durch den südlichen Theil der
vereinigten Nordamerikanischen Staaten, im Jahr

1783

1783 mit zum Augenmerk, dessen Gebürge zu besuchen. 'Da aber meine Zeit überhaupt eingeschränkt war, und ich auch die zu Landreisen in
diesen Gegenden bequemere Jahrszeit so viel möglich benuzen mußte, so konnte ich mich nicht überall
nach Gefallen und nach Erforderniß der Gegen-
stände verweilen. In einem so weitläuftigen Lande
ist es unmöglich, alle belehrende Gegenden selber
zu besuchen, und eben so schwer ist es dermalen
noch, gründliche und zuverläffige Kundschaften über
abgelegene Orte, von einem seiner Einwohner zu
erhalten. Dies wird mich entschuldigen, wenn

ich

ich hie und da Lücken auszufüllen nicht im Stande, oder mir eine und die andere Muthmaſſung
zu erlauben gezwungen bin.   Bey dem Mangel
innländiſcher Communikation durch beſtimmte
Fuhrwerke iſt es einem Reiſenden auch ſchlechterdings unmöglich, ohne übertriebene Koſten,
Sammlungen von Gebürgsarten zu veranſtalten
und an verlangte Orte zu ſchaffen.   Ich habe vie-
les geſammlet, gepacket, und nachher nicht wieder geſehen, welches ich zu beſſerer Ergänzung dieſes Aufſazes nöthig gehabt hätte.

Nie-

Niemand hat bisher noch diesen östlichen Theil von Nordamerika mit philosophischem Auge, nach seinem ganzen Umfange nemlich, betrachtet, wenn ich Herrn Evans ausnehme, der in seiner Analysis (*) verschiedenes, die Richtung und Beschaffenheit der Gebürge betreffend, erwähnet. Von ihm hat Gouverneur Pownall, in seiner

Topo

(*) Geograph. Historic. Polit. et Mechanical Essays; the first, Containing an Analysis of a General Map of the Middle British Colonies in America &c. by *Lewis Evans*. Philad. 1755. 4to. 32 Seiten.

Topographischen Beschreibung von Nordamerika, das nemliche wörtlich entlehnet. Beyde Schriften haben sich in Amerika selten gemacht, und ich konnte solche erst habhaft werden, nachdem ich schon zum zweytenmal die Gebürge durchwandert hatte. Sie vorher gehabt zu haben, wäre mir von grossem Nuzen gewesen; unterdessen war mir es doch auch nicht gleichgültig, meine Bemerkungen größtentheils durch die ihrigen bestätiget zu sehen. Der Bezirk des hintern Gebürges, den ich selber besucht habe, liegt zwischen dem Hudsons- und Potomack-River; von den vorderen

Gegen-

Gegenden aber, habe ich die ganze Länge von Rhode-Eyland bis St. Augustine in Florida kennen lernen, und den Weg von Neuyork bis Charleton in Carolina (960 englische Meilen) zu Lande bereiset. — Ich schmeichle mir, daß ich in den folgenden Blättern, wozu ich den Entwurf sogleich nach geendigter Reise in Carolina machte, den Weg wenigstens gezeichnet habe, der zu mehrerer Kenntniß dieses Welttheils führen, und die Aufmerksamkeit anderer Naturforscher leiten kann; und dies allein rechne ich mir zum Verdienst. Denn auch jede einzelne Widerlegung mei-

ner

ner Irrthümer, bringt uns der Wahrheit näher.

Uebrigens habe ich die Ehre mit aller Hochach-

tung zu seyn

Dero

Bayreuth. Julius 31.

ergebenster Diener

D. Schöpf.

Oeftliche Küfte von Nordamerika.

Die grosse Auffenlinie der dermaligen Küfte von Nordamerika fällt von Nordoften nach Südweften ab. Der öftlichfte Theil von Neuland ift unter ungefähr dem 52ften Grad der Länge; von hier an beugt fich die Küfte immer weftlicher, bis fie mit der Spitze von Kap Florida unter etwa 82° der Länge fich endiget. — Diefer auf jeder Karte deutlich genug bemerkte Abfall macht folglich ungefähr 30 Grade öftlicher Länge Unterfchied.

Diefe Küfte bleibt fich nicht in ihrer ganzen Länge gleich, und der füdlichere Theil ift von dem nördlicheren merklich verfchieden. Von den mitternächtlichften Gegenden von Labrador, Neuland ꝛc. ꝛc. herab ift fie

meiſt ſteil, ſchroff, kühn (a bold ſhore), felſicht, bis
in die Nachbarſchaft des Sunds und Hudſonsfluſſes.
Einige ſchmale vorſpringende ſandichte Bänke, als Kap
Cod, Kap Ann ꝛc. machen keine geltende Ausnahme.
Um den 41ſten Grad der Breite ungefähr, nimmt ſie
eine verſchiedene Beſchaffenheit an. Der ſüdöſtliche
Theil von Long-Eyland, und von da längſt der See
hinab, bis Florida, ſtellen nun ein einförmiges, nie,
driges, flaches, ſandiges Ufer dar. Das letzte hohe
Land in der Gegend ſind die Hügel von Neverſink,
bey Sandy-Huck auf Jerſey, und von da nichts ähn,
liches, bis zu einigen Sandhügeln in Florida, die
aber anders nichts als von der See ſelber aufge,
worfene Dämme, und nur etwas höher als ähnliche
Wälle, die überall an den Ufern von Florida, Karo,
lina und Virginien vorkommen, ſeyn mögen. Ich ha,
be nicht Gelegenheit gehabt, die Neverſink ſelber zu
beſuchen, und weiß daher nicht, ob ſie Felsgrund ha,
ben, oder nur Sandhügel ſind, wozu ſie doch zu hoch
ſcheinen. So wie die Küſte von verſchiedener Beſchaf,
fenheit iſt, ſo iſt es auch die Bildung des inneren Lan,
des. Evans und Pownall bemerken, daß die Gebürgs,
reihen auf der Oſtſeite des Hudſonfluſſes, die zum
Theil durch Neuyork Provinz, übrigens aber durch
Connektikut, Rhode-Eyland, Maſſachuſets ſtreichen',
eine

eine verschiedene Richtung und Gang von denen der
südwestlichen Seite des Hudsons, die durch Jersey,
Pensylvanien ꝛc. gehen, haben, wenigstens nicht die
unmittelbare Fortsetzung derselben sind. Da mir diese
mittäglichere Hälfte der nordamerikanischen Küste und
Landes bekannter worden ist, als die nördlichere, so
will ich von jener erst meine Bemerkungen beybringen,
und das Wenige, was ich von der nördlichen Abtheilung weiß oder kenne, am Beschlusse beyfügen.

2.

Die erwähnte südliche Abtheilung der nordamerikanischen Küste, von Hudsons Mündung herab nach
Florida, hat dieses durchaus gemein, daß sie sich vom
Ufer der See an nach den innern Gegenden und nach
den vesten Felsenreihen zu, wie eine schiefe Fläche,
gemächlich erhebt; eben so aber fällt der veste Grund
vom Ufer See-einwärts nur allmählich ab. Dieser
letztere Umstand ist eine für die Seefahrende wichtige
und bekannte Bemerkung, und lehrt sie die Gefahren
einer an sich so niedrigen und nicht über 5 — 6 Seemeilen weit zu entdeckenden Küste, zu vermeiden. Das
Senkbley, indem es die Tiefe des Wassers anzeigt,
unterrichtet zugleich von der Entfernung des noch dem
Auge verborgenen Landes, wo nicht mit genauer, doch

ziem-

ziemlicher Beſtimmung. Und ſo weit beſtätigte ſich hier die von jemanden gemachte allgemeine Bemerkung: „daß die öſtlichen Küſten aller Länder allmählich und „ſanfter abfallender ſind, als die weſtlichen:„ wegen der dem Umſchwunge der Erde von Abend gegen Morgen, entgegen geſetzten Bewegung der Waſſer, von Oſten nach Weſten; der noch die in dieſer Richtung mit dem Monde fortgehende Meeresfluthen und die Oſt = Paſſatwinde zu Hülfe kommen. Es darf aber dieſe allgemeine Bewegung des Meeres von Morgen gegen Abend hier nicht als die Alleinurſache angenommen werden.

Vom 41ſten Grad der Breite zum 35ſten, oder der Gegend von Kap Hatteras, iſt nach der Angabe aller guten Charten, der ſüdweſtliche Abfall und Einbug der Küſte weniger beträchtlich, als von dieſem Kap an, längſt der Küſte der Carolinen, Georgia und Florida; welche letztere einer Nebenurſache, der größern Wirkung des ihnen näheren Gulfſtroms, vielleicht ihren tiefern Ausſchnitt zu danken haben.

3.

Man hat lange ſchon bemerkt, daß Nord = ſowohl als Südamerika ſich von ſelber, wie andere Länder,

in

in 3 Abtheilungen darstelle: die Ebenen, die Vorge-
bürge und das hohe Gebürge.

Die Ebenen (the flats), von den Indianern
Ahkynt genannt, ist die Gegend von der Seeküste
Land auf- und einwärts, bis an die sogenannte Wasserfälle der verschiedenen in das atlantische Meer sich
ergießenden Ströme.   Sie bilden eine nach der See
abhängende Sandfläche, und erstrecken sich auf verschiedene Breiten in das Land.   An den Küsten von
Long-Eyland nur auf wenige Meilen.   Im nordlichen
Theil von Jersey auf 15 — 20; im südlichern auf 30
und drüber, und so zunehmend durch Maryland, Virginien, Nord- und Süd-Carolina, wo die größte
Breite, mit der sie sich landeinwärts erweitern, zwischen
80 — 100 Meilen beträgt.   Durch Georgien und Flo-
riba scheint, so weit ich Nachrichten erhalten konnte,
ihre Breite wieder etwas abzunehmen, so daß sie im
Ganzen von einer Bogenlinie umzeichnet werden.   Für
den beträchtlichern Theil bilden sie eine todte sanft
abhangende Fläche; näher gegen seine westliche Gränzen nur findet sich einige Abwechslung von unbeträchtlichen Hügeln hie oder da.   Dies ist die Gegend von
Amerika, die Reisenden Anlaß gegeben hat, zu sagen,
daß Virginien, Carolina ꝛc. keine Steine habe.   Und

in

in der That finden sich keine andern in diesem Bezirf,
als weit zurück, und dann nur dünne Schichten von
abgerundeten Kieseln (*), verschiedene Fuß tief unter
Sand begraben; oder die ebenfalls tief liegende ver-
härtete Muschelbetten; aber kein Stein auf dieses ganzen Striches Oberfläche.

4.

Die Beschaffenheit und Schichter dieser vorbersten
Landstrecke des vesten Landes von Amerika sind von
den Jerseys hinab bis nach Florida ganz dieselben.
Wenigstens was ich hie und da, an den Bänken der
Flüsse, hohlen Wegen und Brunnen, in Maryland,
Virginien und Carolina bemerkt habe, stimmt mit den
Nachrichten überein, die Kalm von West-Jersey (**),
Stork von Ost-Florida (***) gegeben. Die Ord-
nung und Folge der Betten ist durchgehends einerley;
nur ihre Tiefe ist hie oder da verschieden, und so ist
die Härte der unter sich verbundenen Materien. Sie

zeigen

(*) Kalm. 2ter Th. Philadelph. S. 267. Abgerundete
Kiesel 8 Fuß tief.

(**) Kalms Reisen, 2ter Th. S. 499. deutsche Ausgabe.

(***) Description of East-Florida, by William Stork.
London 1769. 4to. pag. 4.

zeigen sich in folgender Lage: Gartenerde, Sand, Thon, Seeprodukte.

5.

1.) Die Gewächserde, die überall die äusserste Decke der Erdkugel ausmachet, bekleidet auch diese Sandscholle mit einer dünnen Lage. Meistens nicht einmal rein, sondern noch mit unterliegendem Sand vermengt. Sie wird an den meisten Stellen als eine Rinde von $1 - 1\frac{1}{2}$ Zoll angetroffen. In den weitläuftigen Fohrenwaldungen von Nord- und Süd-Carolina ist sie so dünn, daß, wenn irgend, durch Ackern, oder längst der Strassen durch Fahren, sie auseinander gerissen wird, solche bald durch Regen weggewaschen, oder durch Winde als Staub weggeführt wird, und den klaren weissen Sand zurück läßt. Wo Gräben frisch aufgeworfen, oder Strassen an bedecktern Orten tiefer eingeschnitten haben, zeigt sich diese dünne schwärzliche Rinde, die dennoch mit vielem Sande vermischt, oder öfter noch nur schwärzlich gefärbter Sand ist. Es verstehet sich dieses aber nur von dem höher gelegenen und nicht überschwemmten Lande; Flußbänke und morastige Vertiefungen sind ausgenommen, denn diese haben sich auf Unkosten der höhern Gegenden bereichert.

U

6.

2.) Ein Bette von Sand füllt wohl den beträchtlichsten Raum der Gegenden, von dem die Rede ist.
In den zurückgelegenen Landschaften finden sich Lagen
von kleinen abgerundeten Steinen mit darunter, aber
weder häufig, noch beträchtlich. Näher nach der Küste
herab und längst derselben ist es Sand allein. Die
Tiefe dieses Sandbettes ist verschieden; weniger tief,
ab von — und mehr so, näher an der See; von 2. zu
20—30 und mehr Fussen. Eben so ist die Farbe, Fe-
stigkeit und Bestandtheile dieses Sandbettes abändernd.
Nächst der Küste erscheint es bey Wilmington, und anderwärts an den hohen Bänken der Flüsse, ganz rein
und weis, und in der Sonne für empfindliche Augen
schmerzhaft blendend. Weiter im Land ist es durchgehends mehr oder weniger ins röthliche fallend. —
Die Ufer von Florida, Carolina, Virginien ꝛc. bestehen blos, oder gröstentheils aus feinem Muschelsand,
in welchem man mit Hülfe eines Vergrösserungsglases
die klein zermalmten Ueberbleibsel organischer Körper
deutlich entdecket. Anderwärts, und häufiger an den
Seiten durchgehender Flüsse, so wie weiter Landeinwärts, ist es quarzigter und kieseligter Sand —
oder mit vorigem gemischt. Gemeiniglich ist dieses
Sand-

Sandbette locker. Ein Antheil darunter gemischter Thon macht ihn hin und wieder härter. Um Baltimore, Friedrichsburg ꝛc. hat sich der meiste Theil dieses Sandbettes zu brauchbaren Sand- und Quadersteinen verhärtet, und noch an andern mehr Orten, in den von der See entferntern Stellen dieses Reiches, findet sich das nemliche.

Nicht immer, und am wenigsten in den seichtern Betten dieser Sandflötze, lassen sich Lagen durch Verschiedenheit an Farbe entweder, oder Härte, erkennen. Am öftersten erscheint es als ein einförmiger Sandhaufe; ungeachtet, wie bey Baltimore, man zwischen oben und unten liegendem lockern oder mürben Sande feste Quadersteine herausnimmt, die das entfernte Auge nicht entdecken kann.

7.

3.) Unter dem Sande ist eine Thonlage, ebenfalls an Farbe, Tiefe und Beschaffenheit verschieden. Oft ist etliche Fuß tief ein ziemlich reiner, weisser oder grauer Thon, und längst den von Wassern oder anders durchschnittenen Bänken, in einer horizontalen Richtung fortlaufend zu entdecken. An andern Orten, mehr mit dem darüber liegenden Sande vermengt, und

A 5

durch)

durch Gefühl mehr, als durchs Gesicht aufzufinden.
Wieder anderwärts, in Maryland und Jersey, ist die
Thonlage mehr mit der nächstfolgenden Muschelschichte
vermengt, und erhält daher oft die Eigenschaften eines
unvollkommenen Mergels. Einige Stücke von einem
aus dieser Lage genommenen Thon aus Maryland habe
ich gesehen, der einen grossen Antheil verwitterter
Schaalen enthielt, den vollkommenen Kreidengeruch,
aber gröberes Korn hatte, und zäher der Zunge an-
hieng. Ueberall beynahe, durch den mittlern Theil dieser Sandflächen, zeigt sich die Thonlage oft in unbeträchtlicher Tiefe unter dem obern Sande. Seine
oberste Lage schien mir immer die reinste zu seyn; weiter unterwärts ist er häufiger mit Sand gemenget.
Weiter im Lande ist er auch öfters von einer röthlichern
Farbe, aber doch zeigt hie und da eine weissere Lage
seinen Abschnitt vom darauf liegenden Sand.

Wann ich nicht irre, so scheint es mir doch, daß
diese Thonlage zunächst der See am unbeträchtlichsten
sey, und oft fast vermißt werde, landeinwärts hingegen, an Tiefe mehr und mehr zunähme; so wie im
Gegentheil die auf ihr befindliche Sandlage, in den
westlichen Gränzen des Reiches, davon die Rede ist,
unbeträchtlich, in tiefern Bänken aber, näher der See

zu

zu lieget. Der Thon ist auch tiefer im Land häufiger
mit Sand gemengt, und bildet so, den so allgemein
aus Sand und Letten bestehenden Boden. Auch scheinen sich an einigen Stellen die Thonlagen unregelmäßig
zu vertiefen, und gleichsam von den andern Massen
leergelassene Kesseln zu füllen.

8.

4.) Die unterste Lage endlich des flachen Vorder-
Landes ist ein vollkommenes Muschelbette, das, so
weit ich Nachrichten sammeln konnte, noch nirgends
durchgegraben worden ist, und das sich unterhalb jener
ganzen Fläche von Jersey nach Florida hin erstrecket,
wie der Sand oben. Es würde hier überflüßig seyn,
alle die verschiedenen Stellen zu erwähnen, wo man
Conchylien entdeckt hat. (Ich werde vielleicht sie am
Beschluß anzumerken Gelegenheit haben.) Die Bänke
aller der, das niedere Land von Virginien durchströ-
menden Flüsse, unterhalb ihrer sogenannten untern
Wasserfälle, sind voll davon. Die hohen Ufer des
Potowmacks (*), Rappahannoks, York - und James-
Flusses, eine Menge andere kleinere Flüsse, Mühlgrä-
ben, Hohlwege liefern unzählige Beyspiele davon, und
erregen

(*) Kalm 2ter Th. S. 247.

erregen die Aufmerksamkeit der Fremden mehr, denn der Einheimischen. Die Ströme in Nord-Carolina und Georgia desgleichen. Weniger so aber, die unbeträchtlichern und seichtern Flüsse von Süd-Carolina.

An vielen Orten des östlichen Ufers von Maryland, am Rappahannok an den Bänken von Yorktown, um Neu-Bern, Wilmington, und weiter im Lande von Nord-Carolina, am Savannahfluß und andern Stellen mehr, nahe und ferne von der Küste Georgiens, ist dieses Muschelbett zu wirklichen und harten Felsen zusammengebacken; die aber dennoch ihre fremde Bestandtheile, die Schaalen nemlich, ganz oder zermalmet, mehr oder weniger sichtbar darstellen, und hin und wieder dichte und fest genug sind, zu Mühlensteinen verarbeitet zu werden. Laagen und Schichten lassen sich zuweilen deutlich an diesen Felsenbänken unterscheiden, besonders an den hohen Wänden zu Yorktown.

Die verschiedenen Gattungen von Conchylien sind durchgehends dieselben, als noch itzt längst dem Strande der See vorgefunden werden, Hayzähne, Wallfisch- und andere Knochen mit eingerechnet. Sie sind meistentheils zerbrochen und durch einander gemengt,

mengt, jedoch nicht immer in gleichem Verhältniß.
Es findet nemlich in Absicht auf sie dieselbe Ordnung
gewissermassen statt, die noch an den Küsten in dem
verschiebenen Standorte verschiedener Gattungen der
Conchylien bemerkt wird. So nehmen z. B. Austerschaalen und Clams gewöhnlich die obere Lagen ein,
und diese werden ebenfalls, am weitesten im Lande,
nach der ersten Felsenreihe zu am häufigsten gefunden.
Auf den niedrigen Stellen, zwischen Baltimore und
Annapolis, des sogenannten War-fields, sind Austern
zu Tage ausgewaschen. Austern und Clams sind die
einigen Schaalen, die man in den zurückgelegenen
Theilen dieses Distrikts in Jersey (*) beym Graben
vorfindet, in der Tiefe von 40 Fuß. Weit zurück am
Tar-River, bey Martinsburg, Nord-Carolina, zeigen
sich diese Gattungen vorzüglich nur, und eben so bey
100 Meilen weiter landeinwärts am Savannahfluß; da sie
hingegen an den näher zur See befindlichen Muschelbänken,
um Wilmington ꝛc. seltener sind. So behaupten aber
auch noch die Austern ꝛc. (**) überall die seichtern
Stellen

(*) Kalm. 2ter Th. S. 495.

(**) „Bey niedrigem Wasser siehet man die schlammich-
„ten Ufer der Flüsse und Kriks mit unermeßlichen Betten
„von

Stellen der Meeresufer, und liegen folglich höher, als andere Schaalthiere.

An verschiedenen Orten haben sich diese Schaalen mehr oder weniger ganz und unverändert erhalten. Man kann an einigen sie von eben aus der See ge=nommenen kaum unterscheiden; an andern sind sie theils zerbrochen, theils halb aufgelöset, und wieder ander=wärts in Steine zusammen geknetet. Dieser Unter=schied rührt gänzlich von dem verschiedenen, mit ihnen anfänglich vermischten Stoffe her; je nachdem dies mehr oder minder thonartig, oder Sandgemenge, oder eisenschüßige Erde war; denn bald haben sie dies, bald jenes, bald alles zugleich zum Bindmittel. Daher gleichen einige dieser Muschelfelsen einem unvollkom=menen groben Muschelmarmor; andere schlagen zum Theil Feuer am Stahl, und brausen zugleich mit Säuren auf.

Am

„von (lebenden) Austern, für viele Meilen nach einander „bedeckt. Dies geschieht in einigen grossen Flüssen=bis 30=40 „Meilen von der See. Sie liegen dicht an einander, mit „dem scharfen Theil aufwärts, und machen beynahe einen „soliden Fels von 1½ = 2 Fuß Dicke. Catesby.

Am weitesten zurück in diesen Flächen, und näher
der ersten Felsenreihe, scheint es werden häufiger noch
andere, dem Meere fremde und von ihm eigentlich an
seine alten Ufer angespülte Körper vorgefunden. Als
Seeschlamm in welchem Bäume, Aeste, Rohr, Kohlen ꝛc. (*) vermengt; von welchen Gegenständen, nach
meiner Erfahrung und Augenschein, sich nichts ähnliches in den näher seewärts gelegenen Bänken zeiget;
einige einzelne in den Sand begrabene Bäume ausgenommen. In den neuern Sümpfen finden sich zwar
ebenfalls Bäume versenkt, die aber später dort erst
überdeckt worden sind.

Im Durchschnitt genommen ist dieses Muschelbett
unter den vorigen Lagen, von 10 — 15, allgemeiner
aber 30 Fuß und drüber hoch bedeckt. Auf den östlichen Ufern von Maryland und in Carolina hat man
über 40 Fuß gegraben, ehe man es erreichte. Wie
tief aber die Muschelbette selber sich erstrecken, hat
man gar keine, auch nicht muthmaßliche Angaben, weil
was man davon sieht, immer nur der oberste Theil
davon bleibt, ungeachtet sie in Virginien am York-
River und anderwärts sich wohl in 30 — 40 Fuß hohen
Wänden zu Tage zeigen.

9. Ich

***

(*) Kalm ꝛter Th. S. 343. 496. u. f.

9.

Ich brauche nicht zu erinnern, daß die Lagen der
viererley erwähnten Schichten nicht immer so ganz
rein, eine mit der andern unvermengt seyn sollten.
Oft sind sie es; allgemein aber bleiben die Schichten,
in der angezeigten Folge-Ordnung, immer durch die
vorzüglichere Menge der ihnen zuständigen Bestandtheile
merklich unterschieden, wenn auch etwas mehr frem-
des beygemischt wäre. Aus allem aber erhellet un-
läugbar, daß sie der Niederschlag von langen Jahren
über dieser Gegend gestandener Meere sind, bis auf
die oberste Rinde von neuerlich erzeugter Gewächserde,
und später durch Flüsse angeschwemmtem Geburgssand.

IO.

Diese ganze niedere und vordere Landstrecke, zwischen dem Ocean und der ersten nachher zu erwähnenden Felsenreihe, ist, wie ich schon erinnert, eine vollkommene, gegen die See gemach abhängende Fläche.
Nirgends ist sie durch Unebenheiten unterbrochen, als
längst der verschiedenen theils stehenden, theils fließen-
den Wasser. Alle größere und kleinere Ströme haben
sich tiefe Betten darein gegraben, und indem man
quer durchhin reiset, sieht man deutlich, daß die sämt-

liche

liche Fußbette ehehin ungleich breiter und folglich seich-
ter waren, ehe sie sich auf ihre iezige Canäle ein-
schränkten. Wo man irgends mitten in den Waldungen
die ebene Strasse, es sey immer so wenig, abhängiger
werden sieht, da kann man sicher erwarten, bald irgend
einen Strom oder Bach anzutreffen, der unmerklich
sich nach der See hin bewegt, weil theils der unbeträchtliche Abhang, theils die von Zeit zu Zeit eintre-
tenden Fluthen ihren Wassern keine grosse Geschwindigkeit erlauben. An den meisten Flüssen dieser Landstrecke
bemerkt man, daß die nordöstlichen Ufer gemeiniglich
für eine grössere Breite niedriger und flächer sind, als
die südwestlichen. Vermuthlich daher, weil häufigere
und heftigere Sturme von der erstern als von der
andern Gegend kommen, die so wohl den beweglichen
Sand verwaschen und verwehen helfen, als die Gewalt des Wassers mehr nach der andern Seite drängen.

Erst an den unmittelbar vom Ocean bespülten
Ufern findet man, in den Gegenden von Carolina und
Florida wenigstens die ich gesehen habe, längst ihm
fortlaufende erhabene Dämme, die das Werk des
Oceans selber sind, und die er sich zur Gränze gesetzt
zu haben scheint. Wenn man von Wilmington nach
Charleston die untere oder längst der See gelegene

Schöpfs mih. Beytr.   B   Strasse

Straſſe reiſet, ſo geht der Weg auf 16 engliſche Meilen, unmittelbar an dem Rande des Meers hin, über
die ſogenannte Lange-Bay — und die ganze Länge
dieſes Weges, hat man zur Rechten, in verſchiedener
Entfernung von 1—200 Schritten, eine mit der See
parallel laufende Reihe Wälle, von 3—10— bis 16
Fuß hoch. Der Strand erhebt ſich gemächlich von der
See nach dem Fuß dieſer Wälle, die in ihrer Grund-
fläche 10—12 und oben 3—6 Fuß breit ſeyn mögen.
Dieſer Strand beſteht theils aus quarzigtem feinem
Sand, theils aus zermalmten Muſcheln, die mit andern Dingen von den unaufhörlich gegen ſie anſpülen-
den Wellen ausgeworfen werden. In einigen Stellen
findet man wirkliche Beweiſe, daß hier ſchon der Mu-
ſchelſand anfängt ſich in faſt weiche Steine zu bilden.
Das bloſſe Beſpülen des Seewaſſers ſcheint dem Sande eine beſondere Feſtigkeit zu geben, wenn er auch
nicht andere bindende Theile dadurch erhalten ſollte.
Wenn man ganz dichte an den Wellen auf dem feuchten Sande hinreitet, ſo hinterlaſſen des Pferdes Hufe
kaum einige Spuren, da hingegen des trockenen Sandes Oberfläche ſchon blos vom Winde beunruhiget
wird, und dadurch noch zur Bildung und Erhöhung
jener Wälle beyträgt. Aehnliche Wälle von Sand
ſahe ich nachher mehr in der Gegend von Charleston,

unb

und auf der Nord-Beach in Florida, und nach Berichten sollen sie sich ziemlich allgemein längst den sämtlichen Küsten auf dieselbe Art darstellen, wo nicht Localumstände es verhindern. Sie erschienen mir immer auf ihrer nach der See gekehrten Seite beynahe senkrecht abgebrochen, auf der entgegen gesetzten aber abhängiger und mit Gewächsen bekleidet. In Orkanen, oder wenn heftige Winde stark gegen die Küste wehen, erreichen sie die Wellen, oder überschwemmen sie gar, wenn sich die Fluthen nicht zwischen den hie und da befindlichen Oeffnungen durchdrängen können, und so entstehen unzählige Hügel von lockerem Sande, andere Sandwälle und Unebenheiten, noch hinter ihnen, zwischen deren Vertiefungen, wenn das Wasser fällt, eine Menge Muscheln, Fische, Knochen und anderer Auswurf der See zurückbleibt.

II.

Viele dieser Sandwälle und Hügel hinter den erstern, scheinen obgleich abgebrochen und ungleich, dennoch mit den erstern gewissermassen eine parallele Richtung (*) zu behalten; und noch oft bis auf eine halbe,

B 2 ganze

(*) Dergleichen Dämme werden an mehr andern Orten angetroffen. „Wenn der Strand niedrig ist, und aus einem leich-

ganze oder einige Meilen weiter landeinwärts, bleibt
der sandigte Boden uneben, mit Erhöhungen und Vertiefungen durchgraben, ehe die eigentlichen vorher beschriebenen grossen Plänen ihren fernerhin ununterbro-
chenen Anfang nehmen. Wer nur mit einiger Aufmerksamkeit diese Gegenden bereiset, kann bey diesen
Erscheinungen nicht umhin auf den Gedanken zu ge-
rathen, daß jene nun vom Meere entfernten Hügel,
vormals eben so, wie die ihr noch gegenwärtig nähern,
Sandwälle, aus dem Absatz der anspülenden Wellen
entstanden, und daß folglich das feste Land dieser östlichen Küste in seiner Ausdehnung wachse, und das
Meer sich selber von Zeit zu Zeit engere Gränzen
setze.

„leichten Sande bestehet, so unterstützt der Wind die Wir-
„kung der Wellen, und treibt den Sand höher, als diese
„reichen können. Daher entsteht am Rande des Meers eine
„Wulst von Sande, welche etwa 40 — 50 Schuh hoch, und
„bald breiter bald schmäler ist. Diese Sandhügel werden
„von den Wellen bald aufgeworfen, bald wieder eingerissen,
„bis endlich einige davon durch die Vegetation fest werden.
„Diese nennt man Dünen. Sie sind in Holland und
„Flandern sehr häufig, und an manchen Orten haben
„Wind und Wellen ganze koncentrische Reihen
„davon hintereinander gebildet. De Lüc Ge-
„schichte der Erde 1ster Band S. 172.

ſetze. — Ich konnte aber nirgends aus Erfahrung und Beobachtung beſtätigte Beweiſe darüber ſammlen, ſondern die übereinſtimmende Meynung aller dieſe Gegenden bewohnenden Landleute, gieng dahin, daß die See an dieſen Küſten ſelten eine plötzliche oder merkliche Abänderung mache, ſondern abwechſelnd und allmählich gewinne und verliere. Als wirkliche Thatſachen kan ich aus Catesby's Werke nur folgende hier zum Beweis dieſer Meynung aufbringen. „Ein Grampus, „der am Nord-Ediſto-Uſer ſtrandete und 16 Fuß lang „war, wurde in weniger denn einem Monat mit „Sande bedeckt. Groſſe Winde blaſen oft den Sand „2 — 3 Fuß tief weg, und legen dem Auge eine „Menge Muſcheln und andere Dinge blos, die lange „vorher unter ihm begraben laßen. — An Sullivans „Eyland, welches an der Nordſeite des Eingangs des „Hafens von Charleston liegt, hat die See an der „Weſtſeite ſo viel gewonnen, (obgleich dieſe Seite, die „vom Ocean abgelegene war,) daß es in 3 Jahren eine „Viertelmeile betrug, in welcher Breite eine Menge „Fichten- und Palmbäume umgeworfen und begraben „worden. „ —

Dürfte man aber auch, aus jenen Erſcheinungen der hintereinander gereiheten Sandwülſte, auf eine wirk-

B 3 liche

liche Zunahme des veſten Landes der öſtlichen Küſte
von Amerika ſchlieſſen, ſo wäre dies zugleich eine gegründete Widerlegung der Meynung, daß die öſtlichen
Küſten der Welttheile von dem beſtändigen Strome des
Weltmeers, als einer langſam wirkenden Urſache an-
gegriffen, untergraben und verkleinert würden. Es
hat aber ſchon be Lüc in ſeiner Geſchichte der Erde,
1ſter Theil 24 — 26ſter Brief, die Unzulänglichkeit dieſes Syſtems ſinnreich und gründlich erwieſen, daß ich
nichts beſſers thun kann, als meine Leſer dahin zu ver-
weiſen; da es ohnehin unbedachtſam ſeyn würde, etwas über die Abnahme oder Anwachſen dieſer Küſten
zu entſcheiden, ehe man hinlängliche Erfahrungen
darüber geſammlet, welches, in dem noch neu bewohnten Lande, bisher noch nicht der Fall war.

Daß ſich beſtändige Veränderungen an der Küſte
ereignen, erfahren die Schiffer zu ihrem Verdruß und
Schaden. Alle Eingänge in Flüſſe und Häfen des
ganzen Striches vom Delaware herab bis Florida, ſind
durch quer vorliegende Sandbänke äufferſt beſchwerlich
und oft gefährlich. — Die nach der See ſtrömende
Flußwaſſer, und die ihnen an ihren Mündungen begeg-
nenden Wellen, verurſachen es, daß ſie juſt da, am
unbequemſten Orte, den anderwärts weggenommenen

Sand

Sand anhäufen. Daher entstehen die so gefürchteten
Bars (Bar, Riegel, Hindernisse); die sich aber öfters
in heftigen Stürmen umändern, und einen Kanal mit
Sande anfüllen, den noch kurz vorher Schiffe passi-
ren konnten, anderwärts hingegen einen neuen eröffnen.

Eben so ist diese Küste der südlichen Hälfte von
Nordamerika, kurz und dichte vor dem vesten Lande,
mit einer Reihe niedriger, schmaler und von Norden
südwärts sich erstreckender Eylande versehen, in-
nerhalb welchen kleine Fahrzeuge lange Reisen längst
der Küste machen können, ohne den Gefahren der
hohen See ausgesetzt zu seyn.

II.

Ich habe Eingangs schon erwähnt, daß der Abfall der ganzen Nordamerikanischen Küste, von Nordost
nach Südwest, unverkenntlich sey, ohne es nöthig zu
finden, kleine Abweichungen anzuzeichnen; hier, glaube
ich, möchte es der schicklichste Ort seyn, noch die
Bemerkung hinzu zu fügen, daß dieses ungleich stärker
und auffallender zwischen dem 35 und 30sten Grad der
Breite, oder zwischen Kap Hatteras in Nordkarolina
und Sanct John in Florida statt finde, als längst des
ganzen übrigen Striches. Wenn ich auch die ange-

zeigte

zeigte Richtung der grossen Aussenlinie zu erklären nicht
wagen will, so däucht mich doch, daß die Ursache des
in dem kleinen Bezirk bemerkbaren stärkern Einbugs
weniger schwer anzugeben sey. Aus dem Mexikanischen
Meerbusen drängt sich, um das Kap Florida, längst
dessen östlicher Küste und den Bahamischen Inseln, der
sogenannte Gulfstrom mit solcher Gewalt durch den
nicht über 20 Seemeilen breiten Kanal, daß ihm kein
Schiff, auch mit den besten Winde, entgegen zu stemmen
vermag. Dieser Seestrom, nachdem er dem Zwang seines engern Kanals entgangen, und die nördlichsten der
Bahamischen Inseln vorbey ist, nimmt die ähnliche
Richtung mit jener Küste, und bleibt ihr ziemlich nahe,
so daß die von Nordkarolina aussegelnden Schiffe, oft
nach vor wenig Stunden gelichtetem Anker, sich darinnen befinden. Der Strom setzet seinen Weg zwar
noch viel weiter gegen Norden und Nordost durch den
Ocean fort; indem er aber nach und nach grössere
Breite gewinnt, und von der Meerenge, die seine Geschwindigkeit vermehrte, sich entfernt, so verliert er
auch von der Gewalt, die er in jenem Bezirk zu haben
scheint. — Wenn wir einen mit merklicher Kraft durch
irgend einen Kanal fortgehenden Strom annehmen,
und in der Gegend der benachbarten Küste, an welche
die ganze Gewalt des Stroms, wenn er in seiner

ersten

erſten Richtung bliebe, anprallen müßte, einen merk⸗
lich ſtumpfen Winkel, oder Buſen finden, ſo entſtehet
die gegründete Vermuthung, daß dieſer Strom und je⸗
ner Buſen irgend jemals Bezug auf einander müſſen
gehabt haben. Dieſe Vermuthung muß neue Wahr⸗
ſcheinlichkeit gewinnen, wenn wir die abgeänderte Rich⸗
tung des Stroms, dem eben ſo abgeänderten Laufe der
Ufer, obſchon in einiger Entfernung folgen ſehen, und
uns noch überdies überzeugen können, daß das Erd⸗
reich jener Ufer von der Gewalt der Waſſer zum Theil
bezwinglich iſt. Alle dieſe Umſtände finden genau ſtatt.
Der Gulfſtrom erhält zwiſchen der Küſte von Oſtflorida
und den Bahamiſchen Inſeln und Bänken eine Rich⸗
tung von Nord bey Weſt, in welcher er, alle Hin⸗
derniſſe weggeräumt, an die Ufer von Florida, zwiſchen
St. Auguſtin und St. Mary ungefähr, mit ſeiner
ganzen Gewalt anſchlagen müßte; und hier finden wir
auch den tiefſten Einbug der ganzen Küſte nach Weſten.
Allein der Gulfſtrom nähert dermalen ſich den Ufern
dieſes Buſens auf mehr nicht denn etwa 60 — 80 Mei⸗
len; behält nicht ſeine anfängliche Richtung, ſondern
wendet ſich etwas nördlich über den Bahamiſchen In⸗
ſeln, und nachdem er des ſtärkſten Einfluſſes der Nord⸗
oſt⸗Paſſatwinde befreyet iſt, ſogleich beynahe Nordoſt,
und dieſelbe Windung nimmt die Küſte des veſten Lan⸗

des

des von St. Mary an, und behält sie als vorzüglich
bis Kap Hatteras, wo noch immer der Gulfstrom
nicht über oder kaum eine Tagesfahrt vom Ufer entfernt bleibt. Ein Fahrzeug, das bey Windstille, oder
mit nur schwachem Winde, in dem Gulfstrom sich be-
findet, wird sich unbewußt nordostwärts mit dem
Strome fortbewegt; ist es aber zwischen dem Strom
und dem vesten Lande, so steuert es nach Gefallen und
Beschaffenheit der Winde, ohne an seinem wahren
Wege zu verlieren. Die Wirkungen des Gulfstroms erreichen also nicht die Küsten des vesten Landes, und
können folglich keinen Bezug auf dessen Bildung haben,
wird man mir einwerfen. Vielleicht aber zu voreilend.
Es ist wahr, was ich schon selber eingeräumt, daß die
sichtbare Gewalt der Oberfläche des Gulfstroms dermalen nicht auf die Küste selber stößt, und nur zuzu-
weilen unmittelbaren Einfluß darauf hat. Bey den
heftigen Stürmen, die an der Nordamerikanischen Küste
gemeiniglich mit der größten Wuth aus Nordosten kommen, werden die Wasser des Stroms in ihrer Richtung gehemmt, und schwellen gegen die niedern und
vordern Küsten von Florida, Georgia und Karolina
oft fürchterlich an, und drohten so mit dem vereinigten
Ungestüm des Windes, unter andern Städten, Charleston bereits verschiedenemal den Umsturz. Aber auch
die-

diese zufällige Ereignisse abgerechnet, so folgt noch immer nicht, daß was dermalen der Fall nicht ist, es niemals gewesen sey; daß nemlich, weil dermalen der Gulfstrom nicht die Küste unmittelbar anspüle, er es niemals gethan habe. Man hat noch nicht genau bestimmt, weder wie breit der Strom sey, nachdem er in den Ocean eintritt, noch welche Menge von Wasser seine Gewalt in der Tiefe umfasse und mit forttreibe. Beydes mag sich wohl unter verschiedenen Nebenursachen etwas abändern. Man erlaube ihm aber eine nur mässige Tiefe von 50 — 60 — 80 Faden, nnd erinnere sich dessen, was ich bereits im 2ten §. angemerkt, daß so wie das veste Land allmählig gegen die See abhängt, auch die Ufer allmählig nur in der See abfallen, und daß man gemeinhin zu Schiffe die Anzahl Faden mit denen man Grund findet, als so viele Meilen Entfernung vom Ufer, obschon nicht ganz genau richtig schätzet. Der Strom findet also in seiner Tiefe, an dem seichte abhangenden Meeresgrund, in einiger Entfernung vom vesten Lande selber Widerstand, und ändert seine Richtung, ohne dem trockenen Gestade nahe zu kommen, in der nemlichen Maase, als diese und dessen vom Meer bedekte Fortsätze sich ändern. Ich begnüge mich hier, die Wahrscheinlichkeit einer Verbindung des Gulfstroms und der Gestalt der Küste, eines

Theils

Theils nur von Amerika, als Ursache und Würkung
angezeigt zu haben.. Ob nicht das nemliche auch auf
die ganze Aussenlinie der Küste anwendbar wäre, ge-
traue ich mich nicht zu entscheiden. — Die Richtung
des Gulfstroms bleibt immer noch Nordöstlich bis in
die Gegenden von Neufundlands-Bänken — denn bis
dahin, und wie man behauptet noch weiter nördlich,
erfahren die Seefahrenden seine Würkung.

I2.

Wird es aus der erzählten Beschaffenheit dieses
östlichen Bezirks von Amerika nunmehro als ungezwei-
felt angenommen werden können, daß dieses Ganze
vormals ein von ursprünglichen Felsen, (deren gleich
nachhero gedacht werden wird,) umgränzter Meeresbu-
sen gewesen sey, und die dazu erforderlichen Beweise
in seinen Muschel- Thon- und Sandlagen dem Auf-
merksamen darbiete; so wird man kaum die aufsteigende
Frage unterdrücken können, die uns zu Auffindung des
Zeitpunkts, in welcher sich die Verwandlung von Meer
in vestes Land zugetragen, anlocket. Es ist aber noch
hier nicht der schickliche Platz, mich auf die ganze Be-
antwortung dieser Frage einzulassen, weil aus der
Folge auch erhellen wird, daß nicht nur diese Plänen,
sondern auch die hohen Gebürge von Nordamerika, un-

ter

ter Meer gewesen sind. Ob aber diese Veränderung das Ganze auf einmal betroffen, oder ob,
nachdem die Gewässer die hohen Gegenden verlas-
sen, solche noch eine Zeitlang über diesen Plänen gestanden haben, und diese in einer zweyten und spätern Periode zu trocknem Lande geworden sind, wäre eine andere und genauer hieher gehörige Frage.

Den ersten Anlaß zur Vermuthung, daß der Rückzug des Meers nicht auf einmal bis in seine dermalige
Gränzen geschehen seyn möchte, gab mir die schon an-
gezogene Nachricht Hr. Kalms, im 2ten Theil S. 495. daß
man in der Gegend von Racoon, also in der Nähe
von der ersten folgenden Felsreihe, „nicht nur Schaalen von Austern und Muscheln, sondern auch viel
Schilf und Stücke von zerbrochenen
Aesten, 40 Fuß tief‚‚ gefunden habe. Dies ist ungefähr, was man gemeiniglich überall am Rande der
See ausgestossen findet. Etwas mehr Wahrscheinlichkeit entdeckte sich mir, als ich ferner erwog, daß die
Felsenreihe, die diese grossen Bucht zur Gränze ge-
dient zu haben schien, in der Gegend von Neuyork und
weiter hinauf nördlich, näher und oft unmittelbar an
die See ausläuft, aber hier statt flaches vestes Land

vor

vor sich zu haben, nur mehr oder weniger tiefe, viele und weitläuftige Bänke vor sich hat. — Dahin gehören östlich von Neuengland die Nantucket Schoals, Georges-Bank, Browns-Bank und andere unter dem Namen Neuschottlands-Fischerbänke, bekannte; und dann noch weiter nordöstlich, die noch beträchtlicheren Neuland-Bänke. — Eine Bemerkung, die der Hypothese, daß die grossen südlicheren trockenen Sandflächen ehemals ähnliche Sandbänke möchten gewesen seyn, nicht ganz ungünstig ist. — Und wenn in Voraussetzungen dieser Art, die ähnliche Meynung eines andern Mannes der meinigen etwas mehr Gewicht geben könnte, so hatte ich Ursache mich zu freuen, als ich nachher in Evan's Analysis seiner Karten von Pensylvanien und Jersey fand, daß er ganz geradezu jene erste Felsreihe für das ältere Meeresufer von Nordamerika anspricht, und die vorliegende Sandfläche nach und nach entstehen lässet. Diese Meynung bleibt aber denn doch nur Vermuthung, weil ich keine Data finden konnte, die etwas mehr gegründete Folgerungen erlaubt hätten.

13.

Vergeblich schmeichelte ich mir, als ich jene Gegenden bereiste, daß vielleicht aus der Menge und Dicke der auf den Muschel- und Sand-Schichten liegen-

genden Decke von Gewächserde, einige Aufklärung zu
finden seyn möchte. Wenn man nemlich, dachte ich,
bestimmen könnte, wie viel Erde die auf diesen Flächen
befindliche Gewächse in einer angenommenen Zeit lie-
ferten, so würde man eine nähere Vermuthung auf
die Länge der Zeit, in der sie Pflanzen getragen, an
und für sich, und eine Vergleichung gegen die höhere,
vielleicht länger trockene Gegenden, wagen dürfen.
Allein es standen mehr Schwierigkeiten im Wege, als
ein Reisender zu überwinden im Stande war. Ich
fand oft die ganz der See nahen Stellen auf einige
Meilen völlig ohne Decke von Pflanzenerde, und dennoch ein und andere Gattungen darinn wachsend. Nächst
Flüssen und andern Ueberschwemmungen ausgesetzten
Stellen, einen reichen Vorrath, theils erzeugter, theils
angeschwemmter Moorerde. Der größte Theil der vordern Sandflächen ist zwar mit etwas weniger Erde bedeckt, trägt aber hauptsächlich nur Nadelholz und
magere Grasarten, und ist daher allgemein unter dem
Namen der Pine-Barrens (unfruchtbares Föhren-
Land) bekannt. Etwas weiter zurück erst finden sich
Eichen- und Laubhölzer eingemischt, die noch weiter zurück beynahe gänzlich die Oberhand behalten, und in
eben der Maase findet man die Lage von Gewächserde
an Dicke zunehmen. Nun wäre aber vorher zu prüfen

und

und zu bestimmen, nach welchem Verhältniß Nadelholzungen und Laubholzungen in Erzeugung und Anhäufung der Gewächserde fruchtbarer sind. Wahrscheinlich ist es allerdings, daß Nadelholzungen in diesem Betracht den Laubtragenden nachstehen. Nach allgemeinen Beobachtungen zeigen erstere auch in der äl-
tern Welt überall einen magern Boden an; sie erzeu-
gen wenigere und kleinere Blätter und verlieren sie
langsamer; die verlornen werden überdies nicht so
leicht durch Fäulnis in Erde verwandelt. — Das jähr-
liche Produkt in Blättern beträgt hingegen mehr bey
Laubhölzern, diese fallen häufiger ab, werden schnel-
ler aufgelöset, weil sie weniger harzigt sind; und vermehren vielleicht auf diese Art die Lage von Pflanzenerde um sich her geschwinder (*). — Ich könnte dem-
nach zwar bestätigen, daß dermalen auch hier diese
verschiedene Baumarten auf der Güte nach verschiedenen

(*) „Dammerde eines vor 52 Jahren angelegten Buchen-
„waldes, an den meisten S. ellen 3 Zoll stark. In einem
„10jährigen feuchten Ellern- und Pappelnwald war sie
„21 Zoll stark, und in einem sehr alten Tannenwald auf
„dem Harz, (nur) 13 Zoll bis auf den felsichten Grund.„
Beobacht. Zweifel und Fragen die Mineralogie betreffend,
1ster Versuch S. 103.

nem Boden stunden, aber dennoch aus der da oder dort
dicken Lage der Pflanzenerde, nichts auf den Zeitpunkt,
in welchem Vegetation in beyden angefangen hatte, zu-
rückschliessen; weil mir es noch durch Versuche nicht
ausgemacht schien, ob vom Ursprung an Laubholz
auf besserem Boden als Nadelholz wuchs, oder beyde,
wenigstens in diesen amerikanischen Gegenden, nur in
der Erzeugung und Verbesserung der Erde um sich,
verschiedene Geschwindigkeit beobachtet.

Mitten in den sandigten unfruchtbaren Nadelholz-
waldungen fanden sich häufige Moräste, Sümpfe und
niedere Stellen, die entweder Wasser durchhin fliessend
haben, oder solches aufhalten. Diese Stellen sind mit
einer ungleich tiefern Lage von schwarzer Erde und
Schlamm versehen. Ju ihnen aber wachsen auch vie-
lerley Laub- und immer grünende Holzarten und andere
Pflanzen. Nan fragt sich's, ist diese hier in grösserer
Menge befindliche schwarze Erde, durch Regen, durch
ausgetretene Wasser allein, nach diesen vertieften Betten angeschlämmt worden? Oder ist sie die Folge von
grösserer, wirksamerer und reicherer Vegetation, durch
Feuchtigkeit begünstiget — oder beyder Ursachen zugleich? — Es ist auch noch unausgemacht, wie viel
nach Lokalumständen, Regen, Winde, Ueberschwem-

Schöpfs min. Beytr.   E   mun-

mungen, die Zunahme der obersten Rinde von Gewächserde begünstigen, oder ihr hinderlich sind; und daß
hie und da auf dem magersten Sande ein einzelner
Eich- oder Laubtragender Baum gefunden wird, und
gesund und stark ist, beweißt auch, daß sie nicht durchgehends und immer nur in guter Erde wachsen müssen.

14.

In der vorhergehenden Erzählung war ich schon
verschiedenemal genöthiget, mich auf eine Felsreihe zu
beruffen, die die erstbeschriebene niedere Landstrecken
des südlichen Theils von Nordamerika, als eine Gränz-
linie umgiebt. Es ist diese Linie, und der Gang dieser
Felsreihe, deutlich durch eine in derselben Richtung, in
den grössern und kleinern Flüssen befindliche Folge von
Wasserfällen, von der Natur selbst angezeichnet. Die
meisten Flüsse finden längst ihres Laufs, an dieser Ost-
Seite der Gebürge nach dem Ocean, verschiedene
Stellen, wo sie sich durch und über Felsen zu drängen
und zu stürzen genöthiget sind. Gegenwärtig aber be-
ziehe ich mich einig und allein auf die untersten Fälle
(the lower falls) vom Gebürg her, oder die erstern,
von der See aufwärts. Eine Kette von Felsen, die
in der Nachbarschaft von Neuyork die gefährliche Passage im Sund, die Hell-gate, im Hudsonsfluß aber
keine

keine Hindernisse verursacht, kömmt jenseit des Hudsons hinter Powles-Hoock wieder zum Vorschein; zeigt sich in steilen und schroffen Felsen hinter Braunschweig in Jersey, in Bruchstücken bey Rocky-Hill; wird ab und zu niedriger, bey Trenton, Germantown, hinter Philadelphia, nach Chester, Neu-Castle und Wilmington; erscheint etwas verschieden zwar um Baltimore, George-town in Maryland; wird wieder die vorige um Friedrichsburg und Richmond in Virginien, und setzt nach Nachrichten, in einer ähnlichen Richtung durch Nord- und Süd-Carolina fort. Sie beschreibt zwar eine etwas gekrümmte Linie, (oder scheint nur ge-krümmt, weil sie sich nirgends in ihrer ganzen Breite entblöset,) folgt aber doch der Hauptrichtung von Nordost nach Südwest. Da hingegen der allgemeine Lauf der von dem Gebürge kommenden Ströme von Nordwest nach Südost ist, so müssen sie sämmtlich an einem oder dem andern Orte diese Felsreihe überwin-den, und mit mehr oder weniger Schwierigkeiten und Gewalt ihre Bahn durch sie brechen. Der Hudsons-fluß allein hat seinen Weg frey behalten. In den übrigen Flüssen aber folgen sie beynahe regelmässig:

In

In Pensilva-
nien
{ Delaware, bey Trenton, in ungefähr 75° — westl. Länge von London — in 40° Breite.
Schuylkill, bey Philadelphia, 75. 20.
Susquehannah, unterste Ferry, 76. —

Maryland
{ Cimponder-Creed,
Potowmack, oberhalb Georgetown 77. 30. . . — 39 —

Virginien
{ Rappahanock, oberhalb Friedrichsburg 78. —
James-River bey Richmond, 78. 20.
Uppomatox, bey Petersburg —

Nord-Ca-
rolina
{ Roanoke, bey Halifax — —
Zu Tar und New-River — — — 37. 20.

Die

Die hier genannten sind die allgemein bekanntern,
wovon mir fünfe durch Augenschein bekannt worden sind.
Ich habe die westliche Länge (*) dabey angemerkt, um
gleich hiernach die Wahrscheinlichkeit, wo nicht Gewißheit, zu zeigen, daß die Fortsetzung der Felsenkette, die
diese Fälle verursacht, auch noch weiter südlich entdeckt
werde. Ich finde nemlich auf einer Charte von Carolina (**) folgende Stellen bezeichnet:

Nord-Ca-
rolina.
Ledge   of   Rocks (Felsstrich) in Neuse-River, unter 79° —
Rocky-River, (felsichter Fuß)
ein Arm vom Nordwest-River — 79. 30.

Süd-Ca-
rolina.
Hanging-rock-Creeck (hän-
gender Felsbach) ein Arm
vom Pedee-River —   — 80. 30.
Rocky-Creeck, Rocky-branch,
Rocky-Mount, und felsichte
Stellen in und um den Wa-
teree überhalb Camden, in
ungefähr —   — — 81. —

C 3   Die-

─────────────────────────────

(*) Nach Angabe von *Governor's Pownalls Map of
North-America; London* 1779.

(**) Henry *Mouzon's Map of South & North-Caro-
lina. London* 1775.

Diese letzterwähnten sind zwar nicht als eigentliche Fälle, sondern als merkwürdig felsichte Stellen in den Flüssen angemerkt; gehören aber nichts destoweniger hieher (*). — Weiter aber finden sich auf der nemlichen Charte, ein Fall

Im Congaree, einige Meilen unterhalb
  der Vereinigung des Broad und
  Saluda-River — — 81° —

Im Savannah, Nordwestlich von Augusta 82 —

Der Abfall vom 75. west. Länge, oder Delaware-Fall, nach 82.. im Savannah ist von Nordost nach Südwest. Die erwähnten Stellen sind die ersten felsichten, von der See-aufwärts; und ich glaube nicht, daß es weiterer und anderer Bestätigung über den Strich dieser Felsreihe, den sie von Neuyork südwärts beschreibt, bedarf. — Es ist blos ihre Hauptrichtung, die wir kennen, aber nicht ihre Tiefe, und nicht ihre Breite. Ob sie gegen Westen fortgehet, die Grundlage der andern aufgesetzten Gebürge ausmacht, und vielleicht irgendwo westlich von dem Alleghany wieder zum Vorschein kommt, werden spätere Erfahrungen leh-

***

(*) Eine Linie vom Fall im Savannah, nach dem im Roanoke gezogen, gehet ziemlich nahe durch diesen Strich.

lehrey. Oſtwärts ſcheint ſie ſehr ſchnell und ſteil in
die Tiefe abzufallen, denn man hat noch nirgends,
beym Graben durch das an ſie angelehnte Muſchelbet-
te, wieder darauf getroffen.

Dieſe nemliche Reihe ſetzet aber auch von Neuyork aus, nördlich fort, zeiget ſich längſt der Küſten
von Connektikut, und iſt noch dieſelbe auf Rhode-
Eyland. Höher nördlich habe ich ſie nicht zu ſehen
Gelegenheit gehabt; zweifelsohne aber erſtreckt ſie ſich
weiter.

Sie ſcheint hie und da 2 — 3 — 4 Meilen und
mehr breit zu ſeyn; erhebet ſich höher in den nördlichern der vorerwähnten Gegenden, in York, Jerſey,
Penſylvanien nemlich; wird niedriger nach Süden,
bleibet im Ganzen aber doch immer beträchtlich über
die vorliegende Flächen erhaben, ungeachtet ſie nirgends eigentliche Berge bildet.

15.

Dieſer ganze merkwürdige Felsſtrich beſtehet einzig
und allein aus urſprünglichen oder Grundgebürgs-
Arten, hauptſächlich aber aus einem Granit, der
hie und da einigen Abänderungen unterworfen, und

der,

der mir wenigstens, auf meiner Reise, nicht weiter
Landeinwärts vorgekommen ist. In und um diesen
Strich, und nur da, finden sich verschiedene andere
thon- und talkartige Steinarten, als Asbeste, Glimmer, Schneidestein, Grünstein, Schörl ꝛc.

Granit habe ich gesehen zu Neuyork und Richmond; eine Entfernung von beynahe 400 engl. Meilen
in gerader Linie. Mithin ist wahrscheinlich genug, daß
er sich in der vorhin angezeigten Fortsetzung der Felsenreihe südlicher und nördlicher eben auch zeige. Es
ist aber zu merken, daß diese Felsreihe auf ihren Wege
von Nord nach Süden nicht überall zu Tage liege; sie
ist größtentheils, zumal südlich, so niedrig, daß sie
meist überall mit der gewöhnlichen, aus Sand und
Letten gemischten röthlichten Bodenart überlegt ist, und
das in ungleicher Höhe. Sie zeiget sich nur wo sie
von Flüssen durchschnitten, oder sonst blosgewaschen
worden; und ich erinnere hier nur vorläufig, daß in
diesem Theil von Amerika gerade die umgekehrte Ordnung, von dem, was wir anderwärts finden, statt
habe; hier nimmt nemlich der Granit die vorderste
Reihe, von der See aufwärts, ein, da er hingegen
auf andern Gebürgsrücken die höchsten und letzten
Spitzen ausmacht, die man ersteigen kann.

Längst

Längſt dieſes Striches ſind überall beynahe, die
dem Granitgeſchlechte eigenen und zufälligen Beſtandtheile (*), aber nicht immer in derſelben Miſchung,
nicht immer in derſelben Menge und Verhältniß, zu
entdecken. Ein grobkörnichter, mit viel Glimmer ge-
miſchter, Quarz, ſchien an den meiſten Orten den
reichlichſten Antheil auszumachen. Doch werde ich, beſſerer Ordnung halber, einige der vorzüglichſten Orte
dieſes Striches, von Norden nach Süden genauer erwähnen. Ich muß es aber ſchon hier, wie in der
Folge noch, bedauern, daß ich mich nicht überall mit
vollkommener Zuverläſſigkeit ausdrücken darf, weil der
größte Theil der von mir auf dieſer Reiſe geſammleten
Gebürgsarten, die ich einem Hamburger Kaufmann, in
Philadelphia, zur Beſorgung nach Deutſchland über-
geben, ich weiß nicht auf welche Art, verloren gegangen.

16.

Man wird mir verzeihen, daß ich bey dieſer Gelegenheit etwas von Rhode-Eyland mit anführe, obgleich dieſer Theil auſſerhalb und nördlich des mir anfangs vorgezeichneten Umfangs, vom Hudſon-River
nach Süden, lieget. Längſt des Sundes erſcheint die

C 5   ganze

_____

(*) Cronſt. Miner. §. 268.

ganze Küste von Connektikut erhaben und felsicht, ich habe sie aber nicht betreten. Weiter hin ist Rhode-Eyland auf eitel Felsen gegründet, deren kahle Gipfel überall im Eylande und an den Ufern, uns im Jahr 1779. an den Siß des Hungers erinnerten. Die Hauptgebürgsart hier, ist ein grauer einfacher fein-körnichter, ins röthlichte spielender Felsstein. Er bricht überall zu Tage aus, und längst der Seeküste, zeigt er sich mit blättrichten, perpendikulär neben ein-ander stehenden Lagen. Er nimmt eine grobe Politur an, und wird zu Leichensteinen, Treppen ꝛc. verarbeitet.

In den Vertiefungen, die seine Geschiebe hie und da lassen, stehet ein dickblättrichter, grober, schwarzer Schiefer auf ihm auf; man siehet ihn an den nacktge-waschenen Seeufern deutlich. Ich habe nichts von Thier- oder Pflanzen-Ueberbleibseln darinn gefunden; er mag wohl zu den ursprünglichen Schiefern gehören. Auf einer Stelle hatte man ehemals einen Schacht darein getrieben; ich konnte aber nicht erfahren, ob man nach Kohlen oder Alaun suchte.

Zerstreut an den Ufern und auf dem Eylande, finden sich Bruchstücke und Massen von zusammenge-leimten Felssteinen, oder Breccie (*). Sie enthält die

gemei-

_____

(*) Saxum amnigenum. *Linn. syst.* 3. *p.* 80. *n.* 38.

gemeinen Wafferkiefel in abgerundeter, abgeschliffener Form, in Grössen von ⅛ — 50 ℔, die durch eine feine eisenschüffige, fandigte Maffe zufammengehalten werden. Diefe Felsart zeiget sich hauptfächlich an dem einen Ende von Eaftons-Beach und weiter hinauf. Wo die Wellen frey an fie anfchlagen, oder anfchlagen konnten, zeigen fich auf ihrer Oberfläche eine Menge Höhlungen; die Behältniffe der losgegangenen Kiefel. Sie enthalten nichts kalchichtes, denn weder auf dem ganzen Eylande, noch weiter hinauf nach Providenz, hat man noch Kalch gefunden; den man entweder weiter her holen, oder fich des Aufternkalchs bedienen muß.

Dies Eyland hat fehr viele Anhöhen, und überall auf demfelben findet man auf zwey Fuß tief Waffer, und die meiften davon find beftändig fumpfig. Eine Thonlage, die nur etwa 2 — 3 Fuß tief lieget, fammlet das Waffer, das nun übrigens aus der Atmofphäre entweder, oder aus der das Eyland umflieffenden See, durch feine eigene Wege in die Höhe fteigend, fich verfüffet. Ein fo fchmales Eyland bleibt aber immer, wegen der Menge feiner frifchen Wafferquellen, merkwürdig. Einige davon fetzen Ocher ab.

17.

17.

Die Gegend um Neuyork bestimmte ich anfänglich
als die nördliche Grenze der zu erörternden Anmerkungen.

Oestlich von Neuyork liegt das ansehnliche und
fruchtbare Long-Eyland, und streckt sich eigentlich in Ost-
Nordost. Der östliche und südöstliche Theil desselben
ist flach und sandig; nach der See zu. Die Ebene von
Jamaika oder Hampstead, ist eine vollkommen todte
Fläche, von vielen Meilen lang und breit, und von
allem Gesträuche entblößt. Am Nord- und Nordwestlichen Ende, oder nach dem vesten Lande zu, erhebt
es sich in niedrige Hügel, die zum Theil, wie um Huntingdon, fast ganz aus grobem Sande mit grossen Kieseln, theils, wie um Bokram ꝛc., aus Kieseln und Bruchstücken von Granit, aber alle abgeschliffen, bestehen. Die
Thäler zwischen diesen Hügeln haben nicht alle einerley
Richtung, die mehresten gehen aber doch Nord- und
Südwärts, und enthalten mehr oder weniger Letten,
oder rothe Erde wie um Neuyork, mit Sand und Kieseln gemischt. Hie und da nimmt Flugsand mit schwarzer Erde gemischt, beträchtliche Strecken ein, wie
um Tennifot ꝛc. Anderwärts, um Musqueto-Cove,
und York-Eyland gegenüber, sind ganze Hügel
von

von Letten und blauem und weissen Thon, der auch
mit dünnen Lagen in verschiedener Tiefe unter der
Oberfläche, öfters zum Vorschein kommt.

Auf Butlers-Eyland, (ein kleineres von Long-
Eyland abgerissenes,) im Sand und andern tiefen Orten, zeigen sich Spuren, daß diese Gegenden auch
neuere, blos örtliche Veränderungen erlitten haben.
Unter der obern Lage von Gartenerde kommt reiner
Sand, dann wieder eine Lage von mit Gewächserde
vermengtem Sand. —

Die ganzen obern Schichten dieses Eylandes verrathen einen angeschwemmten und von der See verschiedentlich gebildeten Sandhaufen. Der eigentliche
felsichte Grund mag wohl ziemlich tief unter der Oberfläche wegstreichen; von den Felsen um Kings-bridge
aber, ist doch die Fortsetzung in denen schon weit
niedrigern, meist vom Wasser bedeckten, noch in der
Hellgate zu entdecken.

Unerachtet an verschiedenen Stellen der Ufer dieses Eylandes, noch jetzt tiefe Lagen von allerley Muscheln angeschlämmt werden, so ist mir doch kein Fall
bekannt geworden, daß man Muschelbetten beym Graben

ben gefunden hätte; man gräbt aber auch nicht leicht über 10 — 12 Fuß tief. Es ist keine Spur von Kalchsteinen auf dem ganzen Eyland, eben so wenig als von Versteinerungen aus dem Thierreich. Aehnliche Breccien aber, wie auf Rhode-Eyland, finden sich überall, und auf den angebauten Hügeln um Bockram ꝛc. auch, in Kiesel versteinertes Holz, in kleinen und abgeschliffenen Stücken. Torf findet sich in ausgetrockneten und noch stehenden Sümpfen. Man will auch Kohlen gefunden haben, wovon ich aber nichts zu sehen Gelegenheit hatte.

18.

Neuyork-Eyland selber erstrecket sich ganz gerade von Süd nach Nord, uneben und hügelicht. In der Mitte des Eylandes bey Blumenthal, und längst des Hudsonsflusses erheben sich die Felsen, bis an sein nördliches Ende, wo auf ihren Höhen Fort Knyphausen und andere Werke angelegt waren.

Die allgemeine Decke des Eylandes ist Sand und Letten. Bey Verfertigung der Linien um Neuyork im Jahr 1782. hatte ich Gelegenheit, ihn vielfach bis auf 6 — 8 Fuß tief zu sehen. Es war überall grobkörnichter Sand mit etwas Letten gemischt, der ihm ziemliche

Festig-

Feſtigkeit gab. Schwarze Erde war nicht über 1 — 2
Zoll tief der Oberfläche beygemiſcht oder aufliegend.
In dieſer Tiefe lagen häufige und groſſe Bruchſtücke
von

> theils mürben Glimmerſchiefer, mit ungemein viel
> weiſſem und gelblichtem Glimmer,

> theils eine grobkörnichte ſtark quarzichte Granit-
> art, mit untermengten groſſen Körnern einer
> ſchwarzen Hornblende, und ſeltenern ganz
> kleinen gelblichten Glimmer - Pünktchen.

Verſchiedene andere, aber ſämmtlich untereinander verwandte Gebürgsarten finden ſich auf und um das Eyland, theils in veſten ſtehenden Felſen, theils in
Bruchſtücken. Weil ſich unter der ihnen aufliegenden
Decke, ihre Verbindung und Zuſammenhang nicht erkennen läßt, ſo will ich ihrer auch blos in willführli-
cher Ordnung erwähnen.

Die hohen und gegen den Fluß ſteilen Wände,
am Nordende, beſtehen hauptſächlich aus einer grauen
Felsart, die der Rhodeeyländer ähnlich iſt, und hier
eben ſo zu Leichenſteinen ꝛc. gebraucht wird. Es iſt ein
hartes und veſtes Geſtein, das einen ſehr feinen
Quarzſand zum Grund hat, und mit ebenfalls ſehr fei-

nen

nem ſchwarzen (Glimmer?) Staub ziemlich gleich und
genau gemiſcht iſt, dazwiſchen aber mit einzelnen, äuſſerſt kleinen Pünktchen glänzet. Es ſchlägt nicht überall
Feuer; bricht in ungleichen Schaalen, und zeigt zwiſchen ihnen einen Eiſenroſt-Beſchlag; ſchabt ſich weis;
giebt aber angehaucht keinen Geruch. Es iſt daher
dieſe Felsart, allem Vermuthen nach, der nachher zu
erwähnenden an der Susquehannah, und bey Baltimore ꝛc. verwandt, und vermuthlich einerley mit dem
grauen Felsſtein, den Hr. Kalm bey den Highlands,
nördlich von York, erwähnt.

Eingeſprengt hie und da, und Bruchſtücke von einer dunkelgrünen Felsart — mit weiſſern Adern durchzogen, die ſich dem Bänderjaſpis zu nähern ſcheint. —

Groſſe und loſe Bruchſtücke von dunkelgrauem Horn-
ſtein fand ich am Geſtade des Oſt-Rivers. An einigen Stücken davon zeigten ſich unvollkommene Eindrücke von Muſcheln und Corallen. — Nirgends in der
Gegend habe ich einen würklichen Fels davon getroffen,
und bin alſo ungewiß, ob dieſe Hornſteine in dieſe
Gegend gehören, oder zufällig ſind.

Am Oſt-River, in der Gegend von Kypſies-Bay,
ſtreichen Felswände zu Tage aus, die dem äuſſern An-
ſchein

schein nach in horizontalen Schichten angelegt sind.
Sie bestehen aus feinem Sand oder Quarztheilen, haben viel Glimmer, und sind nicht sehr vest. Wenigstens da, wo das Salzwasser anspület und angesprützt wird, findet man häufige ausgewaschene Lücken. Adern von reinem, einen und mehr Zoll dicken Quarz, streichen in verschiedenen Entfernungen durchhin.

Gneiß, der aus weissem Feldspat, graulichen Quarzkörnern, weissem und gelblichem Glimmer, mit schwärzlichen hornblendigen Körnern und Flecken bestehet.

Granit, der aus röthlichem und weissen Feldspat, weißlichen Quarz, kleinen gelben Glimmerpunkten, und schwarzer Hornblende bestehet. Bricht hin und wieder zu Tage an der See aus. — Die oben erwähnte, und auf Anhöhen ausgegrabene Bruchstücke sind dieselbe Gattung, nur blättrichter.

Schöner, vester Granit, aus weissem, zum Theil etwas ins gelbliche fallenden Feldspat, weniger weissem, theils bräunlichem Quarz, ziemlich grossen durchsichtigen Glimmerblättern, deren Farbe ins grünliche und graue spielt, zusammengesezt, mit eingesprengten wenigen kleinen schön rothen Granaten.

Auf einigen dieser Granitfelsen finden sich zeolith-
artige Krystallen. Sie bestehen aus feinen weissen
etwas glänzenden Fasern, von der Länge eines halben
Zolles, welche concentrisch laufen, und sich in einer
erhabenen Spitze vereinigen. Ganze Stellen vom Granit sind zuweilen dichte damit auf der Oberfläche überlegt, und beym Zerschlagen findet man, daß sie auch
durch die ganze Masse vertheilt sind. Sie verhalten
sich aber im Feuer, nicht wie Zeolithe (*); in starkem
Feuer waren die Fibern nach einigen Minuten unverändert, eher spröder; blieben auch so nach dem Zusatz
von Borax, Salmiak und mineralischem Laugensalz.
Starkes Vitriolöl hatte nach 24 Stunden ihnen nichts an-
gehabt. Sie möchten daher mit mehrerem Recht vielleicht
zeolithartig-krystallisirter Asbest (**) zu nennen seyn.
Und folglich wohl der nemliche mit dem, welchen Hr.
Kalm im Serpentinstein (***) gesehen hat.

Von

(*) Cronst. Miner. §. 108.

(**) Amiantus radians L.

(***) Kalm. Reis. 2ter Theil, S. 437. „Hr. Fränklin
„gab mir ein Stück von einem Steine, den man in Neu-
„engelland braucht, die Schmelzöfen und Schmiedessen auf-
„zumauren. Er bestand aus einer Vermischung von Serpen-
„tin-

Von Erzen hat man auf York-Eyland und den
zunächst umliegenden Gegenden, noch anders nichts
entdeckt, als Eisen-Sumpferz. Auch dieses Eyland, so
schmal es ist, und von Salzwasser umflossen, ist reichlich mit Wasser versehen, und eine besondere Wohlthat
ist es für die Stadt, eine unerschöpfliche Felsquelle
zu haben, die reines vortreffliches Wasser liefert, und
in der höchsten Sommerhitze eine Temperatur von
40 — 45 Fahrenh. behält. Im strengsten Winter zwischen 45 — 50. In der Gegend der Quelle ist das
Eyland keine halbe englische Meile breit, zwischen dem
Ost- und Nord-Revier. Vermuthlich erhält es seinen Vorrath von entferntern Gegenden, durch Fels-
klüfte. Kalch ist nicht in der Nachbarschaft; auch erin-

D 2   nere

„tinstein (ollaris) und Asbest. Der größte Theil davon war
„ein grauer Serpentinstein, der bey dem Angreiffen sehr fett
„und glatt schien, und sich gut schneiden und bearbeiten ließ.
„Hin und wieder aber schimmerten einige Sternchen, die
„ein Asbest bildete, dessen Fäserchen, aus dem Mittelpunkt,
„wie Stralen schossen. — Asbestus fibris e centro radi-
„antibus. Dieser Stein soll nicht aus einem Felsen ge-
„bauen, sondern hin und wieder auf dem Felde zerstreuet
„gefunden werden.

nere ich mich nicht, von aufgegrabenen Austerschaalen in Neuyork gehört zu haben (*).

19,

In dem nächstfolgenden Jersey bin ich nicht so glücklich gewesen, auf dem kurzen Weg, den ich gerade durch machte, eigentliche Granitfelsen anzutreffen. Da sie aber gleich nachher in Pensylvanien, und zwar in der schon erwähnten Hauptrichtung, wieder zum Vorschein kommen, so ist zu vermuthen, daß sie hier größtentheils bedeckt liegen mögen. Die nackten niedrigen Felsen dicht hinter Paulus-hoock schienen in der Entfernung Granitähnlich; ich durfte ihnen aber während den Unruhen nicht nahe kommen. Die ersten hohen Gebürge und Felsen um Boundbrock, hinter Braunschweig, sind ein dem Neuyorker ähnliches graues Gestein; und erscheinen, wo sie entblößt sind, in auf einander liegenden Platten. Abbe Robin (**) will Granit gesehen haben, und erwähnt, daß man Marienglas in diesem Strich fände. Zwischen Braunschweig und Princeton finden sich auf Rockyhill lose Bruchstücke von unvollkommnem Granit, und eben so, aber unbe-

---

unbeträchtlich am Fall des Delaware bey Trenton;
wo man hingegen eine harte blaulichte feinkörnichte
Felsart (*) durch den Fluß streichen siehet.

Die hohen Hügel von Neversink, die dichte an
der See, nächst Sandyhoock auf Jersey liegen, und
das letzte hohe Land dieser Gegend sind, habe ich nie
Gelegenheit gehabt zu besuchen. Sie schienen mir zu
hoch und zu breit gegründet, für blose-Sandhügel.
Vielleicht findet man dort Granit. —

Der Weg, den ich von Elisabethtown über Braunschweig nach Trenton durch die Jersey nahm, gehöret
übrigens zu dem erhabenen und hugelichten Hinter-
grunde der vorliegenden Sandflächen; in dem man aber
mehr Abänderung findet, weil er dem eigentlichen Ge-
bürgsstrich näher ist. Man hat Sand, Sand und
Letten, grauen thonigen Boden; in den Thälern
schwarze Erde, abwechselnd. Ueber Trenton, Princeton und Braunschweig aber, streicht vorzüglich eine Reihe
Hügel, die aus rother, oder braunrother in dünnen
Schichten liegender Steinart bestehen. Ich mache
D 3   keine

(**) Scheint dem Trapp verwandt — braust nicht mit
Säuren, und schlägt nicht Feuer.

keine Verfuche damit auf der Stelle, fondern nahm Pro-
ben davon, die aber mit mehrern andern, auf die fchon
erwähnte Art, verloren gegangen find. Seine Schichten
liegen theils horizontal, theils abfchüffig; er verwittert
an der Luft, giebt zähen Boden, ift aber doch zum
Feldbau tauglich. Hr. Kalm nennt ihn einen rothen
Kalkftein (*), der dem von Kinne-Rulle in Weßgoth-
land ähnlich ift.

20.

Nur einige Meilen von Philadelphia, ift im
Schuylkill, ein zwar nicht aufferordentlicher, aber in
feiner romantifchen Lage angenehmer Fall. Hier ftürzt
fich der Fluß über wahren Granit, aus Quarz, Feld-
fpat und Glimmer; und Quarz und Glimmer. In lezterer Geftalt zeigt er fich an den fteilen Ufern des
Schuylkills, an der obern und untern Fähre bey der
Stadt, um Bartrams Landfiz ꝛc. — aber nur an
den tiefen Ufern, und ift oben mit der allgemeinen
Bodenart überlegt, daß man ihn übrigens nicht zu
fehen bekommt.

In diefem Strich findet fich aber auch an mehreren Stellen der Seifenftein, (Soapftone). Saxum

talco-

talcofum particulis fpataceis granatisque immixtis (*),
wovon die ergiebigſte Grube, und die die größten Tafeln
liefert, in der Gegend von Cheſter iſt. Er iſt grünlich-
grau, glatt und wellenförmig; läßt ſich ziemlich leicht
ſägen und ſchneiden, und wird zu mancherley Gebrauch
verwandt.

Ein talfichter Schiefer, mit Glimmer und einge-
ſprengten Granaten, findet ſich in der Nachbarſchaft
von Schuylkills-Fall.

Berglein, Amiantus fibris feparabilibus molliusculis (**), wird an vielen Orten dieſer Gegend, und oft
in langen und groſſen Stücken angetroffen.

Marienglas (***) wird gleichfalls vielfach und
in groſſen Stücken, zu halben Ellen und mehr, angetroffen. Ich kan gegenwärtig nicht entſcheiden, ob
es wahre Mica membranacea L. iſt; woran ich jedoch
kaum zweifle. Ein kleines Stückchen, das ich von
Baltimore mitgebracht, wo es in dem nemlichen Fels-

D 4 ſtrich

strich gefunden werden soll, ist durchsichtiger Gyps-
spat (*), und riecht im Feuer stark nach Schwefel. Da
aber übrigens weisse durchsichtige Glimmerschuppen in
grosser Menge vorkommen, so kann jenes doch auch
wohl die Mica membranacea L. oder russisches Glas seyn.

Granaten finden sich nicht nur im Seifenstein,
und obigem Talkschiefer, auch wohl im Granit einzeln
eingesprengt; sondern auch losgerissene, in der Dammerde in und um Philadelphia. (Am häufigsten sollen
sich Granaten bey Germantown am Schuylkill, an den
Felsen auf Levering's Lande finden.) So enthält ebenfalls der Sand und die Dammerde hier und anderwärts oft viel, des aus diesen Graniten losgerissenen
Glimmers.

Nicht näher bey Philadelphia, als 15 — 17 Meilen, trift man die ersten eigentlichen Kalchschichten an;
und so weit her muß aller zum Bauen benöthigter
Kalch gehohlt werden. Aber Geschiebe von blättrichter Felsart, „die größtentheils aus schwarzem oder
„grauem in Wogen laufenden Glimmer, der hier und
„da, mehr oder weniger, zwischen den Krümmungen,
„mit

_____

(*) Cronst. §. 18.

„ mit einem grauen, lofen, ganz feinförnigen Kalffteine
„ vermifcht ift, und Quarzförner enthält, findet fich
„ bey Germantown (*), und nach dem Schuylkill hin. „
Auch weiffer kleinförniger Sand, mit fchwarzen klein-
körnigen Glimmer und Quarzförnern; und darunter
Streifen von weiffem Kalkftein allein, ohne Verfaß mit
Glimmer, oder auch Kalkftein und Glimmer gleich ge-
mifcht. Diefe Felsart bricht am Fluffe hie und da zu
Tag aus; liegt in Schichten von ungefähr einen Fuß
dick; ift aber auf dem flachen Lande mit 4 — 6 Fuß
der gemeinen aus Sand und Letten gemifchten ziegel-
farbigen Erde bedeckt. Auch in diefem Steine finden fich Granaten.

Aller Wahrfcheinlichkeit nach liegen diefe Gefchiebe
auf dem Granit, und find nach ihm entftanden.

21.

Der Granit von Newyork, und der am Schuylkill,
die genau Nordoft und Südweft gegen einander liegen,
dienen uns nunmehro zu gewiffen Standpunkten, von welchen aus wir weiter füdweftlich, feine Fortfeßung in der-
felben Linie gewiß irgendwo immer wieder finden werden,

D 5   wenn

(*) Kalm 2ter Theil S. 327.

wenn sie auch hie oder da, durch dazwischen vorkommende Felsarten, unterbrochen zu seyn scheinen sollte. —

Die gewöhnliche Poststraße von Philadelphia führt beynahe in derselben Richtung. Nachdem man den zwischen Granitwänden laufenden Schuylkill bey Philadelphia passirt hat, siehet man fünf Meilen weiter in einem hohlen Weg bey Darby, die mehr erwähnte graue Felsart mit einiger Abänderung; auf ihr liegt grauer Schiefer. Zwölf Meilen von Philadelphia erreicht man Chester, in dessen Gegend der Seifenstein gebrochen wird. Der Weg gehet nun auf hohem, meist ebenen Grund, in einer kleinen Entfernung vom Delaware fort. Bey Wilmington kommt man über den Brandtwein, der hier durch eine Felsenschlucht seinen Weg nach dem Delaware nimmt. Diese Felsart ist derb, aus feinem weissen Quarz, mit sehr vielen untermischten schwarzen Punkten, die aber, so viel ich mich erinnere, hier keinen Glimmerglanz haben, und den Fels grau erscheinen lassen. Aber doch dem Yorker unähnlich. — Der Brandtewein macht hier einen kleinen Fall. Man hat links den in seinem tiefern Thal fliessenden Delaware meist im Gesicht, und sieht hie und da in der Ferne, den zum Grund liegenden Fels zu Tag ausgehen. Man kommt durch Neu-Castle, von da nach Christianbridge,

Eltri

Elkriver, Nordost-River oder Charleston, und Susquehannah, der an der untersten Fähre eine Meile breit ist, und viele verborgene Klippen hat, die von den an beyden Ufern sich zeigenden, aber meist verdeckten Felsen, Fortsetzungen sind. Etwas höher sind die eigentlichen sogenannten Susquehannah-Falls. Die Felsen sind hier nur etwas lichter und grauer, als die nächst zu erwähnenden, und auch den vorhergehenden verwandt.

Gunpowder-Creek, 25 Meilen von der Susquehannah, und 16. von Baltimore; in seiner Nachbarschaft, und besonders in der engen und nicht tiefen Schlucht, worinn er sein Bett hat, und über Felsen brauset, erscheint eine schwärzlichte schuppichte Felsart, deren gleich nachher bey Baltimore soll erwähnt werden, wo sie an Menge ist. Hier unterscheidet sie sich blos durch den grössern Antheil von Quarz, den sie in ihrer Mischung hat. Von der Art, wie die Felsenwände an diesen Ufern sich ablösen und brechen, ist es wahrscheinlich, daß sie ursprünglich Lagen- oder Blätterweise auf einander gesessen haben.

In der Entfernung von 110 englischen Meilen, zwischen Baltimore und Philadelphia, sind die genannten
Flüsse-

Flüsse beynahe die einigen Stellen, wo man den unterliegenden Felsgrund zu suchen Gelegenheit hat, ausgenommen, daß man hie und da Bruchstücke vorfindet.
Die Straße läuft über den darauf gehäuften röthlichen sandigten Boden.

22.

Um Baltimore, welches eine von Neuyork durch
Germantown und Schuylkill-Falls gezogene Linie
ziemlich genau trifft, finden wir unsere Granitreihe
mit einigen ihr verwandten und sie auch in andern
Weltgegenden begleitenden Felsarten, wieder. Hier
treffen wir die bey Wilmington, Susquehannah und
Gunpowder erwähnte graue quarzichte Felsart, theils
in derselben Gestalt, theils mit einiger Abänderung
an; ich habe um deswillen dort nicht viel davon ge-
saget. Jene Stadt liegt am Fuße einer Anhöhe, zum
Theil auch an und auf derselben, am Patapsko-River,
der hier ein geräumiges Becken bildet, ehe er sich
mit der Cheasapeak-Bay vereiniget. Oestlich von der
Stadt lieget die Halbinsel, die sogenannte Eastern-
Shore, welche so wie alles, was östlich von dem Wege
von Philadelphia hieher lieget, zu der ersten Abtheilung, den Sandflächen gehöret. Westlich von Baltimore hat man auf der Anhöhe zum Theil abhangend:

Ph. I.

Plänen, meist aber unebenen, mit tiefen Wasserschluch-
ten durchgrabenen Grund, dessen Oberfläche hauptsächlich röthlicher, sandichter, lettichter Boden ist. Da
ich hier eben so wenig als anderwärts, Gelegenheit
hatte, die Verbindung der verschiedenen Felsarten unter sich aufzuspüren, so werde ich die vorgefundenen
auch blos willführlich erwähnen.

Bruchstücke von Granit, finden sich hie und da
in Schluchten; ein Stück, das ich vor mir habe, bestehet meistens aus grobem undurchsichtigen scharfeckich-
ten weißlichem Quarz, und enthält vielen großblät-
terichten grünlichweissen Glimmer, der spröde ist; an
einigen Stellen aber auf der Oberfläche nicht nur seinen Glanz verlohren hat, sondern auch sich in biegsame
faserichte Blätter aufzulösen scheint. Dieser Glimmer
wird durch das Glühen weisser. In meinem Exemplare
sehe ich zwar nichts weiter; aus einer auf der Stelle
gemachten Anmerkung aber finde ich, daß etwas weniges Feldspat und mehrere Schörlkrystallen sich in andern Stücken dieser Felsart gezeigt haben.

Den größten Theil aber des hiesigen Felsgrundes
macht eine schwarze, schwärzliche, und schwärzlichgrüne,
auch graue Steinart von beträchtlicher Härte. Sie
beobachtet

beſtehet aus einer Miſchung von feinen, dünnen, ſchmalen Schuppen einer ganz ſchwarzen Hornblende (*), mit einem nicht ſehr beträchtlichen Antheil von einem feinkörnigen weißlichen Quarz in verſchiedenem Verhaltniß vermengt, woher die bald mehr, bald weniger ſchwarze oder graue Farbe entſtehet. Von ihr ſind die im §. 21. erwähnten Felsarten mehr oder minder entfernte Verwandte. Die Hornblende iſt auf abgeänderte Weiſe darein vermengt. Bald unordentlich, und dann ſcheint ſie keinen beſondern Glanz zu haben; bald ordentlich, in wagerechten, ziegelartig (imbricatim) über einander liegenden Lagen: und dann hat ſie bey reflectirtem Lichte, theils ihren gewöhnlichen Glanz theils auch ſpielt ſie mit Regenbogenfarben. Dies findet beſonders auf den Oberflächen ſtatt, denn dieſe Felsart iſt blättericht angeleget. Man kann ſich davon theils an den Felswänden ſelbſt, theils an den zum Bauen gebrochenen Steinen überzeugen. Die Blätter ſind Zoll- und mehr dicke, und wo ſie ſich ſpalten, das doch nicht gar leicht geſchiehet, findet man die genau und veſt auf einander paſſenden unebenen Flächen mit einem gelbbraunen ocher-ähnlichen Häutchen bedeckt. Zwiſchen den ſchwarzen Schuppen ſiehet man

---

(*) Corneus ſpatoſus niger. *Wall. ſyſt.* I. *p.* 360. a).

man hie und da äufferst kleine Blättchen und Pünktchen eines gelben Glimmers. Oft kommen auch die
schwarzen Hornblendeschuppen länger und haar = oder
nadelförmig vor. An einigen Stellen sieht man dünne
Lagen von blos schwarzer Hornblende, und dann behält sie eine regelmässiger in die Länge gezogene Lage,
als wo sie mit Quarz durchwebt ist. Dieser Stein
schlägt nicht überall Feuer am Stahl, und braußt nicht
mit dem Scheidewasser. Gestossen giebt er ein graues
Pulver; welches in starken Feuer weder für sich, noch
mit Borax floß, sondern als ein bräunlichtes Pulver
wieder aus dem Tiegel genommen ward (*).

Diese Steine werden in Menge nach Baltimore
geschaft, und zu Aufführung der Grundmauren, der
Keller 2c. gebraucht, wozu sie vortrefflich sind.

Die letzten Spuren davon westlich von Baltimore,
habe ich 7 — 10 Meilen in Bruchstücken am Wege an-
getrof-

(*) Diese Steinart gehört zu dem Saxum grandaevum
Linn. syst. p. 79. n. 35. Saxum ferreum Wall. syst. I.
P. 429. n. 14. Zumal da des darinn befindlichen Quarzes
bisweilen so wenig ist, daß man ihn in einigen Stücken zu
erkennen Mühe hat, oder er gar fehlt.

getroffen; diese waren aber schon mit dem weiter hin
zu erwähnenden Seifenstein vereinigt und vermischt.
Ob sie in der Nähe gegraben, oder weiter hergebracht
worden, weiß ich nicht. Sonst scheint er der ganzen
hügelichten Gegend um Baltimore zur Unterlage zu
dienen, und liegt zu Tage, besonders häufig an Wegen,
und an den Seiten verschiedener kleiner engen Thäler
zwischen dem Viermeilenbach (four - mile - run) und der
Friedrichstowner Straße, nach der Gegend hin, die
ich so eben zu erwähnen im Begriff bin.

23.

An der Straße von Baltimore nach Friedrichs-
town, (ungefähr 10 Meilen von Baltimore, und eine
halbe Meile zur Rechten aus dem Weg,) auf dem südlichen und südwestlichen Abhang eines Hügels, finden
sich eine Menge Bruchstücke von Quarz, mit in dicken
Lagen eingesprengten vortreflich schönen Schörlen.
Diese Bruchstücke sind von verschiedener Größe, liegen
seicht auf und halb in der Dammerde umher zerstreut;
das Holz ist in der Gegend abgetrieben, ausserdem
man sie nicht leicht entdecken wurde; in den benach
barten Waldungen mögen ihrer vielleicht mehr seyn.
Es war mir eine besondere Freude, nicht nur diese
Schörle zu finden, sondern auch der erste Finder zu
seyn.

seyn. Ich hatte zwar vorher, in der kleinen Sammlung des Hrn. du Sumetiere zu Philadelphia, ein ey-
grosses im Wasser abgeschliffenes Quarzstück (*) gesehen, das zwey oder drey kleine, ebenfalls abge-
stumpfte Schörlkrystallen enthielt, das aus einem
Bach bey Charleston in Maryland (etwa 50 englische
Meilen Nordost von dieser Stelle) war genommen
worden; hier aber schienen sie recht zuhause zu seyn.

Die Masse, auf der sie zum Theil schichtenweise auf-
liegen, zum Theil durch sie verbunden werden, ist ein
meist reiner weisser ungeformter Quarz; der auch in
besondern Stücken dortherum vorkommt, und dann nur
zuweilen mit rother eisenschüssiger Rinde umgeben ist,
oder dergleichen Flecken, öfters auch auf der Oberfläche oder in Ritzen, geringe Nester von kleinen
blitzenden Krystallen hat.

Die Schörlkrystalle selber sind schwarz und gla-
sicht; weil sie genau und vest aneinander gefügt sind,
und ohne sich zu brechen nicht trennen lassen, so kann
ich die Zahl ihrer Ecken nicht mit Gewisheit angeben;

(*) Eben so in der Schweiz. v. Saussure Reisen durch
die Alpen, 1ter Theil, S. 9I.

Schöpfs min. Beytr.   E

ben; aber sechsseitig scheinen sie. Sie sind von 1 — 2
Linien im Durchschnitt, mit ihren Seiten enge an
einander und über einander gefügt, und verlängern
sich die einen vor den andern, wie die Pfeiffen einer
Orgel. Doch laufen die einzelnen Krystallen nicht
lange, ohne entweder bloße querüber gehende Absätze
zu zeigen, die aber äusserst genau an einander passen,
oder ihre Absätze und Glieder durch dünne Quarzfugen
verbunden zu haben. Zum Theil sind sie Säulengerade
und parallel, zum Theil aber auch etwas nach einer
oder der andern Seite gebogen, oder auch aus einem
gemeinschaftlichen Punkt nach verschiedener Richtung
auslaufend. Auch behalten sie nicht immer diese schöne
parallele Richtungen; sind oft ganz untereinander und
mit Quarz verworren; und über dies finden sich noch
Stellen, wo ausser der bloßen rohen Schörlmassen und
Quarzadern nichts bestimmtes krystallisirtes zu entdecken
ist. Ich finde kleine Stellen, wo sie mit Talk durchwebt sind, der in grosser Menge an demselben Hügel
vorkommt; und bey einer genauern Untersuchung sehe
ich auch, daß einzelne kleine Punkte hie und da zwischen den Krystallen mit Säuren aufbrausen.

Auf die Magnetnadel wirken sie nicht,
wie Herr Saussure von den Genfischen bemerkt
hat

bat (*); erwärmt aber werden sie elektrisch und
ziehen Glasfäden an.

Daß diese amerikanische Schörle gewiß keines
vulkanischen Ursprungs sind, überzeugte mich nicht nur
die übrige Beschaffenheit der Gegend, so weit ich
sie übersehen konnte; sondern auch der reine unver-
änderte Quarz, mit dem sie in so genauer Verbindung
stehen. Ueberdies finden sich einzelne Schörlkrystallen
auch in mehr andern Gebürgsarten eingesprengt, die
eben so wenig eine Spur von Feuerveränderung verrathen.

Auf demselben Felde mit den Schörlen kommen
gar häufig, ebenfalls Bruchstücke von dem schon §. 20.
erwähnten Seifenstein (Soapstone) (**) vor. Er zeigt
Spuren von einem schiefrigen Gefüge, die glimmer-
artigen Theilchen sind nur klein, und seine Farbe
ist aus gelbbräunlich, grünlich und grau gemengt;
hin und wieder zeigt sich eine dazwischen eingelegte
Schwärze. In diesen Stein finden sich verwitterte

E 2 Kieß-

(*) Saussüre 1ster Theil §. 9 .

(**) Talkartiger Schneidestein. Cronst. §. 263. Talcum
Ollaris. *Linn.* Steatites Ollaris. *Wall.*

Kißwürfel, aber keine Spuren vom Schörl, obgleich
sie so nahe Nachbarn sind. Man bedient sich seiner
auch hier zu Kaminstücken, und die Landleute zu allerley Gußformen. Die Gegend um Baltimore liefert
verschiedene Abänderungen von dieser Steinart. Man
findet sie sonderlich auch von grünlicher Farbe, und
zum Theil mit so häufigen Glimmerblätchen, daß einige Stücke lediglich daraus zu bestehen scheinen. Diese
Glimmerblätchen sind in manchen Stücken kleiner, in
andern von ziemlicher Grösse und runzlich oder wellenförmig gebogen. Mit unter kommen auch Serpentine
vor, von weißlicher, grünlicher und gelblicher Farbe,
und verschiedener Härte, dem Schneidestein bisweilen
so ähnlich, daß man sie für nichts anders als verhär-
teten Schneidestein halten sollte, oft mit schwärzlichen
eisenschüssigen Flecken und in den Klüften mit braunem
Ocker bedeckt. Der grünliche und gelbliche ist zuweilen
auf einigen Stellen halbdurchsichtig. Besonders merkwürdig war mir, seiner schönen zeisiggrünen Farbe
wegen, ein Stück von dichtem Gefüge, aber sehr zer-
klüftet, so daß die Textur fast schiefrig zu seyn scheint;
mit röthlichen und bräunlichen eisenschüssigen sowohl
als weissen Flecken auf dem Bruch, welche letztere
nichts anders als Asbest sind, dessen lange weiche und
zarte Fasern man, wo der Stein nach ihrer Länge
spal-

spaltet, deutlich siehet, weniger aber, wo solches in
die Quere geschieht. In der hellröthlichen Rinde besonders sind Quarzkörner verwebt, daher der Stein
äusserlich hie und da Feuer giebt, da er sich innerlich
schaben läßt. Auf dem Bruch fand ich hier und da
dreyseitige gleichwinklichte in einer Spize sich endende
Hölen, in denen irgend eine Art Kryſtalle geſeſſen
haben muß — die mich an die in dem Speckſtein meines Vaterlandes, bey Wunſiedel, neuerlich gefundenen
Steatitkryſtallen erinnerten. — Dieſe Steine, beſonders die Serpentine, ſind oft mit Hornblende von
bald gröſſern, bald kleinern, geraden und gebogenen
Blättern, und meiſt grüner Farbe, aber in den einzelnen Stücken immer von anderer Schattirung, von
dem ſchwärzlichen an bis ins gelbliche, nach allen
Richtungen durchkreuzt.

Auſſer dem weiſſen verſtreuten Quarz, fand ich
noch auf demſelben Felde eine grobe Breccia, von kleinen abgerundeten Kieſeln mit Sand und Eiſenerde zu-
ſammengebacken.

Ein kleines Stückchen ſogenanntes Marienglas,
erhielt ich in Baltimore, das in der Nachbarſchaft
ſollte gefunden werden, und zu Kütte, (Plaiſter of
Paris)

Paris) Eſtrichen ꝛc. verbraucht wird. Im Feuer giebt es Schwefelgeruch, und iſt alſo nur Spatum fiſſile L.

Daß die, dieſer Granitreihe theils an und vor-liegende, theils ſie deckende Sandſchichte, hier wie an andern Orten, ſich in Quaderſteine verhartet habe, iſt bereits §. 6. angezeigt; der Verwandſchaft und Nachbarſchaft willen, erwähne ich hier, daß auch ein veſtes feinſandiges rothbraunes eiſenſchüſſiges Geſtein mit vielem zarten weißlichem Glimmer gemengt, häufig um Baltimore vorkomme, deſſen Bruchſtücke ſich un-eben, aber horizontal ſpalten.

24.

Ich habe das wichtigſte der Gegend um Balti-more angezeigt; und gehe nun in der nemlichen Rich-tung weiter von Nordoſt nach Südweſt. Einige Mei-len überhalb Georgetown in Maryland, iſt der untere Fall des Potowmack; und ich fand um Georgetown ſowohl als um Alexandria, die ſchon beſchriebene graue, aus feinem Quarz und ſchwarzen Glimmer gemiſchte Felsart.

Zwey Meilen überhalb Friedrichsburg in Virgi-nien, fällt der Rappahannock über ein Felſenbett, das eben-

ebenfalls Rappahannock-Falls genannt wird; und um
diese Stadt findet man bereits Stücken eines vollkow
men, feinen und gleichgemischten Granits, aus Quarz,
Feldspat und Glimmer, mit eingesprengten Schörlkrystallen; auch andere, denen einer oder der andern
dieser Bestandtheile mangelt. Diese Bruchstücke kommen von der Felsreihe am Fall.

Von Friedrichsburg nach Richmond reiset man
über lauter Sand und lettichtes Land; und siehet keine
Steine, als hie und da an hohlen Wegen dünne
Schichten von abgerundeten Kieseln und andern Arten, in verschiedener Tiefe mit Sand ꝛc. überschuttet
Dennoch muß die Granitreihe unter der Straße in
der Tiefe, und in derselben Richtung fortsetzen, als die
Straße; und man hat sie auch wieder, so bald man
bey Richmond von der hohen ebenen Sandfläche herabsteiget; und das enge Thal, welches der James-River
sich hier und weiter Seewärts gegraben hat. Dichte
bey Richmond, ist der unterste Fall dieses schönen,
reichen und lastbaren Flusses. Er stürzt sich eben nicht
über grosse Höhen herab, sondern zwängt sich mit un-
geduldigen Schäumen und Toben über und durch
die niedrige, queer durch ihn von Nordost nach Südwest streichende Granitreihe. Dieser Felsenabhang soll

E 4   sich

ſich von hier auf 4 — 5 Meilen weſtlich erſtrecken, und
doch nur im Ganzen 71 Fuß ſenkrechten Abfall dem
Fluſſe geben.

Das Waſſer hat hier den Granit blos gewa-
ſchen; und dieſe Stelle iſt beſonders merkwürdig. Alle
Haupt-Beſtandtheile des Granits trifft man an, aber
nicht immer gleich und genau gemiſcht. Hier ſind
Klumpen von reinem körnichten Quarz; dort Geſchiebe
von ſchönem und zum Theil kryſtalliſirten Feldſpat, an
einem andern' Ort rohe Maſſen von kleinſchuppichtem
meiſt ſchwarzem Glimmer — hier ſind Glimmer und
Quarz, Glimmer und Feldſpat, Feldſpat und Quarz,
bald alleine, bald alle drey zuſammen gemiſcht. Man
ſieht einen erhärteten Teig, deſſen Beſtandtheile, da
er noch weich und flüſſig war, nicht gehörig durch
einander geknetet worden.

Die Felſen durchſchneßen den Fluß in augenſchein-
lichen Reihen, von Nordoſt — Südweſt; und machen
es höchſt wahrſcheinlich, daß ſie in mehr oder weniger
ſenkrechten, aneinander gelehnten Blättern angelegt
ſind — denn in der Richtung, die der blätterichte An-
ſchein den Fluß queer durch nimmt, kann dieſe Erſcheinung nicht dem Fluſſe zugeſchrieben werden. In
der-

derselben Richtung zeigen sich auch weiffe Abern oder Bänder, vom Quarz sowohl, als vom Feldspat; die sich aber zuweilen auch etwas von der Linie abwärts krümmen. Vom Feldspat laffen sich, wo es am häufigsten liegt, schöne groffe, über Zoll lange Rhombi oder Krystallen ablöfen (*); und hie und da sieht man leere Räume, wo andere ehemals befindlich waren.

Auf den etwas über das Waffer hervorragenden Felsstücken, die aber zu andern Zeiten unter Waffer stehen, sind viele gröffere und kleinere, seichtere und tiefere Höhlungen; sogenannte Riesentöpfe, in den theils Sand, theils allerley Kieselsteine angetroffen worden. Herr Kalm (**) erwähnt daß Bartram ähnliche auch in andern Gegenden der nördlichen Kolonien, bey den Flüffen angetroffen habe, und erklärt ihre Entstehung ganz sinnreich. Hier schien es mir nur, daß losgegangene Feldspatstücke die erste Ge-

E 5   legen-

(*) Vorher schon habe ich bey Hrn. Sumetiere ein groffes Quarzstück, in dem die Hälfte eines leeren groffen Rhomboidischen Raums auffallend war, und ihm deßhalb von einem Landmann gebracht wurde. Hier hatte ein Feldspat-krystalle gesessen.

(**) Kalm K. 2ter Th. S. 269.

legenheit zur Aufnahme eines Kiesels ꝛc., durch deſſen
Umwirbelung die weitere Aushölung entſtanden, mögen gegeben haben. —

Das beſtändige Anſpühlen und gewaltſame Drängen des Fluſſes hat die Oberflächen aller dieſer Gra-
nitfelſen ganz glatt abgeſchliffen. An den Seiten und
zwiſchen den Graniten findet ſich eine groſſe Verſchie-
denheit anderer kleiner abgerundeter Steine, die durch
des Waſſers Gewalt von andern Gegenden ſind her-
geſchleppet worden.

25.

Es findet ſich alſo, zufolge meiner Beobachtung,
wahrer Granit um Neuyork und um Richmond, die
mehr denn 500 engliſche Meilen von einander entfernt,
Nordoſt und Südweſt gegen einander liegen. — Oeſt-
lich von ihnen, werden keine Spuren von ihm angetroffen; zwiſchen beyden gedachten Orten aber, und
genau in derſelben Richtung, erhebt ſich hie und da
eine wahre Granitſpitze, und zeigt ſich, wo irgend
Ströme ſeine ihm aufliegende Hülle weggewaſchen haben. Ueberall ferner, längſt des ſo von ihm bezeichneten Weges, finden wir ſeine Beſtandtheile einzeln,
oder vermengt mit andern ihm verwandten Steinarten;

wir

wir sahen blättrichten Gneis, den stralichten Amiant,
russisches Glas, den Berglein, Granaten, Hornblende,
Schörl, und den Topfstein in demselben Striche, theils
für sich, theils auf verschiedene Weise unter sich und mit
Quarz, Feldspat und Glimmer gemischt. Es ist hinlänglich, diese verschiedenen Arten genannt zu haben,
um meine Leser zu erinnern, daß dieser so bezeichnete
Felsstrich allerdings zu den ursprünglichen Felsarten
gehöre; und immer derselbe, nur unter abgeänderten
Mischungen, bleibe.

Finden wir nun eine ursprüngliche Felsart, durch
einen Weg von 500 englischen Meilen, einerley Richtung folgen, und diesen Weg auf vorzügliche Art durch
Fälle in den Flüssen ausgezeichnet; so dürfen wir
wohl mit ziemlicher Dreistigkeit behaupten, daß dieselbe
ursprüngliche Felsart noch die nemliche bleibe, wenn
in der Fortsetzung der erstern Richtung wir mehrere
Fälle in andern Flüssen, weiter nach Südwesten angezeigt finden. Und so werden die Bemerkungen anderer, meine Vermuthungen im §. 14. in der Zeitfolge
bestätigen. Wird lezteres wahrscheinlich, so hat man
bereits, zwischen Neuyork und Fort Augusta am Savannah, eine Südwest streichende Granitreihe von ungefähr zwölf Graden der Breite; und warum sollte
man

man nicht die Fortſetzung von Neuyork Nordoſtwärts
eben ſo wahrſcheinlich finden? die durch das übereinſtimmende Ganze ſo viel begünſtiget wird.

Zu beſondern Betrachtungen mag es in der Folge
veranlaſſen, daß dieſe Granitreihe die einige iſt, (meines Wiſſens,) die wir irgendwo ſo nahe dem Meer,
ſo niedrig, und ſo ununterbrochen fortgehend finden.
Was der erhabene Montblanc, in einer Höhe von
2426 Klaftern über dem Meere, der Büct, Gotthard ꝛc. und andern in ihren höchſten Spitzen enthalten, findet ſich hier dem Meere theils gleich, theils
nur wenig erhabener. Was ſich beym Herabſteigen
von den zugänglichſten Gipfeln jener Berge in die
niedern Gegenden findet, beobachtet man in Amerika
beym Aufſteigen nach den weſtlich und hinter der Granitreihe ſich ſtuffenweiſe erhebenden Gebürgen. Ich
habe nirgends auf und in den Gebürgen Granit oder
Granitähnliche Steinarten angetroffen, wie ich in der
Folge anzeigen werde. Hier alſo findet ganz eine
umgekehrte Ordnung ſtatt.

Daß in der Tiefe der Granit, der doch das
Hauptgewölbe unſers Planeten auszumachen ſcheint,
ſich unter den auf ihn gelaſteten Bergen fortziehe,
gebe

gebe ich zu; aber westlicher habe ich ihn nirgends gesehen (*).

Auch zeichne ich nochmals die schon mehrmalen
erwähnte Richtung der Granitreihe von Nordost nach
Südwest als merkwürdig an, weil sie nicht nur dem
Hauptumriß der Küste, sondern auch den westlicheren
und erhabenern Bergreihen getreu und parallel bleibt;
und noch um deswillen, weil verschiedene andere Granitreihen der alten Welt, in ungleich grösserer Höhe,
dieselbe Richtung haben.

Erze hat man noch nirgends in der eigentlichen
Granitreihe entdeckt, wohl aber in den ihr aufsitzen-
den Geschieben und Flözen; wo man aber auch bisher
sie nur Nesterweise getroffen; dahin rechne ich die Spuren von Kupfer um Braunschweig, Rockyhill rc. in
Jersey.

26.

(*) Man hat nirgends das Vergnügen, ihn in so grossen
Massen zu sehen daß man etwas bestimmtes über seine Anlage in Schichten urtheilen könnte. — Meistentheils erscheint er aber doch in Blättern; es könnte aber auch dieser obere Granit nur nachentstandener seyn.

26.

Weſtlich von dieſer Linie des Granits, erhebt ſich das Land überhaupt; und verſchiedene Reihen Berge, einer hinter den andern erhaben, beobachten in ungleichem Abſtand von ſich, eine regelmäſſige Abwechslung, von Felſteinarten, oder Felsgebürge und Kalchboden, die immer alle der Hauptrichtung von Nordoſt nach Südweſt, mehr oder weniger folgen, und wo ſie irgend abzuweichen ſcheinen, findet man bey genauerer Nachſicht, daß es bloſe Vorſprünge (Spurs) ſind. Einige merkwürdige Thäler machen die Gränzen zwiſchen den Hauptreihen, deren eigentlich drey ſind, und die keinen Kalch auf ihren Rücken tragen.

Dieſe uberhaupt anzuzeigen, bediene ich mich zwar des Wortes, Felſteinarten, oder Felsgebürge, vielleicht uneigentlich; um aber nicht mißverſtanden zu werden, ſo erkläre ich mich, daß ich unter dieſer Benennung, in dieſer Abhandlung, blos diejenigen erhabenern Gebürgsketten anzeigen will, die zwar aus verſchiedenen thonichten, quarzichten, ſandichten ꝛc. Steinarten beſtehen, aber keinen Kalch haben.

Kalchthäler hingegen nenne ich die zwiſchen dieſen Felsreihen liegenden tiefern, ihnen gleichlaufenden Grün-

Gründe, die hauptsächlich nur mit Kalch, Marmor, oder auch spatartigem Gestein angefüllt sind, und wo sie sich auch in Hügel erheben, dennoch niedriger bleiben, als die ihnen zunächst westwärts anschließende Reihe der Felssteine.

Beyde bilder, das Hauptgerippe dieses östlichen Theils von Nordamerika, und verdienen, ihrer auszeichnenden Ordnung wegen, die genauere Aufmerksamkeit des künftigen amerikanischen Naturforschers, dem es mit der Zeit leicht seyn muß, ihre Striche mit abwechselnden Farben auf der gemeinen Landcharte zu bezeichnen. Man kan und wird von einem Reisenden keine vollkommene Beschreibung, eines noch unbekannten Gebürges erwarten, oder verlangen, zu dessen Beobachtung er gar keine vorläufige Kenntniß sich verschaffen, noch die erforderliche Zeit und Gelegenheit dazu finden konnte. Man muß erst mehrere Theile eines Gebürges gesehen haben, bevor man sich über dessen Richtung, Anlage, Eintheilung, einen Umriß denken kann. Die Erklärung dessen, was man an einer Stelle gesehen hat, findet man vielleicht erst an der zwenten oder britten, weit davon entfernten; oder wird da erst auf andere neuere Bemerkungen geleitet, zu deren Bestätigung man sich wieder an die erstere Stelle

Stelle zurück wünschet. Unterdessen, da ich den Weg
vom Granit an nach Wyoming an der Susquehannah,
und nach Pittsburg am Ohio, und wieder zurück, gemacht, folglich zweymal, und an zwey verschiedenen
Gegenden, über das Gebürge weg, und lange Strecken
zwischen und an dem Gebürge gereiset habe, so werde
ich wenigstens eine Skizze zu entwerfen mir erlauben,
die durch weitere Beobachtungen zu berichtigen ist, aber
andern Reisenden zu ihren Bemerkungen Erleichterung
und Vorschmack geben wird. Meine Nachrichten be-
ziehen sich also hauptsächlich auf die Gebürgsgegend
zwischen Philadelphia und Wyoming, und zwischen
Pittsburg und Baltimore, eine Durchsicht von ungefähr 120 englische Meilen von Nordost — Südwest. —
Wenn ich nun hie und da eine Vermuthung auf andere, nicht besuchte Gegenden, wage, so stütze ich mich
hauptsächlich auf die an entfernten Orten, in gleichen
Richtungen von mir beobachtete allgemeinere Uebereinstimmung, theils aber auch auf Nachrichten, die zwar
nicht von Mineralogen, aber doch von Leuten kommen,
die Kalch von andern Sand und Felssteinen zu unterscheiden, besonders aber den erstern, weil man ihn
überall sucht, anzugeben wußten.

27.

27.

Erſte Kalchlage hinter dem Granit.

Eine Kalchlage ſcheint dicht hinter dem Granit an-
zuſchlieſſen. In nicht groſſer Entfernung von Schuylkill-Falls hat man einen Bruch von weiſſem, hellgrau
und blaulicht theils geadertem, theils geflecktem
Marmor eröffnet, der in Menge zu Grabſteinen
Tiſchen, Kaminen ꝛc. verarbeitet wird (*); er iſt weich,
und nicht der feinſte, und ſpringt dünnſchaligt unter
dem Meiſſel. An andern Orten iſt es blos ein ganz
einförmig hellgrauer, feiner und dichter Stein, und
wird zum Kalchbrennen verwandt. Dieſer Strich zeiget ſich um die Gegenden von Plymouth, White-
marſch, Chesnuthill (**), Seven-Stars, Swedes-
Ford. Seine Breite ſoll an einigen Orten 1 — 2 Meilen oder mehr betragen; er ſchiebt hie, und da Aeſte
(Spurs) etwas weiter vor und rückwärts von ſich.
Bey Swedes Fort iſt ein Marmorbruch, an der
Spitze eines ſteilen Hügels, unmittelbar über dem
Fluß

(*) Kalm R. ater Theil S. 234. 235.

(**) Dies ſind die nächſten Orte, die Kalch in Menge
nach Philadelphia liefern; zwiſchen 14 und 18 Meilen davon.

Fluß offen. Er bricht in Schaalen, die beynahe senkrecht, etwa in einem Winkel von 80 Graden, nach
Osten abfallen. Was ich von diesem Strich zu Tage
gesehen, schien theils Ost zu West- theils West-
Südwest zu streichen; seine Hauptlagen aber sind größtentheils verdeckt.

Als seine südwestliche Fortsetzung findet sich, einige
Meilen West von Baltimore, eine Ader von sehr schö-
nem weissen, und weissen blaugefleckten Marmor, die
queer durch die Susquehannah von Nordost nach Südwest herabkommt. Ich habe den Ort nicht gesehen,
sondern die Nachricht von einem Steinhauer, der ihre
Breite nicht bestimmen konnte, weil sie damals nur
noch an einem Orte, und blos da, wo sie vom Flusse
losgewaschen wird, entdeckt war. Er ist von verschiedener Güte und bricht schaalicht. Der ganz weisse ist
vollkommen dem schuppichten krystallinischen Marmor
ähnlich, der bey Wunsiedel bricht, und sich hier, wie
dort, an den Granit und Gneiß anschließt; er enthält
zuweilen gelbe, aber wenige, Glimmerschuppen, und
löset sich gänzlich in Säuren auf. Die oberste Lagen
sind reicher als die untersten; in der Tiefe verliert er
sein blendendes Weiß, und wird gelblich. Bey der katho-
lischen Kapelle zu Baltimore sieht man an einigen schö-

nen

ren Leichensteinen, daß er eine gute Politur annimmt.
Man hat ähnlichen, auch in dem Pensylvanischen
Striche, der aber dort, weil er weicher ist, nicht so
sehr geliebt wird.

Dieser weisse Marmor wird mit Recht zu den
ursprünglichen Gebürgsarten gezählet; und ist gänzlich
ohne fremde Körper (*), hier sowohl, als in der alten Welt.

Auf der Oberfläche dieses erstern Kalchstriches
finden sich an mehrern Orten, weisse, ganz durchsichtige Bergkrystallen; von der Grösse eines kleinen Fin-
gers, bis zu einem Schuh lang und Schenkel dick (**).
Ganze grosse Drusen davon habe ich in einem Thale
bey Swedesforb gesehen; sie sitzen auf einer mit Quarz
und Kalch vermengten Mutter, die hin und wieder,
selbst zwischen den Krystallen aufbrauset. Die Kry-
stalle selbst sind hart, schlagen Feuer und schneiden
Glas. Oft sind es nur ganz kleine, in Ritzen zwi-

schen

(*) Schuppichter Kalchstein ist überall ohne Versteinerungen. Crell. N. Entd. V. 139.

(**) Crystallus hexagona, pellucida, non colorata.
Waller. min. p. 108. Kalm. 2ter Theil. S. 233.

schen dem Kalchstein enthaltene Krystallen. — Vorzüglich schöne aber sollen in der Nachbarschaft von
Seven-Stars (Sieben-Sterne) gefunden werden.

Die weitern Fortsetzungen dieses Striches sind
mir unbekannt.

28.

Zweyte Felsreihe.

Die nächstfolgende Fels- oder Gebürgsreihe ist
zwar nicht sehr hoch, erhebt sich aber jennoch beträchtlich, hinter dem vorliegenden Lande. Ihre obersten Lagen scheinen vorzüglich eine grünlichte, talkichte,
thonichte Bergart eigen zu haben; sie hat aber unterwärts
auch andere Felsarten. Zu dieser Reihe gehören die
Elk-Ridge in Maryland, südlich von Friedrichtown,
welche wenigstens 10 — 16 Meilen im Durchschnitt
breit, auf ihren Rücken aber mit einigen kleineren
parallelen Vertiefungen und Thälern gefurcht ist. In
dieser Elfridge sind Stevensons Kupferwerke. Die Gebürgsart, aus der man etwa 60 — 70 Fuß tief das
Erz holet, ist eine Mischung aus röthlichtem brausen-
dem Spat (Spar), und hie und da Quarz, ohne Glimmer. Die aufliegende Decke aber dieser Gegend für
mehrere Meilen (von 30 — 39 Meilen westlich von
Baltimore) ist ein dunkelgrauer dünnblätterichter aber

hoch

doch fester etwas glänzender Thonschiefer, er brauset nicht, schlägt nicht Feuer, und schabt sich weiß; ist mit mattweissen Adern durchzogen.

Aus der Gegend von 24 — 28 Meilen westlich von Baltimore an der Conegacheag-Strasse, habe ich eine graugrünlichte Art Thonschiefer, dicht und hart, am Bruche matt; er hat beygemischte Kalchtheile, die ihn an mehrern Stellen aufbrausen machen, ohne daß sie mit dem Glas zu entdecken wären. Naß wird er hellgrün; er schabt sich weiß und erhält an der Luft, einen röthlicht-braunen, hie und da dendritischen Beschlag. Springt im Feuer. Liegt dort in blätterichten Bruchstücken (*).

Noch allgemeiner ist auf diesen Hügeln, zwischen Friedrichtown und Baltimore, für eine Strecke von 18 — 24 Meilen, ein mehr glänzender Thonschiefer mit Glimmer und Quarztheilen vermischt. Dieser ist sehr dünnblätterich, grünlicht; fühlt sich fett und weich, und brauset nicht (**).

F 3   Am

(*) Er scheint zu dem Schistus viridis *Linn.* zu gehören, ob er gleich etwas härter ist, als dieser beschrieben wird.

(**) Er könnte beynahe schon für einen Glimmerschiefer gelten. Ein ähnlicher findet sich um den Fichtelberg, auch im Sächsischen Voigtlande.

Am öftlichen Abhang eines Hügels, 22 Meilen von Baltimore an der Conegacheag-Straffe, bricht ein feiner blaßröthlichter Thonschiefer von dünnen Blättern, und ungleichen oder unebenen Flächen; er fühlt sich fett und talkicht an. Aehnlicher kommt auch anderwärts von andern Farben vor.

Zwischen 16 — 18 Meilen weftlich von Baltimore, in der Gegend von Allens-Mühle, finden sich unter der Dammerde häufige Geschiebe, von dünnblätterichtem weißlichem ftarkglänzendem Glimmerschiefer, mit nur sehr wenigen und feinen Quarzkörnern vermischt.

Um diefelbe Gegend, 18 Meilen weftlich von Baltimore, findet sich noch eine der vorliegenden Granitreihe verwandte gneissige Steinart, aus groben Quarzkörnern, grünlichem und schwarzem Glimmer; und vielleicht Feldspat (der aber verwittert ift), gemischt; sie bricht in dünnen Schaalen. In einem niedrigen Hügel, der dort in Nord-Nordoft und Südweft ftreicht.

Diefe Elk-Ridge, in Maryland, gehet südlich vor dem Thale, in welchem Friedrichtown. lieget, fort nach dem Potomack, kurz vor welchem sie sich in einen hohen kegelförmigen Hügel endiget, der unter dem

Namen

Namen Sugar-Loaf-hill weit herum sichtbar und bekannt ist. Jenseits des Potomacks weiß ich die Fortsetzung dieser zweyten Reihe nicht genau anzugeben, vermuthe aber, daß die Bull-run-Mountains, die zwischen sich und dem South-Mountain ein Kalchthal haben, (welches in diesem Betracht die Fortsetzung des Friedrichtowner Kalchthals wäre) zu ihr gehören; so wie ebenfalls die weiter hinab nach Südwesten in Virginien vorkommende South-West-Montain und Green-Mountain, damit in Verbindung stehen mögen. Da, wie ich schon erwähnet, hinter Baltimore diese Reihe vorzüglich eine grünlichte Thonschiefer-Decke hat, so verleitet mich der bloße Name dieses in derselben Richtung sich findenden, mit dem Namen Green-Mountain, (grüner Berg) bezeichneten Berges, zu glauben, daß eine ähnliche grünlichte Bergart ihm diese Benennung erworben.

In der nemlichen Richtung werden auf Jeffery's Karte von Virginien noch einige andere Berge, als abgebrochene, angemerkt; nemlich der Long- und Smith-Mountain, und Mount-Ararat. Wer diese Gegenden besucht, wird aus ihren Richtungen und Bergarten, aus dem dazwischen liegenden Kalchthal 2c. ihren Zusammenhang auffinden können.

Wenn

Wenn ich blos nach der Karte die nordöstliche Fortsetzung dieser Kette von Hügeln aufsuchen will, so nehme ich das schon erwähnte Friedrichtowner Kalchthal als seine westliche Gränze an. Ich finde sodann, daß sich eine Reihe Hügel, disseits Hannover, Heydelberg, York, nach der Susquehannah hinziehe, zwischen Nelsons-Ferry und Wrights-Ferry ungefähr, durch diesen Fluß setze, dann wieder auf der Nordseite von Susquehannah, disseits Lancaster fortgehe, unter dem Namen der Welsch-Mountains sich den Flying-Hills bey Reading etwas nähern, aber weiter mit Coventry- — Limerick- und Rockyhills anschliesse, und so, (enger schon zwischen den zwey nächsten Reihen, dem Granit und dem South-Mountain eingeschlossen) nach dem Delaware zu, in der Gegend des Hancocks ausgehe.

Daß dieses ungefähr die Richtung sey, die diese Reihe, mit einer Breite von vielleicht 10 — 15 — 20 Meilen, mit verschiedenen Vor- und Absprüngen, mit ungleichen Höhen ꝛc. durch Pensylvanien nimmt, beweißt mir die Entstehung kleinerer Ströme, wie sie in der Karte von Pensylvanien angemerkt sind, und die von diesen erhabenern Theilen herab, die einen östlich, die andern westlich sich von dieser Kette abwenden.

Da

Da sind der Gunpowder, Deer- und Muddy-Krick;
Conewingo- Octararo- Brandtewein- Pickering's- und
Neshamenn-Krick, die östlich von der angezeigten
Gränze entstehen, und östlich fliessen. Der Coborus,
der Saucon gehet aus demselben Bezirk westlich; der
erstere nach der Susquehannah, der andere nach dem
Delaware.

Daß ich mich in meiner Angabe nicht ganz irre,
beweißt mir ferner und hauptsächlich noch die Uebereinstimmung der Geburgsarten an verschiedenen Stellen
dieses Striches. So fand ich auf den Hügeln hinter
Valley-Forge, bey Potts-grove und anderwärts, ganz
den obigen grünlichten Schieferarten nahe verwandte
Gattungen; unter den mir übriggebliebenen, sind
folgende:

Von den Hügeln um Coventry, ein schmuzig grü-
nes, thonichtes Gestein, mit kleinen glänzenden Schuppen und kalchichten Nestern; es brauset hie und da
nur, schabt sich weiß, bricht schaaligt. — Kommt
aber auch dortherum schöner und heller grün vor; und
ist blosse Modifikation des oben S. 85. von der Conegacheag-Strasse in Maryland, (bey 100 Meilen
Südwest) erwähnten.

F 5   Aus

Aus Thon mit Sand gemengtes schiefrichtes graues Gestein, mit. kleinen weißlichen Glimmerschuppen, und einzeln eingelegten kleinen Schörlartigen? Kryftallen. Ist hart; bricht schaaligt; ist naß doch auch grünlicht spielend; gibt angehaucht einen Thongeruch. Von der Ostseite, von Valley-Forge-Hill in Pensylvanien.

In diesem Strich ist auf Sculls Karte von Pensylvanien, am Susquehannah eine Stelle, mit Blue-Rock, (blauer Fels) bezeichnet; weit davon nordöstlich, an der Straße nach Bethlehem, bey Swamp-Meeting, oder Quäkertown, habe ich eine blaue, harte, dem Trapp ähnliche Steinart gesehen, wovon ich aber nichts mehr habe.

An andern Stellen (westlich von Baltimore) bricht eine (nicht sehr feste) Felsart, die aus weissem Quarz und Feldspat gemischt ist, und einzeln eingesprengte kleine Körner von Hornblende? da und dort zeigt. Quarz und Feldspat wechseln zuweilen in parallelen ebenen Blättern, nicht viel dicker als ein starker Bogen Papier, ab, welches ihr ein besonderes streifiges Ansehen gibt. Der Feldspat verwittert gern, zu einem Porcellänthon? und dann bleiben die Quarzblätter allein stehen. Wenn sie härter wäre, würde sie dem

Grit-

Gritstone um Bedford und andern Orten des Gebürgs, ähnlich seyn; sie bricht in mehr oder weniger Zoll dicken Lagen, zwischen denen sie eine fahle
Ocherfarbige Rinde hat.

An den Seiten von Warwicks Hügeln, in Penſylvanien und anderwärts, bricht eine andere quarzichte
Felsart; ebenfalls in Lagen, eine lange Strecke; die
Quarzkörner scheinen äusserlich schuppicht oder fletschicht
zu seyn, am Bruch aber zeigen sie sich von mittlerer
Grösse, weiß, röthlich und schwärzlicht, mit Farben
schillernd, halbdurchsichtig, haben nichts frembes zwischen sich, sind eckicht und äusserst fest unter sich vereinigt.

Wenn diese Reihe dem Delaware nahe kommt,
so nähert sie sich zugleich den Leheigh Hügeln. Auf
der Nordseite 'des Delawares weiß ich ihren Weg
durch die Jerſey nicht anzugeben, weil ich diese Gegenden nicht besucht habe. Wer sie hier verfolgen will,
wird genauere Aufmerksamkeit anwenden müssen, weil
sich alle die verschiedene Reihen durch die Jerſey
theils mehr drängen, theils weitere Vorsprünge abge-
ben, indem sie sich dem Hudson nähern, und in dasigen
Gegenden nur engere Thäler bilden. Muthmaßlich
aber

aber ist mirs, daß man ihren Strich über Alexandria, Sunburn, Hoffs, Mendum, längst Suckasany-Plains, Rockaway, Hibernia, Pempton ꝛc. entdecken möchte.

Es enthält diese Reihe einen grossen Vorrath von Erzen.

Kupfer hat Stevensons Grube in Maryland; (Kupferglaserz in röthlichem Kalkspat mit einer talfichten Rinde. Auf den Halten liegt auch der weichere, schwärzliche Thonschiefer, mit Berggrün angelaufen. — Schöner Malachit mit theils stärkern, theils feinern, theils unkenntlichen Strahlen und Fasern. —) und die Gruben um Limerick und Saalford in Pensylvanien; leztere werden, meines Wissens, dermalen nicht betrieben. — In diesem Strich einige Kupfergruben in Jersey?

Bley, grobwürfelichtes in Spat, am Pequea-kric in Pensylvanien.

Eisen in Menge, in verschiedenen Hügeln, seichte unter der Dammerde, die Erze wie in Haufen zusammengeschlämmt. — Gruben und Hämmer sind: Mary Ann-Furnace, bey Heydelberg, Marticks-
Wind-

Windſor ⋅ Reading ⋅ Warwick ⋅ und Coventry⋅
Burdsborough ⋅ Hopewell ⋅ Vincents ⋅ Pool⋅
M'Calls ⋅ Pottsgrove⋅ und mehr andere Häm⋅
mer, Oefen und Gruben, die aber nicht alle
mehr gangbar ſind.

Dahin gehören: mit weichem Speckſtein, Glimmer
und Quarzkörnern vermiſchter Eiſenſtein, von Jones's
Grube, in Berks⋅County, Penſylvanien; liegt ſchich⋅
tenweiſe ganz ſeicht, und bildet ganze Hügel.

Zwiſchen den Lagen des Eiſenſteines liegen andere,
von dünnblätterichtem mildem weisgrünlichtem Speck⋅
ſtein (*), mit ocherichten horizontalen Adern; den
Speckſtein oder Schneideſtein nennen die daſigen Ar⋅
beiter auch Soapſtone oder Iſinglaſs. Er brauſet an
einzelnen Stellen.

Einige Meilen nordöſtlich von der vorigen Grube,
wird in Warwicks Gruben, ebenfalls ſeichte unter der
Oberfläche, ein etwas derberer und ſchwererer Eiſen⋅
ſtein gegraben, der wie jener mit Speckſtein durch⋅
knetet

(*) Der Speckſtein im Bayreuthiſchen iſt wie dieſer, mit
Eiſen oft vermengt.

knetet ist, und zwischen Lagen von ihm Nieren- und Nesterweise bricht.

An und um den Hügeln von Vallen-Forge, in Pensylvanien, grosse Strecken von braunem Eisenmulm; mehr oder weniger hartes aus Thon, quarzichtem Sand und Glimmer mit Eisenerde gemischtes Gebürg; zum Theil ganz weich, locker und schmierig.

So weit mir nun diese Reihe bekannt worden, scheint sie in der Tiefe, Spat- und quarzichten soliden Felsgrund zu haben, durch welchen Kupfer und andere Erzgänge streichen; scheint weiter aufwärts mit Gneisartigen, oder blätterichtem quarzichten derben und weicherem Gebürg überlegt zu seyn, und in den noch höhern Lagen, thonicht-talkichte Schiefer, von mehr oder weniger grünlichter Farbe, zu tragen; Eisen scheint vorzüglich nur Nesterweise auf Anhöhen und in Hügel zusammengeschlämmt zu seyn. Da beynahe durchgehends Spuren vom Talk- und Speckstein, in der Teufe sowohl, als in der Höhe, vorkommen, so möchte man diese Reihe vielleicht nicht ganz unrecht die Talkichte nennen.

In den längst und auf den Rücken verschiedentlich gefurchten Vertiefungen, finden sich hie und da kleine unbedeutende Striche von Kalch.

29.

29.

Zwente Kalchlage.

Zwischen der vorhergehenden Reihe und dem South-Mountain habe ich bereits eines Kalchthals erwähnt. Zehn oder zwölf Meilen von Potomack ist Friedrichtown in Maryland, und weiter Nordöstlich, Tonyton, Peter-Littletown, Mac-Callisterstown, York-town, Lancaster, Neu-Holland in diesem Thale, das sich heraufwärts bis Jones-tavern an den Welsch-Mountains ununterbrochen verfolgen läßt. Hier scheint es sich zwischen einigem hohen Land abzuschneiden, von dem ich aber nicht einmal weiß, ob es nicht aus Kalch-hügeln bestehet. Vielleicht auch setzet es auf der andern Seite fort; ich kenne es aber nicht weiter.

Es krümmt sich nach dem Lauf seiner zween Nach-barn. So wie diese hie und da Vorsprünge in das Thal schicken, so sendet dieses wieder an andern Or-ten Buchten zwischen die Berge. Dieses Thal ist 3 — 6 Meilen breit, ziemlich eben, auffer wo es von Flüssen durchschnitten wird, die, wenn sie nicht eine bequeme Oeffnung durch die vorerwähnte Felsreihe finden, eine Strecke lang an dem südlichen und südöst-lichen Abhange des Thals hinlaufen; daher es gemei-

niglich

niglich einen gröffern Fall nach diefer Seite zu hat.
Der allgemeine, einförmige, graue, blätterichte Kalch-
ftein, von dem ich weiter hin zu reden Gelegenheit
nehmen werde, füllet es ganz. Ich habe keine fremde
Körper darinnen gefehen.

Auf der fübweftlichen Seite des Potomacks habe
ich es bis Leesburg in Virginien in derselben Richtung verfolgt; von dort aber, indem sich mein Weg
füböftlich nach Richmond wendete, kam ich wieder über
niedere gneifichte Hügel der zweyten oder vorigen Felsreihe, und verlor es.

30.

Dritte Felsreihe.   Der South-Mountain.

Deutlicher als die zweyte Felsreihe, höher, gedrängter, und nicht weniger Erzreich, zeichnet sich die
dritte aus.   Obgleich auch diefe sich hie und da zu verlieren scheint, fo erhebt fie sich doch bald wieder in
derselben Richtung von Nordoft nach Südweft.

In Nordkarolina, um den 35ften Grad der Breite
ungefehr, beginnt fie eine befondere Reihe auszumachen.   Südlicher von da, konnte ich nicht erfahren,
ob fie deutlich ift; vielleicht wird fie dort mit den übri-

gen

gen Gebürgen niedriger, und weniger bemerkbar.
Durch Virginien streicht sie in einer ziemlich regelmäſſigen, weniger unterbrochenen Kette, unter den Namen
des South-Mountains, Blue-Ridge, und Pignut-
Mountain, (wenn dies leztere nicht etwa 'ein besonderer
paralleler Zweig davon iſt.) Unter demselben Namen
gehet sie durch Maryland, aber hier so wohl als dort,
mit verschiedenen Aeſten. So bald sie zwischen dem
39 und 40 Grad in Pensylvanien kommt, wird sie gebrochener, schwingt sich etwas mehr nördlich, und
nähert sich den hintern Gebürgen, gehet aber dennoch
in ähnlicher Richtung mit ihnen fort, und erhält da
die verschiedenen Namen, der Oley-Flying-und
Leheigh-Hills. Unterhalb Bethlehem setzet sie durch
den Delaware, und macht jenseits in Jersey, die zunächst an die Drowned-Lands (ersoffenes Land)
südlich gränzende hohe Gebürge, die nach Pownall
Mesapetcung genannt werden, und sich nach dem
Hudsons-River hinziehen, wo sie mit den übrigen
Highlands (*) einfallen. Um den Delaware und
durch ganz Jersey, sollen sie nach Beschreibungen
höher

(*) Kalm zter Theil S. 206.

Schöpf min. Beytr.   G

höher und steiler seyn, als irgendwo südlicher, und kommen ebenfalls dem Nord-Mountain näher.

Nach der Anlage auf Jeffery's Karte von Virginien, wäre dieser South-Mountain, der südlichste Zweig vom Alleghany; er läßt nemlich beyde durch eine Querkette sich vereinigen; ich kann ihm nicht aus Erfahrung widersprechen, es wäre aber erst zu untersuchen, ob diese Querkette, nicht wie ich vermuthe, Kalchstein ist? —

Evans (*) sagt von ihm, daß er nicht mit solchen geraden Reihen, als die endlosen Gebürge, sondern in kleinen gebrochenen steilen Hügeln streiche; daß er sich an einigen Orten beynahe gänzlich auf einige Meilen verliere, und anderwärts wieder auf einige Meilen ausbreite. Er spricht aber hauptsächlich von seinem Gang, nur durch Pensylvanien. Den Zwischenraum von der Granitreihe, bis an den South-Mountain, setzt er auf 50 — 70 Meilen; aber auch nur im mittlern Theil von Pensylvanien. Von Neuyork bis an die ersten Highlands, sinds 36 — 40 Meilen (**); von Philadelphia bis an die Oley- und Leheigh-

---

(*) Analysis pag. 7.
(**) Kalm 3ter Theil S. 201.

Leheigh-Hills 40 — 45.; von Baltimore nach Frixdrloo-
town am Fuß des South-Mountains etwa 60. Die
lezten beyden Entfernungen kenne ich aus Erfahrung,
und zeige sie an, um zu bestätigen, daß sich die Gebürgsreihen, wie ich bereits angemerkt habe, Nord-
westwärts gegen den Hudson enger aneinander ziehen.

Ich bin hier wieder genöthiget, den Verlust der
nach Bethlehem hin auf dieser Reihe gesammleten Gebürgsarten zu bedauren, der mich hindert genauere
Nachrichten darüber zu geben.   Als eine allgemeine
Bemerkung aber darf ich sagen, daß man sie hauptsächlich mit blätterichtem, quarzichten oder gneißichten
Gestein überlegt findet.   In Maryland, auf dem Weg
von Scharpsburg über diese Reihe nach Friedrichtown, oder von einem Kalchthal nach dem andern,
kommt man über verschiedene niedrige und mittelmässige
hohe, gleichlaufende Hügel-Rücken, die durch schöne,
schmale, gut gewässerte Thäler angenehm werden, und
beyde größtentheils mit röthlichem Bodenart überdeckt
sind.   Man findet hie und da, grauen, blätterichten
Sandstein, mit Quarzadern.   Bruchstücke von grobem eisenschüssigem Quarz.   Geschiebe von grau-
röthlichtem Porphyr, mit eingekneteten kleinen durch-

sichti-

sichtigen Quarzkörnern, und milchweissen undurch-
sichtigem Feldspat, fand ich an einer Stelle des Weges.
Am östlichen Abhang dieser Reihe war ein blättrichtes sehr hartes gneisichtes Gestein, aus schuppichtem und
körnichtem Quarz, mit etwas feinem Glimmer, sehr
häufig; es brach in Tafeln, von $\frac{1}{4}$ Zoll, und schien
noch blättricht.

Auf der Westseite hingegen, zwischen Scharpsburg
und Middletown, nachdem man ganz über den Kalchstein weg ist, zeiget sich ein graues, ebenfalls
blättrichtes gneissiges Gestein noch häufiger; es hat
etwas sehr feinen Glimmer, und kleine braune eisen-
schüssige Punkte eingemischt. Angehaucht giebt es
Thongeruch, und schabt sich weiß, brauset nicht, und
ist hart.

Der South-Mountain in seiner ganzen Lage, enthält reiche Klüfte, Gänge und Nester von Erzen; besonders Eisen und Kupfer. Die Eisenwerke bey Chamberstown, Carlisle, Middletown, Easton ꝛc. die beynahe unerschöpflichen Eisenhügel des Obersten Grubbs,
und mehr andere, gehören dahin. Man hat ihn aber
noch nicht so genau durchsucht, als die vorige Kette.

Noch

Noch habe ich von dieser Reihe sowohl als der vorhergehenden anzumerken, daß ihr östlicher Abhang sanfter und schräger ist, als an der westlichen Seite.

31.

Dritte Kalchlage.   Das große Kalchthal.

Ein schönes Thal, und merkwürdig wegen seiner Lage und Fruchtbarkeit, scheidet den South vom Nord-Mountain. Es hat keinen allgemeinen Namen (*), könnte aber mit Recht und Vorzugsweise das große Kalchthal, oder auch wegen der vorzüglicheren Menge seiner deutschen Einwohner, das deutsche Thal genannt werden. Vom Delaware an, bis zum Potowmack, und noch jenseits, habe ich es beynahe 120 englische Meilen verfolgt. Es erhebt sich vom Hudson-River, und man kennt es von da an durch Jersey, Pensylvanien, Maryland, Virginien, bis in Carolina, und bis (wie man mich versicherte) Georgien, in derselben Richtung, von derselben Beschaffenheit, und als unmittelbar vor dem nächstfolgenden Berge hergehend. Die ersoffene Lande (drowned Lands) in

G 3   York

(*) Evans will es Piemont genannt haben, weil es am Fuße des Hauptgebürgs liegt.

Porf und Jersey, sind seine nordöstliche Fortsetzung,
nach Pownalls Angabe. In Pensylvanien ist ein Theil
dieses Thals, zwischen dem Schuylkill und Susquehannah unter dem Namen Tulpehocken-Thal, allgemein als besonders ergiebig bekannt. In Virginien
wird es nur an einem Ort in der Gegend von Staun-
tön, durch von beyden Seiten vorspringenden Bergen,
etwas unterbrochen, welche Berge aber nach aller
Wahrscheinlichkeit aus Kalchstein bestehen (*). Nachher
aber

* * *

(*) Der Roanofe ist es, wenn ich nicht irre, der sich in
dieser Gegend einen Weg durch den Felsen ausgehöhlet, und
so eine natürliche Brücke über sich gebildet hat. Dieser Umstand allein schon macht es höchst wahrscheinlich, daß die erwähnte, den South- und North-Mountain verbindende Berge, aus einer Steinart bestehen müsse, die durch Wasser er-
weicht und ausgefressen werden kann; welches der in diesem
Striche fortgehende Kalch ohne Zweifel seyn wird. Das
Verbergen anderer Flüsse, in andern Weltgegenden, bestätigen
es ferner. Blätterichter Kalchstein giebt der Rhone Gelegenheit, sich zu verbergen. Sauffäre 2ter Theil §. 406. Und
eben so verkriecht sich die Pegnitz, im Bayreuthischen, durch
einen weichen blätterichten Felsen derselben Art. (Meine
obige Vermuthung erhält durch das, was ich von dieser na-
türlichen Brücke in der *Voyage de M. le Chévalier de*
Cha-

aber gehet es wieder in voriger Gestalt weiter süd-
westlich, und soll sich, nach Evans, etwa 200 Meilen
von der Apalachian-Bay verlieren. Die Breite dieses Thals ist ungleich, von 6 — 10 — 12 bis 20 Meilen; im Ganzen aber so, daß seine Breite gegen Süden zunimmt. Von den durchhin gehenden Flüssen erscheint es öfters uneben, hügelicht, und wie das vorige, allgemein südöstlich abhängend. Mit dem vorigen
hat es auch denselben grauen, mehr oder weniger harten und feinen, meist in Blättern verschiedener Dicke
liegenden Kalchstein gemein; welcher zu Tag aus
meistentheils blässer, tiefer hinab aber dunkler und
schwärzlich wird. Oft auch erscheint er als ein dünn-
blättrichter, schwarzer oder grauer Schiefer. Diese
Kalchlage ist meines Wissens noch nirgend durchgegra-

G 4   ben

Chastellux en Amérique p. 107. finde, mehrere Gewißheit.
Le rocher, heißt es, est de nature calcaire, et ses
couches sont parallèles à l'horison. Der Hr. v. Chastellux wundert sich dennoch gewaltig, wie le petit ruisseau
qui coule sous cette arche immense, da durchkommet;
denn er findet nulle trace d'un embrasement subit, ou
du travail lent et pénible des eaux. — Die Breite des
Bogens ist nur 40 Schritt, also weniger, als bei über die
Sarpin. — Die Höhe ist nicht angegeben.)

ben worden. Vermuthlich enthält dieses Kalchthal auch
feinere Marmor; wenigstens habe ich bey Schippensburg einen schönen leberfarbenen gefunden.

Eine Menge zum Theil ansehnliche natürliche
Höhlen und Grotten finden sich in diesem Striche,
z. E. bey Easton, bey Hummelstown, bey Carlisle
und anderwärts, die ihren Ursprung losgegangenen und
gesunkenen Schichten der Kalchlage zu danken haben,
und mit allerley Tropfsteinen ausgeschmückt sind. Beym
Graben nach Brunnen finden sich grössere und kleinere Klüfte, mit Kalchspat und Spatdrusen ausgefüllt.
Auf der Oberfläche aber sind Krystallen vielfach anzutreffen, und vorzüglich als ein getreuer Begleiter, und
richtiger Anzeiger von unterliegenden Kalchboden, wenn
man diesen auch nicht siehet, findet man überall
schwarze Kiesel, (flint, silex,) und weissen Quarz. Der
Kiesel hat beynahe immer eine weisse Rinde.

Mir hat es nicht geglückt, irgend eine Spur von
Versteinerungen in den mannichfaltigen Brüchen, die
ich gesehen und fleissig durchsucht habe, zu finden; nach
Erzählungen aber muß ich glauben, daß hie und da,
aber nur auf der Oberfläche, einige, und das nur selten, angetroffen wurden. Meine Erfahrungen lassen
mich

mich mit vielem Recht vermuthen, daß dieser Kalchstein
zwar im oder unterm Wasser entstanden sey, aber nicht
von zerstörten Schaalthieren seinen Stoff erhalten habe; man müßte denn voraussetzen, daß diese erst in
einen vollkommen gleichförmigen Brey aufgelöset worden wären, so daß auch nicht die kleinste Spur von
einem organisirten Körper übrig geblieben sey, wovon
auch mit dem besten Glase nichts zu entdecken ist.
Seine blätterichte Schichten, von Zollen, bis ein und
mehr Fuß dick, zeigen sich deutlich und überall. Sie
liegen aber nur selten horizontal; ob dieses den unebenen Flächen, auf die sich der kalchichte Niederschlag
setzte, oder nachfolgenden gewaltsamen Veränderungen
zuzuschreiben sey, kann ich nicht entscheiden.

32.

Das Hauptgebürge.

An der Westseite des vorhergehenden Thals finden wir nunmehro das Hauptgebürge des östlichen
Theils von Nordamerika, das aus mehreren, nahe
hintereinander, und parallel, (wenigstens die aller-
meisten) laufenden Reihen bestehet; welche einzeln durch
verschiedene Namen bezeichnet sind, alle zusammen genommen aber, das Gebürge schlechthin, die blauen

G 5   Berge,

Berge, die endlosen Berge, das Apalachische Gebürge, das Alleghany Gebürge genannt werden.
Eigentlicher aber versteht man unter dem Apalachischen
Gebürge den südlichern Strich dieser Berge, die gegen
Abend von Virginien, und den Carolinen ꝛc. liegen,
und von einem Indianischen Stamm den Apalaches,
seinen Namen hat, so wie der Apalachianfluß, der in
die Bay von Apalache, im Mexicanischen Gulf, sich er-
gießt. Der nördlichere Antheil des Gebürgs, hinter
dem obern Theil Virginiens und Pensylvaniens ꝛc.
werden von einem andern Stamm, die Alleghannschen
Berge genannt, der auch dem in den Ohio sich ergiessen-
den Alleghannfluß den Namen gegeben. Den Namen,
endlose Gebürge (Endless Mountains) haben ihnen um
ihres weiten Umfangs und Ausdehnung willen die Indianer gegeben; er ist aber freylich dem Wortverstand
nach einzuschränken. Oefters nennt man sie auch zum
Unterschiede des vorigen, den Nord-Mountain, welches aber eigentlicher der erstern östlichen Wand alleine
zukommt; so wie auch ein besonderer Zweig des Gebürgs, den Namen der Alleghany-Reihe vorzugsweise
führt.

„Die endlosen Gebürge, nach Evans Schilde-
„rung (*), sind nicht unordentlich durch einander ge-
„worfe-

_____

(*) Evans Analysis p. 8.

„worfene und sich überthürmende Spitzen, sondern
„lange einförmige Reihen, die kaum eine halbe (engli-
„sche) Meile senkrecht, (die englische Meile hat 7384
„Rhein. Fuß, oder 1230 Toisen; auch das Drittel davon,
„ist eine zu große Angabe für irgend einen dieser
„Berge,) an irgend einer Stelle über die dazwi-
„schen liegende Thäler erhaben sind. An einigen
„Orten, als gegen Raatskill (Neuyork-Provinz)
„und dem Ursprung des Roanoke, sollte man bey-
„nahe glauben ihr Ende gefunden zu haben; man
„sehe sich aber nur etwas um, und man wird sie mit
„neuen Zweigen sich erheben sehen, die an Ausdeh-
„nung den vorigen nichts nachgeben. Die westlichere
„Kette, oder die eigentlichere Alleghany-Reihe, bleibt
„größtentheils parallel mit der Granit-Reihe, und en-
„digt sich in eine rauhe felsichte Gegend am Ursprung
„des Roanokes und New-Rivers. Die östliche
„Kette, indem sie nach Süden hinab läuft, ziehet sich
„zugleich mehr und mehr westlich; dies ist die Ursache,
„daß das große Kalchthal oder Piemont, in Virginien
„breiter wird, als es weiter nördlich ist. Dieses
„Drängen der östlichern Reihen nach Südwesten
„macht, daß sie dem Alleghany sich nähern, und an
„einigen Stellen ihn durchschneiden und in neuen
„Berg-Reihen fortsetzen; welches, wie ich glaube,

„der

„der Fall mit dem Ouaſioto iſt. Wo die verſchiede-
„nen Reihen einander durchſchneiden, oder die Haupt-
„Reihen kleinere Vorſprünge (Spurs) von ſich ſchicken,
„da zeigen ſich die Berge gebrochen, und in einzelne
„Hügel zerſtreut, und geben die ſchicklichſten Plätze,
„um Straſſen durchzuführen. Es ſind noch verſchie-
„dene Reihen der endloſen Berge, welche mir unbe-
„kannt geblieben ſind, und mich dahero, unausgefüllte
„Stellen auf der Karte zu laſſen, genöthiget haben.
„So weit wir ſie aber kennen, bemerken wir, daß
„jede einzelne Reihe eine eigene, und von den übri-
„gen verſchiedene Gebürgsart enthalte. Als ich ſie
„bereiſete, entgieng mir dieſe Bemerkung, und ich ver-
„gaß ihre verſchiedenen-Gattungen zu zählen. Einige
„dieſer Reihen ſind einzelne enge Bergrücken, wie
„z. E. der Kittatinny; andere ſind auf ihren Rücken
„zwey bis drey Meilen breit; einige ſind ſteil an der
„einen Seite, und gemach abfallend an der andern,
„und je ſteiler ſie ſind, deſto felſichter; aber ſie ſind
„überall mit Wald bewachſen, wo nur hinlänglich
„Erde, die Baumwurzeln zu befeſtigen, angetroffen
„wird. Gegen Nordoſten zu enthalten die weſtlicheren
„Reihen gutes reiches Land, und ſind an einigen Or-
„ten nur breite und ſtarke Dämme (Bancks) von
„3 — 4 Meilen breit. Auf dem Weg nach dem Ohio
„über

„über Frankstown, nachdem man den Alleghany über-
„stiegen hat, wird die Gegend rauh und uneben, bis
„nach jenem Fluß. Um diese Gegend entspringt der
„Laurell-Hill von dem Geburg, und erstrecket sich
„in einer zwar nicht breiten, aber regelmassigen Kette,
„wie mir deucht, bis nach den Ouasioto. Denn ob-
„schon der Alleghany die westlichste Reihe am westli-
„chen Arm der Susquehannah, West von Pensylvanien
„und Neuyork, ist, so ist er es doch nicht mehr in den
„hintern Gegenden von Virginien. Die westlicheren
„Reihen ausgenommen, findet sich nur wenig gutes
„Land im Geburg; und gewiß nicht der zehnde Theil
„ist urbar zu machen; der wenige gute Boden, den
„man antrifft, sind schmale Streifen von sehr reicher
„Erde, an den Flußbetten, die aus dort abgesetzter
„Schlamm bestehen; welche gemeiniglich vormals ober-
„halb von Wasserfällen sich anhäufte, nachdem aber
„die Flüsse sich Kanäle durch die Felsen gegraben, nun
„weiter geschlemmt wird.

Ich habe keinen Anstand genommen, diese ganze
Stelle einzuschalten, theils weil Evans Bemerkungen,
der als Landmesser die Geburge bereisete, die meinigen
bestätigen; theils weil vor und nach ihm niemand mehr
Rücksicht auf die Anlage der Geburge genommen hat;

denn

denn Pownalls Nachrichten find nur von Evans ent-
lehnt.

33.

Der Kittatinny.

Die erste und öftlichste Reihe des Gebürges, die
sich dem Neisenden, der von der Küste herauf kommt,
darstellet, ist der Kittatinny, der aber eben so oft
der Nord-Mountain, der Blew-Mountain, genannt wird. Der Weg von der See nach diesen Bergen zu, führt stuffenweise über die verschiedenen höher
und höher gelegenen Gegenden; die breiten dazwischen
liegenden Thäler und Flächen machen den Abhang aber
weniger auffallend und ermüdend. Die Entfernung
vom Granit, bis an den Fuß dieser ersten Wand, ist
von 60 — 70 — 100 Meilen. Zum erstenmale sahe ich
sie auf dem Wege nach Wyoming, hinter Nazareth
und ich muß gestehen, daß ich mich in meiner Erwar-
tung betrogen, und nicht den steilen, hohen, und ehr-
würdigen Berg fand, den ich nach den Beschreibungen,
die man sich einander in den niedern Gegenden davon
macht, erwartet hatte. Ich wurde aber durch den
mehr unerwarteten Anblick, von einförmiger Ausdehnung und prachtvoller Regelmäffigkeit schadlos gehalten,
für das, was ihm in Vergleichung mit unfern Alpen

am

am Erhabenen und Schaudervollen mangelt, und was
ihm unbeträchtliche Höhe und minder steiler Abhang
nicht zu geben vermag. Da wo ich ihn zuerst erblick-
te, und an mehr andern Orten, stellt er sich dem Auge
als eine anscheinlich in schnurgerader Richtung fortgehende Wand dar; denn die dort und da befindliche
Vorsprünge und Einschnitte, laſſen sich in der Ferne
und unter dem dicken Forste, der ihn vom Fuß bis
zum Gipfel bekleidet, nicht leicht entdecken, und be-
nehmen folglich dem Eindruck der einfachern und groſſen
Hauptlinie nicht viel. Ich sahe in der Folge, auf
dem Weg zwischen Nazareth und Carlisle, diese Wand
auf mehrere Meilen gänzlich ununterbrochen, und genau in demselben Strich des Compaſſes fortgeſetzet;
sogar der Rücken bleibt für beträchtliche Längen in derselben wagerechten Parallele mit dem Fuß. Im Ganzen aber ist der Rücken dieser Wand horizontal, und
stuffenweise gegen Süden abfallend. Zuweilen siehet
man verschiedene dieser Stuffen oder Abfälle kurz hinter einander, und dann wieder eine lange Strecke gerade aus den Rücken fortstreichen. Nur da, wo die
verschiedenen gröſſern, oft auch kleinere Flüſſed urch-
hingehen, bemerkte ich, in der von mir beobachteten
Strecke dieser und anderer Reihen, daß das nächstge-
legene und so durchschnittene Ende der Kette, sich
mehr-

mehrmals in etwas erhabenern und oft abgerundeten
Spitzen zeige; und daß die meisten dieser Erhöhungen
auf der nördlichen Seite der Flüsse sind.

Diese östliche Wand macht, indem sie der Hauptrichtung von Nordost nach Südwesten folgt, dennoch
hie und da einige kleinere Lagen. Ein beträchtlicher
Einbug nach Westen zeigt sich zwischen der Susquehannah und dem Potowmack, oder zwischen Carlisle
und Schippensburg; welchem Einbug alle andere da-
hinter liegende Berg-Reihen mehr oder weniger zu
folgen scheinen. Vielleicht wird sich auch in den davor
liegenden Reihen eine ähnliche Wendung entdecken
lassen. Es scheint wenigstens, daß der Bogen, den
die Delaware in der Gegend von Philadelphia macht,
einigen Bezug darauf habe? —

Die Gebirgsart dieser ersten Wand, ist zu Tage
ein fester, feinkörnichter Sandstein, grau, weißlicht,
auch ins rothe fallend; theils mit weniger, theils ganz
ohne Glimmer, der aber immer sehr fein ist. Auf
dem Weg nach Wyoming, sieht man in und um die
sogenannte Wind-Gape eine unsägliche Menge von
nicht grossen Bruchstücken dieser Art am Wege; grosse
und solide nackte Felsen aber nicht, weil diese mit dem

Ueber-

Ueberſchutt von Erdreich und Bäumen bedeckt ſind.
Er iſt blättricht, aber in dicken Lagen.

34.

Da es mir unmöglich war, die ganze Länge dieſer
Gebürgsketten von einem Ende zum andern zu verfolgen, ſo bediene ich mich der Freyheit, einige zur weitern Ueberſicht der nächſtfolgenden Berg-Reihen gehörige Bemerkungen, aus den beſten Karten Jeffery,
Scull, Evans, Pownall zu entlehnen; die aber, weil
ihre Verfertiger ſich weder die genaue Zahl und Richtung der verſchiedenen Aeſte des Gebürges zum Haupt-
Gegenſtand ihrer Arbeiten machten, noch in den unzu-
gänglichen unbewohnten Wildniſſen, die ſie bedecken,
machen konnten, viele Verbeſſerungen und Berichtigun-
gen in folgenden Zeiten erſt erhalten werden.

Um den 36ſten oder 37ſten Grad der Breite ungefähr, theilt ſich das Hauptgebürge, das unter dem
Namen des Apalachiſchen von Süden herauf kommt,
in verſchiedene, mehr abgeſonderte und regelmäſſige
Zweige. Der weſtliche und beträchtlichere Arm davon,
der in faſt allen Karten als die mehr unmittelbare
Fortſetzung des Apalachiſchen Gebürges, und weiter hin
unter dem Namen des Alleghany-Berges (the Al-

leghany - Ridge) angezeichnet iſt, ziehet ſich erſtlich in
jener Gegend etwas nordweſtlich, bleibt aber nachher
für den größten Theil, durch Virginien, Maryland
und Penſylvanien, mit dem öſtlichſten Arm in einer
Parallele. Dieſer öſtlichſte Arm iſt der erſtbeſchriebene
Kittatinny. Da erſt, wo ſich dieſe beyde, nach Angabe der Karten, in einem ſcharfen Winkel theilen,
und der Alleghany durch ſeine Abweichung mehrern
Raum giebt, erheben ſich zwiſchen beyden verſchiedene
andere Reihen, die überhaupt genommen, als parallel
laufend, hie und da aber abgebrochen, und nicht in
einer genau auf einander paſſenden Linie fortgeſezt,
oder auch mit mehr neuen Zwiſchenäſten vorgeſtellt
ſind. So zeigen die Karten tief unten in Virginien
4 — 5 — 6, höher hinauf aber 7 — 8 — 9 dergleichen Reihen an; die aber gar nicht als geltende Beweiſe hier angeführt ſeyn ſollen. Nach der nämlichen
Karten-Angabe entfernt ſich, weiter nördlich durch
Jerſey und Neuyork, der eigentliche Allegany-Berg
etwas mehr vom Kittatinny, obgleich die übrigen
Reihen gedrängter und enger an einander gerückt erſcheinen.

Ohne mich aber weiter auf die vielleicht mehrmals willführliche Anlage der Bergreihen in den Karten

ten zu stützen, werde ich meine, zwar unbeträchtliche, Erfahrungen darüber beybringen. Vorher aber erinnere ich, daß die Abwechslung zwischen Kalch- und andern Felsarten sich beynahe eben so ordentlich quer durch die Gebürge hin zeige, als zwischen der Küste und dem Hauptgebürge. Die meisten Thäler, oder Zwischenräume von einer Felsreihe zur andern enthalten Kalch, oft Kalchberge, oder Kalchhügel, die dann ebenfalls in paralleler Richtung mit ihren beyderseitigen Nachbarn gehen, und an einer oder der andern Seite, oder allen beyden, fliessende Wasser, die Ursachen ihrer Hügelgestalt haben. In vielen Thälern zwar weis man noch von keinem Kalch; weil man entweder noch nicht darnach gesucht hat, und in den undurchdringlichen Sümpfen, und niedrigbewachsene, vermoßten, überschlämmten Gegenden Entdeckungen zu machen, nicht leicht ist. Vielleicht fehlt er auch in solchen Thälern gänzlich, die eigentlich nur vertiefte Rücken von andern Felsarten sind; die meisten haben ihn aber dennoch auf dem Wege nach dem Ohio besonders.

35.

Berg-Reihen zwischen Heller's Hause am Fuſſe des Kittatinny, und Wyoming am öſtlichen Arm der Susquehannah.

Von Nazareth über Schöneck bis auf einige Meilen von Hellers Hauſe, hat man meiſtens hügelichten Kalchboden. Eine Meile hinter dieſem Hauſe gehet man über den Kittatinny; man überſteigt nicht den höchſten Rücken deſſelben, ſondern kommt durch eine nach deſſen obern Theile zu befindliche natürliche Lücke, die von einer halben bis zu einer Meile breit ſeyn mag, bis auf die Hälfte der Höhe des Berges herein kommt, und überall mit Bruchſtücken, von dem zerbrochenen Rückgrad des Berges, beſäet iſt. Es flieſſet kein Waſſer durch dieſe Lücke, und man ſiehet auch keine Spuren, daß ehemals ein Strom dadurch gekommen ſey; man nennt daher, zum Unterſchied von andern, dieſe Oefnung die Windkluft (Wind-gape). Auf der andern oder Nordweſtſeite hat man einen langen und ſanften Abhang, bis nach Eckardts Haus, 3 Meilen von Hillers, längſt welchem ſich rothe thonichte Lagen, auch Neſter und Nieren von brauner Umbra-ähnlicher Erde, finden.

2) Hin-

2) Hinter Eckardts, — ein Kalchhügel von keiner
beträchtlichen Höhe; er enthält den gewöhnlichen
grauen Kalchstein; ist aber mit Sandsteinen nach
dem Gipfel zu überlegt, und hat viele zerstreute
schwarze Kiesel. So weit man ihn übersehen
kann, streicht er in gleicher Richtung mit dem
erstern; man weiß aber nicht wie weit.

3) Nach diesem Hügel, über Brinkers-Mill, bis
nach Dieters's hat man zwey oder drey niedere
Reihen von Sandstein-Hügeln, die zwar alle,
wenn man sie von einer folgenden Höhe übersieht,
in die Länge Nord und Südwärts gezogen, aber
etwas ungleich und gebrochen sind. Diese Anhöhen sind trocken und arm, in den Grunden aber
ist hie und da gutes Land, auch Kalch und Mer-
gelboden, und schon viele Einwohner. Auf dem
Rücken eines Hügels, hinter Brinkars-Mill, ist
ein See von einer Meile im Umfang, an dessen
Rand ich Bruchstücke, von einer aus abgerundeten, glatten, perlförmigen, milchweissen Quarzkörnern, durch kein sichtbares Verbindungsmittel
zusammengeleimten Felsart, fand. Dieser See
hat auch auf diesem Hügel kein höheres Land um
sich. Es sollen noch einige andere Bergseen in
diesen Gegenden seyn.

H 3
4) Der

4) Der Pokono. — Von Dieters aus reiset man durch enge Thäler und Flächen, kommt einigemal durch den sich stark windenden Pokono-krief; und siehet längst der Strasse nichts denn tausende von blätterichten, tafelförmigen, dickern und dünnern Sandstein-Bruchstücken. Sechs Meilen von Dieters kommt man zu Sebitzens Haus, meist immer aufwärts steigend; zwey Meilen hinter dem Hause passirt man durch eine breite Kluft, (Gape,) an deren Seiten sich seine Wände noch hoch erheben; und über einige kleine Anhöhen und Vertiefungen, hat man noch etwa 4 Meilen weiter nach dem White-Oak-Run, an der Westseite dieses Berges. — Man siehet längst des Weges nichts, denn schaalichten Sandstein in Bruchstücken.

Von Sebitzens Hause am Pokono, bis nach Wyoming sinds 37½ englische Meilen, durch eitel dicken Wald, Sumpf und Wildniffe; der Weg ist gräßlich; nur 6 Fuß breit, zwischen hohen Bäumen ausgehauen, und mit Steinen dick besäet. Dieser ganze Geburgsstrich ist theils unter dem Namen von St. Antonius Wildniß, theils des grossen Sumpfs, (the great Swamp), bekannt.

Vom

Vom White-Oak-Run, hat man theils sanften Abhang, theils schmale Flächen und unebenen Boden, bis man an den eigentlichen Anfang des
grossen Sumpfes kommt, den man 51 Meilen lang
schätzet. Die mehr ausgezeichneten Reihen, die
man passirt, sind:

5) Ein Rücken (Ridge), von hauptsächlich röthlichtem Sandstein: jenseits fließt der Tunkahannok-
Kriek;

6) zwischen diesem und dem Tobyhannok-Kriek —
eine andere Reihe, von röthlichtem Sandstein und
vieler rother thonichter Erde.

7) Etwas ebenes Land, dann ein hoher Berg, der
Locust-hill, rother lettichter Boden, und röth-
lichter schaalichter Sandstein; er hat einen steilen
langen Abhang nach Westen, gegen den Leheigh-
kriek, und bildet mit dem nächstfolgenden Berge
ein enges tiefes Thal, wo unter den hohen
Gipfeln der Bäume Kälte und Dunkelheit herrscht,
und das seines schaudernden Anblicks wegen, die
Schatten des Todes, (Shades of Death) genannt wird.

H 4   8) Vom

8) Vom Leheigh aufwärts, einen steilen hohen Berg; der nemliche Sandstein, aber grau und graublaulicht; jenseits einen längern, weniger jähen Abhang nach dem **Bear-Swamp-Kriek** (Bären-Sumpf-Bach.)

9) Vom Bach an, erst steil aufwarts, denn mehr gemächlich Berg an, über einen Rücken von weisserem und feinerem Sandstein; jenseits ein langer und sanfter Abhang nach einem Bergthal, oder in eine hohe ziemliche Ebene, **Bullocks-Meadows,** auch die lange Wiese genannt.

10) Von diesem Bergthal, eine geringe Anhöhe, auf der Westseite aber tiefer und steiler Abhang.

Hier findet sich rother Letten und allerley Sandsteine. An einigen steilern Stellen aber, theils Bruchstücke, theils stehender nackter Fels, aus grössern oder kleinern, scharfen, weissen, enge und genau unter sich vereinigten Quarzkörnern; ohne Beymischung eines fremden sichtbaren Bindemittels. Dergleichen Stellen kommen hoch oben am Berge vor; der Gipfel selber ist aber doch mit dem blätterichten Sandstein überlegt.

11) Ein

11) Ein anderer Rücken — enthält an der Ostseite
weissen, an der Westseite rothen Sandstein; hie
und da rothen Letten, und grobförnichte Quarz-
Fels-Bruchstücke.

12) Ein anderer Rücken; sein östlicher Abhang, nicht
beträchtlich, hat ähnlichen quarzichten Fels, nach
der Mitte hoch und oben blos liegend; übrigens
aber und nach dem Gipfel, rothen und grauen
Sandstein; sein westlicher Abhang nach dem Laurel-
Run, (Lorbeer-Bach), wenn ich nicht irre, ist
steil und hoch; von diesem Bach hat man noch

13) und 14) zwey mässige Hügel oder Reihen vor
sich, um an den östlichen Arm der Susquehannah
zu kommen, an welcher Wyoming lieget.

Man ist aber hier noch nicht über das gesammte
Geburge weg, sondern hat noch einige Reihen westlich,
die mit den Bald-Eagle-Mountains (Bald-Eagle) und
weiter hin mit der Alleghany-Ridge einzutreffen
scheinen.

So weit ich mir also, auf einen engen Weg eingeschränkt, und ohne weitere Nachrichten von den Ein-

H 5   woh-

wohnern erhalten zu können, einen Begriff über die Anlage dieses Theils vom Gebürge machen kann, ist es folgender.

Es bestehet aus mehrern hintereinander, meist parallel laufenden Reihen; ich habe nur die am deutlichsten ausgezeichneten angemerkt.

Die Grundlage des Ganzen, ist nicht Granit; sondern die erwähnte Felsart, welche aus scharfen, eckichten, weissen, halbdurchsichtigen, genau in einander passenden Quarzkörnern, bald grössern, bald kleinern, bestehet, zwischen welchen keine bindende Materie gesehen werden kann (*). Ich habe keine Probestücke vor mir, erinnere mich aber, daß ich die so beschriebene Felsart oft und genau besehen. Diese Felsart kommt an der Ostseite, und am Fluß des Kittatinny, hinter Easton vor, wo man sie gemeinhin Mühlenstein (Millstone) nennt, weil sie dazu vorzüglich gut gefunden, und nach Philadelphia von da verführt wird; sie kommt aber auch an der Westseite, nach Wyoming zu, vor, und dies berechtigt mich zu glauben, daß sie die Stütze, die Grundlage des Gebürges, und der folgenden aufgeschichteten blätterichten Felsarten sey.

(*) An Saxum quartzosum acutangulum albidum — Linn. ? nisi Cos molaris L. —

sey. Ob sie selber irgendwo in Lagen, in Blättern, oder in ganzen Massen liegt, habe ich nicht Gelegenheit gehabt, mich zu überzeugen.

Sämmtliche Berg-Reihen oder Rücken sind mit einer blätterichten Sandsteinart, nur gedeckt, oder überlegt, aber freylich oft in hoch angehäuften Schichten. Sie haben einen mehr oder weniger feinen weissen Sand zum Grunde, der durch beygemischte fremde Theile, oder auch gefärbten Sand, bald röthlich, grau, blaulicht ꝛc. erscheint, und so eine Reihe von der andern, eine Seite von der andern auszeichnet. Angehaucht geben die meisten einen Thongeruch; auf dem Bruch lassen sie sich hie und da schaben; an der Rinde aber sind sie hart. Sie brechen in Blättern von $\frac{1}{4}$ — 2 Zoll dick, die zwar ein solides Stück zu machen scheinen; bey genauerer Untersuchung aber entdeckt man mehrere, dünne, dicht aufeinander liegende Blättchen. Glimmer scheinen sie nur sehr wenig, sehr feinen selten zu haben; wenn mich nicht glänzende Sandförner betrogen. Sie gehören sämmtlich zu dem Geschlecht der Wezsteine, (Cos), liefern allerley Arten davon, und sind auch allgemein, unter dem Namen Grindstone und Whetstone, dafür bekannt und gebraucht.

Unter

Unter der Wezſtein-Rinde liegt auch öfters noch, eine etwas ſolidere Felsart, aus feinerem gleichgemiſchten Sande beſtehend, die die Einwohner Gritſtone nennen; ich habe aber auf dieſem Weg nur weniges davon geſehen.

Die oberſte Wezſtein-Rinde iſt überall geborſten, und erfüllt mit ihren Trümmern, alle ebene und abhängige Stellen und Orte.

Man hat einige Spuren von Eiſen und Kupfer, in dieſen Gegenden. Um Wyoming hat man Eiſen-Sumpferz, und Anzeigen von andern Metallen.

36.

Berg-Reihen zwiſchen Schippensburgh und Pittsburg am Ohio.

Schippensburg iſt das lezte Städtchen, das man auf der gemeinen Straſſe von Philadelphia nach dem Ohio im groſſen Kalchthal trift. Die Straſſe wendet ſich von da weſtlich, und gehet noch 4 — 6 Meilen über kalchichten Boden, nach dem blauen Berge oder Kittatinny hin; kurz vor welchem man über einige an ihn lehnende Hügel von loſen Schiefergeſchieben kommt, die noch mit grobem Sand und abgerundeten

Kie-

Kiefeln überlegt find. Der blaue Berg fowohl, als der
South-Mountain, erfcheinen in der Gegend von der
Ferne fteiler und höher als gewöhnlich; lezterer, den
man links im Geficht hat, fällt aber gleich nachher beträchtlich ab; fo fchneidet fich auch der Kittatinny hier
plözlich ab, und verliert fich in einen erhabenen abgerundeten Gipfel, Parnells Knob genannt; man wird
es aber nicht fogleich gewahr, fondern indem man auf
einer fich oft windenden Straffe, zwifchen hohen Waldungen hinreifet, erblickt man, mit nicht geringer
Verwunderung, auf einmal erftgenannten Parnell's
Knob hinter fich, den man erft glaubte überfteigen zu
müffen. Es ift nemlich hier die Wand des Kittatinny
auf einige Meilen ganz unterbrochen; erhebt fich erft
wieder weiter fübwärts, und erleichtert fo den Eingang
in das Gebürge. Ein unbeträchtlicher Fluß der größern
Conecacheague-Kriek kommt hier aus dem Gebürge. An
dem Wege, der um diefes Bergende (*) herum führt,
finden fich quarzichte Felsftein-Bruchftücke, von mittel-
mäffig feinem Korn; man nennt ihn hier Free-ftone,

bedient

(*) Nach Sculls Karte vereinigt fich von Nordoften her,
im Parnells Knob, die Conecacheague-Ridge mit dem Kittatinny, und laffen zwifchen fich das Horfe-Vallay, und andere Thäler.

bedient sich seiner aber doch auch zu Mühlsteinen; es
finden sich auch Wezsteine, und in dem Thal, das sich
rechts hinauf und Nordostwärts hinter dem Kittatinny
ziehet, Path-Valley genannt, auch Kalchstein. Auf
den Gipfeln der Berge ist gutes Ackerland, und einige
sind bewohnt.

Die Strasse gehet erst etwas nördlich, ehe sie
über den nächstfolgenden Berg kommt, und an dessen
Fuß fort, der hier erst die Cove-Ridge, weiter hin
aber der Tuskarora heißt. Die Cove-Ridge, mit
einigen andern gebrochenen Reihen, umschließt zwey
fruchtbare und bewohnte Thäler, die grosse und kleine Cove.

Der Tuskarora, die zweyte Reihe, hat am
Fusse sowohl als weiter aufwärts, röthlichen Sandstein, und röthlichen Quarz, in dessen Ritzen häufig kleine Krystallen anzutreffen. Er ist mässig hoch,
die Strasse gehet aber nach verschiedenen Wendungen
durch die Thäler mit einem male steil die Wand hinauf.

Auf seinem Rücken finden sich grosse Bruchstücke einer
Jaspisartigen Felsart. Sie ist dunkel rothbraun; sehr hart,
giebt stark Feuer; ist auf dem Bruche wenig convex; von

nicht

nicht sehr feinem oft schuppichten Korn, matt mit kleinen
glänzenden Punkten; giebt angehaucht keinen Geruch;
bey genauerer Betrachtung aber, und besonders wenn
naß gemacht, entdeckt es sich deutlich, daß sie aus
dünnen, übereinander liegenden, aber äusserst fest und
innigst vereinigten Blättern bestehe, die sich durch
so viele parallele blässere Streifen verrathen. Die
Stücke geben gegeneinander geschlagen einen hellen
klingenden glockenähnlichen Ton.

Um und an dem Tuskarora fanden sich auch kleine
Stücken, von der oben erwähnten quarzichten, perl-
förmigt-abgerundeten Felsart. Am häufigsten aber
deckte ihn ein grauer Sandstein, der hier doch nicht so
regelmässige Blätter zeigte. Der westliche Abhang des
Berges ist lang und gemächlich, von der Höhe herab
bis Fort Littleton sinds 10 Meilen, über niedrige Hügel und durch verschiedene Thäler; man findet abwechselnd rothen Boden, weissen Sand und Sandstein,
Letten und mergelichten Boden. Kalch ist in den benachbarten Thälern, in Cove-Aughwick und Shirley-
Valley. Fort Littleton liegt in einer etwas niedern
Gegend; ehe man aber ganz hinkommt, siehet man
rechts zwey Bergreihen, nemlich die Shade-Mountain-Ridge, und die Black-Log-Ridge, sich in
der

der Gegend abschneiden, und gleichsam für die Bequem-
lichkeit der Strasse Plaz lassen; links aber einige Berge, die zu den Cove-Mountains gehören. Man hat
also, wenn man das Fort erreicht, eigentlich bereits
4 Bergreihen hinter sich, ohne sie alle überstiegen zu
haben. Und von da aus hat man noch weiter
9 Meilen einen ziemlich guten, meist ebenen Weg;
über rothen lettichten Grund, und hier und da Thonlagen in niedrigen Hügeln, bis an den Fuß der nächsten Haupt-Reihe. Man findet Eisen, und schöne
Kryllalle in diesen Gegenden.

Sideling-Hill-Ridge macht nunmehr die fünf-
te Bergreihe, die man auf diesem Wege sieht, und noch
immer, wie die vorigen, von Südwesten und Süd sich
nach Norden und Nordost ziehen. Es ist dieser einer
der ansehnlicheren Berge; und ziemlich steil und stei-
nigt zu ersteigen; auf seinem breiten Rücken aber hat
er verschiedene breite und ebene Flächen, oder weniger
gebrochenes Land. Er enthält die meisten der ange-
merkten Felsarten. Feine und grobkörnichte Quarz-
stücke, mit scharfen Körnern dann mit abgerundeten
weissen Körnern; groben Wezsteine in dicken Schaalen, und von verschiedenen Farben, an den Seiten
und auf dem Gipfel; hie und da auch etwas feinern
Wez-

Wezstein; lange Strecken von seinem quarzigten losen Sand, sind ganz oben; auch der Grit-stein, (Grit-stone) kommt vor; hier besteht er aus kleinen Quarzkörnern, mit feinem Sand, seltener und kleiner Blende und einigen schwarzen (Schörl?) Körnern. Sein westlicher Abhang beträgt nicht viel; in der Richtung aber, die die Strasse nimmt, steigt man nicht ganz herab in das Thal, das ihn von dem nächstfolgenden scheidet, sondern folgt einigen Vorsprüngen (Spurs), durch welche er mit

Rayshill zusammenhängt; welcher weiter süblich auch der Ragged-hill, und weiter nördlich der River-hill genannt wird, übrigens aber mit dem vorigen von einerley Beschaffenheit und Struktur ist; und mit ihm vielleicht nur einen breiten gegründeten Berg ausmacht. Der westliche Abhang von Rayshill ist beträchtlich und lang. Zwischen seinem Fuß und dem östlichen Fuß von Sibelinghill hat man wenigstens 10 englische Meilen, und mehr. Man kommt nachher noch einige Meilen über kleine vorliegende Hügel von rothem Sand- oder Wezstein, und röthlichten Letten, und hat doch noch einen kurzen aber steilen Abhang über Crossing-hill, an dessen Fuß, welchen ich für den eigentlichen Fuß des Rays-hill ansehe, man erst dem Juniatafluß erreicht. Dieser lezte Abhang, auf der Wasserseite,

zeigt durchaus zoll. (mehr oder weniger) dicke Schichten von dunkelrothem Wezstein; mit Lagen von grauem,
theils zwischen dem rothen, theils über ihn, auf dem
Gipfel.

In dem rothen Wezstein läßt sich, wie in den übrigen weiter vorkommenden dieser Art, nichts unterschei-
ben; sie haben fein gemahlnen Sand zur Basis; geben
angehaucht einen Thongeruch; schaben sich blaß; schlagen kein Feuer; er hat wie andere dieser Wezsteine,
kleine schimmernde Punkte, die aber schwerlich Glimmer sind.

Jenseits der Juniata, (die hier erst gerade von
Westen nach Osten entgegen kommt, sich kurz um einen
vorspringenden Hügel wendet, und an dessen andern
Seite eine Strecke den entgegengesetzten Weg nimmt,
bis sie endlich Nordostwärts ihren Lauf nimmt,) gehet
die Strasse über den Rücken einer schmalen und niedrigen Anhöhe beynahe 4 Meilen, an dessen beyden
Seiten man die Juniata links und rechts, an einigen
Stellen kaum eine halbe Meile von einander hier nach
Osten, dort nach Westen fliessen siehet. Dieser Aus-
sprung ist ganz mit röthlichten Sandsteinen, in Blättern, belegt, deren Bruchstücke man hier sowohl, als

anber-

anderwärts, sehr häufig in beynahe vollkommenen Vier-
ecken erblickt. Es führt dieser Ausſprung ziemlich unmerklich aufſteigend, nach der ſiebenten Hauptreihe,
welches die

Alleguippy-Ridge iſt; ungeachtet man nicht über
ihren höchſten Rücken, ſondern durch eine Vertiefung
kommt, ſo hat man doch an der Weſtſeite wieder einen
beträchtlichen Abhang vor ſich; und noch immer die
nemlichen blättrichten Santſteine, die in der Gegend in
beſonders regelmäſſigen Schichten, von allerley Farben
und unterſchiedener Feinheit erſcheinen. Die Bruchſtücke, wie ſie am Weg lagen, hatten öfters gröbere
dendritiſche Zeichnungen auf ihrer Oberfläche. Nachdem
man wieder herab und das nördliche Ufer der Juniata
erreicht hat, ſo führt der Weg längſt dieſes Fluſſes
bis nach dem Städtchen Bedford, meiſt eben; vor-
hero aber paſſirt man noch die von dieſem Fluſſe ge-
theilte oder geſpaltene anſehnliche hohe Wände des

Evits-Mountains, wenn ich nicht irre, auch
Great-Warriors-Mountain genannt; ſeine offne immer
abrollende Seiten ſind ſteil, und endigen ſich an bey-
ten Seiten des Fluſſes in hohe Kuppen. Die unten
liegenden Bruchſtücke ſind eine Art Gritſtone; ſeiner

J 3   quarzich-

quarzichter grieslichter Sand, fest und hart; meistens weis, hie und da etwas röthlich, oder mit röthlichten Adern; die ganze Wände erscheinen meist weis, und man sieht keine Schichten, wenn sie nicht von den losen Geschieben überdeckt und unbemerkbar gemacht sind.

Weiter hin und näher gegen Bedford, wird das Gebürge etwas niedriger, und der Fluß gehet durch eine offnere hügelichte Landschaft; nunmehro trifft man aber schon theils grauen, theils schwärzlichen Kalchstein an, der größtentheils den Zwischenraum, vom letztern Berg bis zum Alleghany, ausfüllt, und sich hie und da in mässig hohe und den vorigen parallele Reihen erhebt; dies bemerkt man unter andern am deutlichsten on

Wills-Mountain, der sich südlich gegen Fort Cumberland am Potomack, und nördlich nach Frankstown ziehet, und fruchtbare Thäler um sich hat. Am Wege kamen Bruchstücke von dem Kalchstein vor, der theils weisse Adern, theils kleine leere Löcher hatte, worinn vermuthlich Spatkrystallen gesessen hatten. In der Gegend um Bedford scheinen zwar diese Kalchhügel unordentlich und verwirrt zu seyn, man muß aber erwägen, daß die Flüsse und Wasser mehr Eindruck auf

sie

sie machen, sie in verschiedener Richtung durch- und
ausgraben, und so verschiedene anscheinliche Fronten geben. Viele von ihnen sind doch auch mit sandigten
Geschieben überlegt.

Bey 6 — 7 Meilen von Bedford gehet die Strasse
noch in Thälern fort, und man hat bald Kalchstein,
grobe Kiesel und Flint, (Silices), bald Sand- und
Gritsteine auf den Seiten. Nachher aber erhebt sich
der Weg, und gehet bey 12 — 13 Meilen über ein
schmales vorspringendes Gebürge des nächsten Bergs,
lange und viel aufwärts; oben aber hat man einen
theils ebenen, theils gemach auf und ab gebogenen
Rücken, und sieht nichts als die vorhin erwähnten rothen
Weßsteine, in kleinen, sehr häufig viereckichten Tafeln.
Dieser ganze Vorsprung (Spur) heißt die Dry-Ridge,
(trockne Höhe), weil man kein Wasser auf seinen engen
Rücken findet; sie gehet vorzüglich Südwest, und an
beyden Seiten bemerkt man andere ihr ähnliche; sie
machen das Vorgebürg des Alleghany, oder man hält
sie für Zweige von ihm. Am Ende der 12 Meilen hat
man einen ziemlichen Abhang nach Westen, und kommt
dann an Irelands-Run; und etwa zwey Meilen
weiter, über einen andern niedrigen Hügel, endlich
selber an den Fuß des

J 3

Alleg-

Alleghany-Berges — der da, wo die Straße
sich ihm nähert, eine gerade Wand vorstellet, so weit
man ihn übersehen kann. Man hat etwa eine Meile
auf einen windenden Weg bis hinauf, und dann einen
sanften Abhang von einigen Meilen, über eitel schaa-
lichte Bruchstücke von Wetzsteinen, (Grindstone), welcher beyde Seiten des Berges deckt: weißlicht mit roth
untermischt; grau; röthlicht; schwärzlicht; dieser lezte
hat einige feine glänzende (Glimmer?) Punkte; die andern scheinen nichts davon zu haben; sie sind von verschiedener Härte; an den steilern Seiten des Weges
sieht man sie in Schaalen, von $\frac{1}{2}$ — 1 — 2 — 4 Zoll
übereinander liegen, oder aus der Erde hervorragen.
Man hat mich versichert, daß diese Reihe bis nach
Südkarolina gehe, und die nemliche Felsarten und
Struktur behalte. Doch zeigen sich auch Spuren von
quarzichtem und körnichtem Gestein.

Dieser Bergrücken und Reihe wird für einen der
höchsten, oder für den höchsten gehalten, welches auch
seine Lage, und die Richtung der vielen von ihm aus-
gehenden Flüsse, an der Ost- und Westseite des ge-
sammten Gebürges zu glauben berechtiget. Er selber
erscheint nicht hoch, und raget auch nicht sehr über
die andern hervor; allein sein Grund ist schon hoch.
Von

Von ihm herab kommt man in die sogenannten Glades (*), unter welcher Benennung man hier ein Bergthal, oder niedere, freyere und breite Gegenden zwischen dem Gebürge versteht. Diese Glades, welche
man zum Unterschied von andern im Gebürg, die langen, oder die grossen nennt, sind von 8 — 10 — 12
Meilen breit, zwischen den beyden angränzenden Bergreihen; und man kennt sie bey 40 — 60 Meilen nach
der Länge; sie haben viel gutes Land und schon zahl-
reiche Bewohner. Im Grossen genommen, ist es ein
hochgelegenes Thal, das aber von kleinern und niedern
Hügeln verschiedentlich durchschnitten ist; es enthält
vielen Kalchstein; seine westliche Gränze ist der

Laurell-hill, nach dessen Rücken, von den Glä-
des aus, man aber so einen mässigen Aufweg hat,
als vom Alleghany herab in die Glades. Sein Rücken
ist breit, und hat hie und da gutes Land; mitunter aber
grosse Strecken mit Bruchstücken von schaalichtem Wezstein besäet, und dick übereinander liegend; und noch
mehr so längst seines westlichen Abhangs, der verschiedene Meilen lang und oft jähe ist. Man rechnet 14

J 4   Mei-

(*) Nach dem Wortverstand, eine Oeffnung, ein freyer
langer Plaz in einem Wald.

Meilen, von dem Fuſſe des Berges in den Glades, bis
an ſeinen andern Fuß, und findet keine Wohnung auf
dieſem Weg. Seine Struktur und Felsarten ſind die
nemlichen wie der vorhergehenden.

Vom Laurellhill ſagt man, daß er in dieſen Gegenden erſt vom Alleghany ausgehe; oder mich deutlicher auszudrücken, daß ſeine ausgezeichnete Reihe, die
von Südweſten herkommt, ſich etwas Nord von hier,
gegen den Alleghany anſchlieſſe oder verliere. — Nach
ihm hat man noch die

Chesnut-Ridge zu überſteigen, welche zwar unbeträchtlich, aber noch von ähnlicher Struktur iſt. Sie
iſt die eilfte der am vorzüglichſten ſich auszeichnenden
Bergreihen, die ich auf dieſem Wege beobachtet habe,
und die weſtlichſte der eigentlicheren Gebürgsreihen.
Von ihr aus ſinds noch etwa 35 Meilen nach dem
Ohio; und dieſen Raum füllen mehrere niedere Hügel,
auf denen man aber ſchier durchgehends doch nichts
anders als röthlichten, oder grauen ſchaalichten Wezſtein findet. Im Ganzen aber ſind ſie mit ungleich
beſſerem, fetterem, braunſchwarzem Boden überlegt,
und man vermißt nunmehro die blaßrothe, ſandigt-
lettichte Oberfläche der Landſchaften, auf der Morgen-
ſeite

seite des Gebürges gänzlich. Näher nach dem Ohio
hin, und in einigen andern Thälern, findet sich Kalchstein.
Die Breite der Gebürge zwischen der Ostseite des Kittatinny, und der Westseite der Chesnut-ridge möchte
etwa 120 englische Meilen betragen, nach der Strasse
gerechnet; im geraden Durchschnitt aber weniger.

Die Haupteinrichtung der Gebürge von dieser
Seite ist also der im vorigen Abschnitt erwähnten ganz
ähnlich. Sie haben nemlich eine Grundlage von
quarzichter Felsart; sind ohne Ausnahme, Seiten und
Gipfel, mit blättrichten Steinarten überlegt; streichen
alle mehr oder weniger von Südwest nach Nordost, und
haben Kalchstein nur in ihren Thälern.

Sie enthalten Spuren von verschiedenen Erzen hie
und da; aber noch wenig untersucht, entdeckt und bekannt. Es findet sich Eisen in Menge; Anzeigen von
Kupfer, und Bley im Ueberfluß; sie haben ferner Zink,
Vitriole, Alaun, Schwefel, Salpeter und Salz.

37.

Ausser den in den vorigen Abschnitten erwähnten
Felsarten, finden sich eine Menge anderer und verschiedener Erd- und Steinarten, auf und unter der Ober-

J 5 fläche

fläche dieses amerikanischen Geburges und seiner Vor-
geburge. Man hat aber noch zu wenige Data, um
etwas über ihre Anordnung zu sagen.

Ueberhaupt genommen aber, ist die allgemeinere
oberste Decke der Fels- oder Kieselreihen sowohl, als der
Kalchsteinlagen, längst der erhabenern trockenern Stellen, eine röthlichte aus Sand und Letten ge-
mischte Bodenart von verschiedener Tiefe; die, ebenfalls vom trocknen Lande gemeynt, nur eine dünne
Decke von schwarzer Gartenerde hat. Und durchgängig
findet man Eisenerde, Eisenmulm, oder überhaupt Ei-
sentheile in mancherley Gestalt, über diese sämmtliche
Oberfläche reichlich verbreitet und den andern beygemischt.

Thonlagen, von verschiedenen Arten, Güte,
Farbe und Härte, sind häufig hie und da in den nie-
d'rn Gegenden, Thälern, an den Füssen und Seiten
niedriger Hügel, anzutreffen. Ich konnte nicht bemerken, daß sie irgendwo eine besondere Richtung, oder
Lage beobachten, sondern es scheint vielmehr, daß sie
Zufallsweise an einem oder dem andern Ort zusammenge-
schlemmt worden sind, und die, von andern Materien un-
ausgefüllten Plätze eingenommen haben. Man hat ziemlich
fei-

feinen Porcellainthon, Töpferthon, Ocherartigen, und
andere, die dem Spanischbraun nahe kommen, oder
sonst zum Anstreichen gebraucht werden können.

Schieferwände und Betten, sind in den Thälern
des Hauptgebürges, und der vorliegenden, und längst
der Flüsse (*) daselbst sehr gemein. Sie finden sich
immer an der abhängenden Seite der übrigen Höhen,
Hügel oder Berge, an Feinheit, Farbe und Härte
ebenfalls verschieden. Die Schiefer liegen eben so oft
auf den quarzichten Felsarten, als auf dem Kalchstein;
auch Quarzfelsen, Kalchstein und Schiefer übereinander.
Abdrücke von Farnkräutern habe ich in den Schiefer-
wänden bey Wyoming, an der Susquehannah gefunden.

Markasite oder Schwefelkies, gelb und weis, in
Nieren und in Blättgens, finden sich häufig an und
zwischen den Schiefern im Gebürge.

Ostwärts vom Gebürg aber, hat man in Vergleichung gegen das Hauptgebürg und seiner westlichen
Gegenden, noch wenige und nicht mächtige Schiefer-
betten

(*) Kalm 2ter Theil, S. 469.

betten gefunden. Der meiste dieſſeits der Berge, iſt bis
daher längſt einigen Ufern der Flüſſe, um Nelſons
Ferry am Susquehannah, am Schuylkill, am Slate-
River in Virginien ꝛc. ꝛc. und dieſer iſt nicht überall
der beſte.

Mit dem Schiefer, und unter oder zwiſchen ihm,
finden ſich gemeiniglich im Gebürge, wenn das Bette
tief genug iſt, Steinkohlen. An mehrern Orten, beſonders wo die Kohlen an Flußwänden zu Tage aus-
ſtreichen, wie bey Wyoming, und bey Pittsburg ꝛc.
zeigt der unläugbare Augenſchein, daß Kohlen und
Schiefer einerley Urſprung gehabt haben müſſen. Grober ſandichter dickblätterichter Schiefer, liegt an ſolchen
Orten ganz oben; nimmt aber tiefer herab an Feinheit
der Blätter, und an Schwärze immer mehr und mehr
zu, bleibt im Ganzen aber doch weicher und bröcklich-
ter, als bloſſer Thonſchiefer, bis er ganz allmählich in
eine Ader von dichten, glänzenden, ungleich brockich-
ten Kohlen ſich verliert; oft ſind dieſe Adern zwar nur
unbeträchtlich dünne, und nur kohlenartige Schiefer
(Brandſchiefer); oft aber auch ſehr mächtig; wie die am
Ohio, welche durchaus auch blättericht angelegt ſind.
Die Kohlen um Wyoming und anderwärts, hatten
wieder groben Schiefer zur Unterlage; die am Ohio
baben

haben Marmor unter sich; ob aber unmittelbar, weiß
ich nicht. Daß diese Kohlen, aus vormaliger ange-
häufter Torf- oder Moorerde, durch Gährung und
Pressung (*) entstanden, leidet wohl keinen Zweifel.
In dem Schieferdache der Wyomings-Kohlen, finden
sich die oben erwähnte Pflanzen-Abdrücke. Die Kohlen kommen nur in den Thälern der Gebürge, und da
in verschiedener Teufe vor. Wo sie zu Tag ausbre-
chen, geschieht es blos durch Gelegenheit der Flüsse
oder Bäche, die sich ihren Weg durchgegraben, und sie
so an den Bänken oft hoch über dem Wasser blos ge-
lassen. Der Hügel gegenüber von Pittsburg ist zwar
über 100 Fuß hoch, und ziemlich steil gegen den Mo-
nangbahela; die sehr mächtige Kohlenlage mag ungefähr in der Mitte des Hügels seyn, so daß man mit
gar geringer Mühe die gebrochenen Kohlen, durch Gräben, gerade herab in die unten stehende Boote schaffen
kann; der ganze Hügel besteht aber dennoch nur aus
Flözen.

Merkwürdig ist in der Absicht, daß die meisten,
oder wenigstens viele Schiefergeschiebe, an solchen
Stellen der Flüsse vorkommen, wo in kleinen Entfer-
nun-

(*) v. Gerolbingen Beobacht. die Mineral. betr. S. 106.

nungen vor ihnen, sogenannte Fälle sind, d. i. wo die
Flüsse über eine untiefe Felsreihe weggehen. Dies ist
der Fall bey Nelsons-Ferry, und bey Wyoming ꝛc.
Aber eben so findet sich das einzige beträchtliche Stein-
kohlenflöz, das man noch bisher an der Ostseite
der Gebürge entdeckt hat, hinter dem Falle des James-
Rivers in Virginien; so findet sich in andern
Gegenden, in ähnlichen Lagen, hinter Wasserfällen
schwarze lockere Dammerde, in der Dicke von 6 — 8 — 10
und mehr Fuß angehäuft, wo noch in den spätern Zeiten sich das nemliche ereignet hat, was länger zurück
zur Entstehung der Schiefer und Kohlen dort Gelegenheit gegeben haben mag, nemlich Stemmung der Flüsse,
oder wenigstens verminderte Geschwindigkeit derselben.

Die schon bemerkten, verhältnißmäſſig seltenen
Schieferlagen, an der Ostseite des Gebürges, mögen
also auch einerley Ursache mit den dießseits eben so seltenen Kohlen haben. Auſſer den so eben genannten
am James-River, hat man nur noch unweit Reading,
und an der Susquehannah, (20 Meilen von Lancaster
bey Elisabeth-Furnace) bisher Kohlen gefunden. Auf
Long-Island sollen welche gefunden worden seyn; und
möglich ist es, denn in seinen sumpfichten Orten hat
es beträchtlichen, obschon nicht bearbeiteten Torfvor-
rath;

rath; die aber dann von nicht so hohem Alter seyn
würden, als erstere. (Weiter nördlich hat man reiche
Kohlengruben in Neuschottland, und Neufoundland.)

In der Nachbarschaft einiger Steinkohlenflöze,
trifft man theils Quellen, theils fließende Wasser an,
auf welchen Bergöl schwimmt; dies ist der Fall bey
Wyoming. Anderwärts aber findet sich Bergöl, oder
Spuren davon, wo man noch keine Kohlen zur Zeit
entdeckt hat; da die Bergöle aber wahrscheinlich Aus-
geburten von den Steinkohlen sind (*), so kann man
in der Folge daher, sie aufzufinden, geleitet werden.

38.

Es gehöret zwar nicht unmittelbar zur Uebersicht
des Gebürgs, aber mit dem Inhalt des vorhergehenden Abschnitts, stehen einige Anmerkungen über die
späteren Veränderungen, so Regen, Flüsse, Ueberschwemmungen auf der Oberfläche von Amerika be-
würkt haben, in näherer Verbindung. Unfruchtbaren
schlechten Boden nennt der amerikanische Landmann
allen den, der nicht 20 — 30 Jahre hinter einander
ohne Düngung reichliche Früchte trägt; und Boden von
                                                    dieser

(*) v. Beroldingen Beobacht. die Mineral. betr. S. 139.

dieser gesegneten Beschaffenheit findet sich häufig, längst
den grösseren und kleineren Strömen, in und vor dem
Geburg, und an den übrigen tiefer gelegenen Stellen,
Sümpfen und Morästen. Hier findet sich alles das
wieder, was Regen und fliessende Wasser, von ihren
ersten Quellen an, dem höhern Boden entzogen haben.
Dieses ist zwar nichts mehr, als was sich überall ereignet; eine Ursache aber scheint es vorzüglicher in
Amerika zu bewürken. Alle die von der Ostseite der
Gebürge kommende Wasser, haben in ihrem Wege
nach dem Atlantischen Meer, durch die beschriebenen
von Nordost nach Südwest streichenden Bergreihen ihren Lauf; und eine gerade gezogene Linie, vom Ursprung der meisten (vielleicht aller?) Flüsse, nach ihrer
Mündung, fällt gerade entgegen gesetzt von Nordwest
nach Südost. Daher die vielfachen sogenannten Fälle, die
der inländischen Bootsfahrt so hinderlich sind; denn jene,
so ich bey der Granitreihe, als die ersteren von der
See herauf, angezeiget, sind nicht die einzigen. Die
Hindernisse, welche die Ströme, besonders bey niedrigem Wasser, in ihrem Lauf finden, geben der von
den höhern Gegenden abgeschwemmten Erde, Schlamm
und Sande Gelegenheit, sich zu setzen. Dies wird am
meisten da geschehen, wo die Hindernisse am beträchtlichsten, und daher findet man hauptsächlich die ergie-

bigsten

bigsten und fettesten Ländereyen, oberhalb jener Fälle, wo es nichts seltenes ist, zwar schmale Striche, die aber doch viele Aecker betragen, von 6 — 8 — 10 und mehr Fuß tief, blosse schwarze Erde von unerschöpflicher Fruchtbarkeit anzutreffen. Wo keine Fälle in der Nähe waren, ist häufig das nemliche, durch die Krümmungen der Flußbetten verursacht worden; denn viele Flüsse, im Gebürge besonders, müssen sich vielfach wenden und drehen, ehe sie ihren Weg zwischen den Reihen durch finden. Die Länge der Flüsse, von ihrem Ursprung zur Mündung, mit allen ihren Aesten, erwogen, läßt es sich leicht vermuthen, daß diese fette Gründe vielfach seyn müssen, und in der That finden sie sich meist überall, wo die Ströme nicht schlechterdings zwischen Felswänden sich zu drängen haben. Die Frühlings- und Herbstregen, die die sogenannten Fluthen (freshes) verursachen, helfen den Vorrath immer unterhalten, und den Abgang der niedern Gegenden ersetzen.

Wo das über die höhern Gegenden sich ergiessende Regen- und sonst sich sammlende Wasser nicht Kanäle findet, sammlen sich Moräste und Sümpfe in den Thälern und flächeren Stellen; so gar an den abhangenden Seiten der Gebürge geschieht das, wo übereinander gestürzte Bäume und Steine einen zufälligen Damm verursachen. Alle dergleichen Stellen, die gleichfalls einen nicht unbeträchtlichen Theil der Oberfläche einnehmen, sind ausserordentlich fruchtbar; nur hat Mangel an Industrie, an Geld und Arbeitern, ihre Benutzung durch die nöthige Vorbereitungen, noch nicht allgemein genug gemacht.

Die Wurzeln der Bäume, die das Gebürge bekleiden, verhinderten daß die Gipfel davon noch nicht kahl gewaschen sind, und vermehren, oder unterhalten wenigstens, durch Blätter, Zweige und Stämme, die obere Lage von Gewächserde; und so bleibt immer ein Vorrath, das, was die Flüsse allenfalls aus den Gründen losreissen und nach der See führen, wieder zu ersetzen. Wo hingegen über die Berge, Wege durchgehauen, oder sonst die obere Kruste bewegt ist, kommen bald die nackten Felsen zum Vorschein. Die beträchtlichsten Flüsse, zwischen dem Hudson und Florida, sind vom Delaware herab zur Roanoke. Die hinter diesem Striche liegenden Gebürge sind höher, und breiten sich in mehr Aeste aus, als die hinter Nord- und Südkarolina und Georgien befindliche Reihen. Virginien hat diesem Umstande die erheblichen Vortheile zu

dan-

tanken, die es von seinen vielen bis zur Granitreihe
schiffbaren Flüssen zieht.

Nachdem die Ströme alle die verschiedenen Hin-
bernisse der ihnen quer vorliegenden Gebürgsreihen
überwunden haben, so kommen sie in die weniger abhangenden Sandflächen; wo folglich ein langsamerer
Lauf ihren Wassern ebenfalls Zeit gestattet, die von
oben herab gebrachte fremde Theile anzulegen. Dies
wird noch mehr, durch die meist bis an die Granitreihe vordringende Fluth und Ebbe begünstiget, indem
zwischen dem Aufhören des einen, und Anfange des andern, die Wasser schier ganz ohne Bewegung sind.
(Slack Water.) — Daher bestehen die niedrigen Ufer
der Flüsse und Kriks, in Maryland, Virginien, Karolina, Georgien ꝛc. größtentheils aus einer schwarzen
fetten, mit kleinem Sande gemischter Gartenerde; und
die so beschaffenen Bänke liegen tiefer, als die sandigte
Fläche, die sie durchschneiden; oder bilden in der Mitte
der Flüsse Eilande, die kaum über die Wasserfläche erhaben, und voll schöner Pflanzen sind. Dergleichen
bald breitere, bald schmälere Ufer, machen eigentlich
das in Karolina und Georgien so schätzbare Reisland
aus. Andere niedere Stellen in den Sandflächen, die
nicht mit fliessenden Wassern in Verbindung stehen,

K 2   samm-

sammlen die Regen ꝛc. von den umliegenden Gegenden,
enthalten ebenfalls auf beträchtliche Tiefe dieselbe fette
Erde, prangen mit dem schönsten Immergrün, und
einem Reichthum von Gewächsen. Diese Moräste, durch
Kunst oder Zufälle ausgetrocknet, werden nachher die
ergiebigsten Torfgruben.

39.

Ich habe bis daher einen Umriß der Anlage des
mittlern und östlichen Theils von Nordamerika entwor-
fen. Mehr durfte ich nicht wagen, als diese Aussen-
linien zu ziehen, weil mehrere Beobachtungen erfor-
derlich sind, um ein vollständigeres Ganzes zu liefern.
Nachdem aber die vorhergehenden Bemerkungen es
deutlich genug erweisen, daß dieser Erdstrich und seine
Gebürge zu den Flözgebürgen gehören, oder wenigstens
sämmtlich mit Flözlagen und Schichten überdeckt sind,
so hat man daher, nach allgemein angenommenen Voraussetzungen, nicht zu zweifeln Ursache, daß sie durch
irgend eine Ueberschwemmung ihre gegenwärtige Bildung
und Beschaffenheit erhalten haben. Beynahe möchte
es unnöthig scheinen, Beweise beyzubringen, daß die
höheren Theile dieses Gebürgs ehemals unter Wasser
gestanden haben, nachdem dieses schon von den ungleich höheren Cordilleras in Südamerika hinlänglich
erwie-

erwiesen ist, und die Höhe der über jenen gestandenen Wassersäulen es als eine nothwendige Folge vermuthen läßt, daß auch diese niedern Gebürge im nördlichen Amerika vom Wasser bedeckt gewesen seyn mußten.

Es fehlt aber auch nicht an eigentlicheren Belegen darüber. In dem schaalichten Sandstein, der die verschiedenen Reihen der endlosen Gebürge deckt, finden sich Abdrücke von Seemuscheln; nicht in dem Stein selber, sondern zwischen seinen Lagen. Am Alleghann und bey den warmen Quellen (Warm-Springs) in Virginien, hatte ich das Vergnügen, Abdrücke von kleineren Pectiniten in schaalichtem Wetzstein, und Entrochiten aufzulesen; an beyden Orten aber nur an den niederen Theilen der Berge. Ob jemand sie auf den Rücken eines oder des andern Berges gesehen, konnte ich nicht erfragen. Sie scheinen auch nicht in einer übergrossen Menge vorzukommen, wenigstens war die Verwunderung über die wenigen, so ich gefunden, Bürge für ihre Seltenheit, aber zugleich hinlänglicher Beweis für die Sache selbst. Vielleicht ist es nur Mangel an Aufmerksamkeit, daß man sie nicht häufiger entdecket, und nach Evans Zeugnisse müssen sie wohl an einigen Gegenden des Gebürges zahlreich seyn; ich war aber, aller Aufmerksamkeit ungeachtet, nicht so glücklich als

K 3

er,

er, welcher versichert: „daß die Steine in allen Thei-
„len des Gebürges voll von Seemuscheln sind. Nicht
„etwa nur in den durch die Thäler zerstreuten losen
„Steinen findet man sie, sondern auch auf den Gipfeln
„der Berge. Ich sahe, sagt Evans, einige mit dem
„felsichten Grund eines hohen Berges vermischt; und
„in Wishoochon-Creeck fand ich einen weichen Stein,
„5 — 6 Fuß lang, voll von allen Sorten von Mu-
„scheln, als hätte man sie in einen Klumpen braunen
„Thons geknetet; da war alle die Verschiedenheit, die
„man sich denken konnte, unter andern eine grosse
„Korbmuschel (Escolop) mit Bändern, so schön als die
„von den Jakobsmuscheln (Cockles). „

Viele Versteinerungen finden sich auf Waldons-
Ridge, einen Arm des Allighani-Gebürges, zwischen
Virginien und Kentucke, wo der ganze obere Theil
des Gebürges eine Fuß hohe Lage von Muscheln enthält; ich habe aber noch keine davon in der Hand gehabt, um zu bestimmen, ob die Mutter Sand oder
was anders ist. —

In der Nähe von Huntingdon an der Juniata,
bewundert man den sogenannten stehenden Stein,
(standing Stone) der gleichfalls ganz mit Muscheln angefüllt seyn soll.

Die

Die Kalchschichten und Hügel in den Thälern sollen ebenfalls hie und da, aber selten und nur auf ihrer Oberfläche, Beyspiele davon liefern. Ich erhielte
einige unvollkommene Nachrichten darüber zu Bedford;
man konnte mir aber die Stelle nicht mehr zeigen, wo
man Muscheln, schon vor mehreren Jahren, in Kalchstein gesehen zu haben sich erinnerte.

40.

Von den Landschaften, jenseits der Gebürge, kenne
ich zwar nichts aus eigner Erfahrung; verschiedene
mündliche Nachrichten von andern Reisenden aber,
stimmen mit der kurzen und allgemeinen Beschreibung,
die Evans davon gegeben, genau überein. „Nordwest-
„lich von den endlosen Gebürgen, sind flachere und
„weit ausgedehnte Gegenden, die gewissermassen so
„hoch als die Berge selbst sind. Man bemerkt ihre
„ausserordentlich hohe Lage und Erhabenheit über die
„Oberfläche der See, am auffallendsten da, wo sie
„steil gegen den Hudsonfluß abgeschnitten sind, wie
„z. E. an dessen westlichen Ufern, unterhalb Albany;
„denn die Höhen von Raats-Kill, obschon sie erha-
„bener scheinen, als andere Berge dieser Gegend von
„Amerika, sind doch auf ihren Rücken nur die Fort-
„setzung der Ebenen, die mit steil abgeschnittenen Wän-

K 4   den

„den hier gegen Kinder-hoock Fronte machen.
„Diese erhabeneren Flächen (Upper Plains) enthalten
„ausserordentlich fruchtbares und ebenes Land, und er-
„strecken sich vom Mohawkfluß durch das Land der
„verbündeten Indianer. Ihre nördliche Gränzen sind
„in kurzer Entfernung vom See Ontario; wie weit
„sie sich aber westlich erstrecken, ist unbekannt, denn
„die weitläuftigen Ebenen des Ohio sind nur ein
„Theil davon, die sich nach Westen hin immer mehr
„und mehr erweitern, und jenseits des Mißißippi
„ziehen (*); eine Reihe gebrochener Hugel macht
„10 — 15 Meilen südlich vom Ohio ihre mittäliche
„Gränze. Es ist merkwürdig, wie im Hudsonfluß die
„Ebbe und Fluth weit hinauf bis in die Nachbarschaft
„des Ursprungs des Delawares und Susquehannahs
„vor-

(*) „Die grossen Ebenen, die jenseit der Gebürge unter
Kentucke sind, nennt man great und litte Barrens. Die
erstern laufen sehr weit bis über die Mißißippi, sind über
500 Meilen lang und auf 40 Meilen breit; alles flach, kein
Baum, keine Staude, sondern nur das schönste, längste
Gras. Das Land sonst gut, das Wasser lauft nie weit. Es
soll kein Schall entstehen, wenn man schießt, und wenn man
nachgräbt, findet man überall die größten Bäume flach im
Boden liegen. „ —

„vorbringt; da diese zwey Flüsse einen so weiten Weg
„in ihren eigenen Kanälen zu machen haben, ehe sie
„(erst bey der Granitreihe) der Meeresfluth begegnen.
„Die Ursache ist, weil Delaware und Susquehannah
„ihren Ursprung in jenen erhabenen Ebenen selber,
„der Hudsonfluß aber die Ebbe und Fluth an ihrem
„wirklichen Fuß hat. „

Verschiedene Reisende, die die Gegenden zwischen
Fort Pitt, und Detroit, Sandusky, Niagara durchwandert haben, beschreiben solche als grosse ausgedehnte Flächen, die an den meisten Orten mit Manns
hohen Gräsern bewachsen sind. Die anscheinlichen Un-
gleichheiten entstehen vorzüglich nur von den Vertiefungen der Flußbetten; eigentliche Gebürge sollen sich
nicht da vorfinden. Nach den Quellen und der Vertheilung
der vielen Wasser, die von diesen Gegenden um die
Nachbarschaft der Canadischen Seen aus, sich, nach
Westen in den Illinois und Mißißippi, nach Süden in
den Ohio, nach Norden in die Seen und den Laurenzefluß
begeben, gehören sie allerdings schon zu dem erhaben-
nern Antheil dieses Erdstriches; die erhabenste über
der Meeresfläche würde aber denn doch, nach Carvers Bemerkung, noch weiter Nordwestlich, und westlich
von der See, in die Landschaft der Assinipoils und

Nau-

Naudowessies fallen, wo in einem Bezirk von etwa 30 Meilen, 3 — 4 der ansehnlichsten Flüsse von Nordamerika entspringen, deren jeder gegen 2000 englische Meilen bis an die verschiedene Meere, darein sie fallen, zurücklegt (*); diese sind der Laurenz, der Mißißippi, der Bourbon, und der Oregon oder der West-River, davon der erste in Lorenzo-Bay, der zweyte in Hudsons-Bay, der dritte in Mexico-Bay, und der vierte gegen Westen ins Meer läuft.

Die hohe Lage der Gegenden um die Canadischen Seen und der Seen selber, erhellet weiter aus verschiedenen andern Umständen. Viele Bäche und Flüsse entspringen ganz in der Nachbarschaft der Seen, wenden sich aber doch von ihnen westlich oder südlich ab. Der ausserordentliche Fall von Niagara stürzet die Wasser des Sees Erie allein 170 Fuß senkrechter Höhe in den Ontario, von da aus durch den Lorenzo ein langer Abhang ist, bis seine Wasser der Meeresfluth bey Trois-Rivieres begegnen.

Es trennt aber darum doch kein beträchtlicher Fluß, wenn wir den Hudson ausnehmen, die beschriebenen
Gebürgs-

(*) *Carvers* travels pag. 71. die englische Ausgabe.

Geburgs-Reihen, woburch diese hintern Gegenden von
den Südwärts gelegenen abgesondert werden; und man
könnte ohne Bedenken muthmaſſen, daß eben diese Gebürge, zu irgend einer Zeit, Dämme der über den hintern Gegenden geſtandenen Gewäſſer abgegeben, und
daß die Canadiſchen Seen noch in ihren tieferen Becken
die Ueberbleibſel jener Gewäſſer aufgenommen haben.

41.

Unter den merkwürdigern Gegenständen der hieſi-
gen Gebürge, verdienen die häufig vorkommende Oefnungen zwiſchen ihren Reihen, allerdings eine Erwäh-
nung. Man kennt sie unter dem Namen *Gapes*, (ein
offner Weg, ein Ausſchnitt, eine Lücke eines Zauns
oder Damms) und unterſcheidet sie in solche, wo Flüſſe
und Ströme durchhinkommen (Water - Gapes) und
trockene (Wind-Gapes). Erſtere haben eben nichts be-
ſonderes, indem die noch durchflieſſende Waſſer ihre
erſte Entstehung und allmähliche Erweiterung leicht
begreifen laſſen. Unterdeſſen ſcheint doch hie und da
die Menge und Stärke der gegenwärtig durchhin gehenden Waſſer, bey weitem unverhältnißmäſſig zu der
vorhandenen Oefnung. Es wird daher wahrſcheinlich,
daß verſchiedene Flüſſe in vorigen Zeiten ſtärker und
waſſerreicher müſſen geweſen ſeyn, und nachher ver-

muth-

muthlich in andere Kanäle gefallen sind. Weniger deut-
lichen Ursprungs aber sind die verschiedenen trockenen
Gapes, wo nemlich in einer gerade fortgehenden Berg-
wand sich plötzlich ein mehr oder weniger beträchtlicher Ausschnitt zeiget, der den Reisenden die Mühe,
über den ganzen Rücken des Berges zu steigen, freund-
schaftlich erleichtert. Von der Art ist die allgemeiner unter dem Namen der *Wind-Gape* bekannte Oeffnung
des blauen Berges, hinter Nazareth. Es fliesset nicht
nur kein Wasser daburch, sondern es findet sich auch
keine deutliche Spur, daß hier ehemals ein Flußbette
gewesen; wenigstens sind die am Wege verstreute Bruchstücke, nicht von der Beschaffenheit. Mehrere und genauere Beobachtungen können vielleicht einen Aufschluß
hierüber geben.

42.

Man könnte vielleicht einen entfernten Verdacht
über die Entstehung dergleichen durchbrochener Berg-
wände auf unterirrdische Erschütterungen werfen. Es
wird aber aus mehreren Ursachen und Umständen höchst
unwahrscheinlich, daß weder Feuer, noch daher rüh-
rende Erdbeben, zu der Bildung der Oberfläche dieses
Theils von Nordamerika etwas beygetragen haben.
Es widerspricht die grosse und bisher allgemein beobachtete

achtete Folgeordnung in den Lagen, Schichten und Streichen der Gebürge, die nirgends eine so merkliche Zer-
rüttung wahrnehmen läßt, daß man auf so mächtig
würkende Ursachen zurück gehen müßte. Die Haufen
von zerstreuten Bruchstücken der blätterichten Wezsteine,
die sich auf den Gebürgen und Gebürgsthälern vorfinden, und die allenfalls eine gewaltsame Zerberstung
der obersten Rinde könnten muthmassen lassen, sind
nicht hinlänglich beweisend; weil n dergleichen blätterich angelegten Felsarten, Absonderungen der Lagen
eben so leicht durch Gefrieren der zwischen die Lagen
eingesogenen Feuchtigkeiten entstehen konnten (*). Es
widerspricht ferner die bis daher noch gänzlich man-
gelnde Bemerkung von Spuren oder Ueberbleibseln von
Vulkanischen Produkten. Mir ist nichts vorgekommen,
das die entfernteste Aehnlichkeit davon hatte; denn die
oben

(*) Ich erinnere dieses mit Bedacht, weil wirklich einige
von den Landleuten in Amerika in dem Wahn stehen, daß
ihre Berge noch wachsen, oder gewachsen haben; und sich das
ganz augenscheinlich aus der geborstenen oberen Rinde eben so
erklären, wie das Bersten einer Baumrinde von der Ver-
grösserung des Stammes. Sie haben also die nemliche Meynung von Erhebung der Berge aus der Tiefe, wie der Herr
Consistorialrath Silberschlag.

oben erwähnten Schörle in Quarz, find nicht dahin zu
rechnen. Vor vielen Jahren schon legte die Königl.
franzöſ. Akad. der Wiſſenſchaften, der Philadelph. Aka-
demie mehrere Fragen vor, die die Berichtigung der
Anzeigen von Vulkaniſchen Ueberbleibſeln in den amerikaniſchen Gebürgen zum Gegenſtand hatten. Es fand
ſich aber niemand, der genauer mit den Gebürgen bekannt war, als Bartram, und ſeine Antwort war, daß
ihm nichts von allem dem, wornach gefragt wurde, auf
ſeinen vielen Gebürgsreiſen, vorgekommen ſey.

Erdbeben ſind überdieß noch, ſo lange Nordamerika von Europäern bewohnt iſt, eine äuſſerſt ſeltene
Erſcheinung geweſen; man erinnert ſich deren nur etwa zwey oder drey in den vordern Gegenden, deren
Wirkung aber niemals hinter der Granitreihe empfun-
den wurde, ſondern die ſich blos auf die der See nahe
liegenden Provinzen einſchränkten.

Die ſonſt ſehr wahrſcheinlich gemachte Vermuthung, daß bey allen den Stellen, wo Bergharz oder
Bergöl gefunden wird, noch würklich brennende, oder
offenbare Spuren bereits ausgebrannter Berge (*) in
der

(*) v. Beroldingen Beobacht. die Mineral. betr. S. 166.

der Nachbarschaft angetroffen würden, trifft nun wohl
in diesem Theil von Nordamerika nicht ein. Bey den
so vielfach vorkommenden Anzeigen von Bergöl und
Steinkohlenflözen im Gebürge, und jenseits desselben,
hat man doch noch weder wirkliche Entdeckung, noch
zuläßliche Muthmassung, vom Daseyn brennender Steinkohlenflöze, gemacht, von deren chemischen Auseinan-
dersetzung durch unterirrdische Feuer das Bergöl entstehen sollte (*). Aber freylich muß ich auch beken-
nen, daß die meisten dieser Steinkohlenflöze vielleicht
zu unbeträchtlich und seicht sind, um die Spuren ihres
innern Brandes auf der Oberfläche bemerkbar zu machen, oder feuerspeyenden Bergen ähnliche Erscheinungen hervorzubringen; und der erwähnte Verfasser der
Mineral-Bemerkungen, zeigt auch aus andern Beyspie-
len, daß dieses nicht immer geschehe. Als die einigen
Anzeigen unterirrdischer Wärme in diesen Theilen
von Amerika, kenne ich blos die sogenannten warmen
Quellen (Warm-Springs) in der Nachbarschaft des
Potomacks, in Virginien; die ich aber nur 74° Fahrenh.
Thermom. gefunden; und die Schiefer und Markasiten
gänz in der Nähe ihres Ursprungs haben.

Eine

(*) Ebend. S. 147. 155.

Eine wärmere Quelle aber trifft man bey den Augusta-Springs, ebenfalls in Virginien an, die 120° Fahrenh. haben sollen; die ich aber nicht gesehen. Nach mündlicher Erzehlung eines Bewohners der Gegend um den Ohio, wurde dort einst im Walde von einigen Holzfällern eine Stelle angetroffen, die ihnen besonders warm, nach den Empfindungen ihrer Füsse zu seyn däuchte; sie überzeugten sich weiter durch ihre Hände davon, und gruben auch einige Fuß tief das Erdreich auf, ohne etwas Merkwürdiges zu finden.

Als wirklich Feuer speyend aber kennt man in Nordamerika keinen andern Berg, als den erst neuerlich von Cook auf der Westseite, am stillen Meere entdeckten; der aber mit diesen östlichen Gegenden gar keine Verbindung haben kann.

43.

Werfen wir nun noch einen allgemeinen Blick auf diesen ganzen östlichen Theil von Nordamerika, von dem bisher die Rede war, nemlich zwischen dem Hudsonfluß und Florida-Bay, und zwischen dem Hauptgebürg und dem Atlantischen Meer; so kann man sie im Grossen, als eine einfache Fläche betrachten, die einen allge-

allgemeinen Abhang nach Südosten hat, und mit grossen
Furchen oder Vertiefungen in der Länge von Südwest
nach Nordost durchgraben ist; die nach Norden hin
sich verengern, so wie die sie bezeichnende Erhabenhei-
ten, oder Bergreihen, im Ganzen genommen nach Norden hin höher erscheinen, und in Süden niedriger
werden.

Diesen erwähnten Abhang erklärt und beweißt die
allgemeinere Richtung und Lauf der Flüsse in diesen
Gegenden. „So lange sie in irgend einem Thale
„fliessen, ist ihre Richtung Südwest, und wo sie ir-
„gend durch Oefnungen und ununterbrochene Reihen
„der Berge einen Weg nach Osten finden können,
„nehmen sie solchen und stürzen und drängen sich über
„Felsen und Abgründe, in beständigen Catarakten und Fäl-
„len südöstlich; und so ist längst den verschiedenen
„Reihen, und von einer zur andern, ihr Lauf in
„grossen Zikzaks von Südwest und Südosten.   Die
„ist die allgemeinere Richtung des Delawares, der
„Susquehannah, des Potomacks rc. (die im Gebürge
„oder jenseits entspringen;) die kürzeren Flüsse aber,
„die nur von dem östlichen Abhang der Berge sich er-
„heben, als Rappahannek, James-River, Roanoke
„und die übrigen Flüsse von Karolina, dringen in

Schöpfs min. Beytr.   L   „aller-

„allerley Richtungen (nach Beschaffenheit des Grun-
„des) füdöftlich nach der See (*). „

Ein Blick auf irgend eine der Charten des nord-
amerikanifchen Continents, wird den Lefer, durch die
Anlage und Richtung der beynahe fämmtlichen Flüffe,
von der Wahrheit diefer Bemerkung überzeugen.

Man wird diefen Abhang zwar ganz natürlich und
nothwendig finden; er zeichnet fich aber doch durch feine
Anordnung auf eine merkwürdige Weife aus. Es haben Waffer ehedem über den höhern und hintern Bergreihen, oder über dem Hauptgebürge geftanden, und
mit dem Niederfchlag der Waffer find jene Gebürge-
rücken überlegt. Diefes mochte fich ereignen, wenn es
wollte, fo mußten unter Bedingung des erwähnten Abhangs nach der See zu, die niederen und vorderen
Bergreihen, zu gleicher Zeit mit den hintern und
höhern vom Waffer bedeckt gewefen feyn. Erhielten
nun diefe höhere Rücken des Hauptgebürges einen beträchtlichen Zuwachs, durch den auf ihre Grundlage
von quarzichtem Fels, aus dem darüber geftandenen
Meere abgefetzten Sand und Thon, der nun als Wez-
feftein

ſtein erſcheinet, (§. 35. 36.) und Ueberbleibſel und Abdrücke von Seethieren enthält; (§. 39.) ſo fragt ſich
allerdings, warum geſchahe nicht das nemliche auf den
davor liegenden niederern Bergreihen? Aber auf der
Granit- der zweyten und dritten Felsreihe, findet ſich
nicht nur gar keine ähnliche Schichtung von Wezſtein,
und gar keine mir bekannt gewordene, oder vielleicht
nur zufällige Anzeige von Seethieren, eben ſo wenig
als in den dazwiſchen gelegenen Kalchthälern. (§. 31.)
Und obgleich die Felsarten der vordern Reihen ebenfalls meiſt blätterich angelegt ſind, ſo beſtehen ſie doch
dem größten Theile nach aus ſolchen Beſtandtheilen, die
man nicht geradezu für den unmittelbaren Bodenſaz
eines lange darüber geſtandenen Gewäſſers anſprechen
kan, wie die obern Schichten des hintern Gebürges.

Hätte zu der nemlichen, und für dieſelbe Länge der
Zeit, das Meer die ganze beſtimmte abhangende Fläche,
mit einer ruhigen Ueberſchwemmung, zwiſchen dem
Alleghann und der Granitreihe überdeckt, ſo würde je-
dermann geneigt ſeyn zu glauben, daß der Niederſchlag
aus dieſem Meer, in Anſehung der Beſtandtheile ſowohl, als der Menge, in einem Raum von nur etwa
100 engliſchen Meilen, nicht ſonderlich verſchieden ſeyn
konnte. Man ſieht aber mit Verwunderung, in den

L 2   niedri-

niedrigern Stellen des Abhangs, Graniten und Gneisse,
die kein Produkt des Waffers an sich selber sind, aber
auch mit andern nicht überlegt sind, die sich auf den
höhern Hauptreihen erst einfinden. Bey jedem Niederschlag aus einer unbewegten Flüssigkeit, fallen durchgehends die festen Theile dergestalt zu Boden, daß sie
jeden Theil des sie aufnehmenden Bodens gleich hoch
bedecken. Ist dieser Boden eben, so wird es die Oberfläche des Niederschlags gleichfalls seyn; ist er uneben, so wird es die Oberfläche des Niederschlags
zwar ebenfalls seyn, aber doch unter den meisten Umständen so, daß die Materie des Niederschlags, die
Unebenheiten des Bodens dennoch gleich hoch bedeckt.
Bey einer fortdauernden und ruhigen Ueberschwemmung also hätte sich eben sowohl ein ähnlicher Bodensaz auf den niederen Vorgebürgen verhältnißmässig
häufen müssen, als auf dem Hauptgebürge, wenn
auch der ursprüngliche Boden der erstern schon an sich
niederer und abhängender gewesen wäre, als der andere; und jene durch die nemliche Menge Niederschlags
auch nicht zu derselben Höhe mit diesen gebracht worden wären. Da sich aber keine Uebereinstimmung von
der Art in den obern Lagen der vordern und hintern
Gegenden findet, und man auch nicht annehmen kann,
daß das über den vordern und niedern Reihen gestan-
dene

dene Gewäſſer vielleicht nur mit wenigern ſoliden und
anders beſchaffenen Theilen wäre geſättiget geweſen,
oder ihr Abſaz durch andere Urſachen wäre verhindert
worden: ſo muß dieſer auffallende Unterſchied, der Ge-
genwart von Seekörpern in den Hauptgebürgen, und
ihre Abweſenheit in den Vor- und Mittelgebürgen,
andere Ereigniſſe zum Grund haben.

Die bekannten und höchſten Gebürgsketten der
ganzen übrigen Welt beſtehen aus Granitſpitzen und
Reihen, die mit den übrigen, allgemein zu den urſprünglichen gezählten Gebürgsarten, dem Topfſtein,
Granaten, Glimmer, Schörlen, weiſſen Marmor ꝛc.
begleitet ſind, bey einer ehemaligen Ueberſchwemmung,
oder langdauerndem höhern Meeresſtand, über die
Meeresfläche erhaben geblieben. Niedriger als dieſe,
und um ſie herum, liegen die aufgeſchichteten Gebürge
der zweyten Ordnung, mit Muſcheln verſehene Sand-
oder Kalchflöze. — Man mag von irgend einem der
europäiſchen Seen nach irgend einem Gebürge aufſteigen, ſo trift man immer zuerſt auf die Flöze, die Muſcheln enthalten, und zulezt erſt auf den Granit und
ſeine Bekleidung. Obgleich auch der Granit öfters in
den übrigen Weltgegenden in niedrigen Lagen vorkommt, und vielleicht den größten Theil des Meer-

grun-

grundes selber und die Unterlage der übrigen Gebürgsarten ausmacht; so muß man in dem Falle vor uns,
immer erwägen, daß hinter ihm Gebürgsarten der
zweyten Ordnung aufgeschichtet sind, ohne daß er selber
damit überlegt ist, und ohne daß er etwa wieder in
noch weiter zurückgelegenen und noch höhern Gebürgsreihen zum Vorschein komme.

Aus dieser umgekehrten Ordnung, und dem um-
gekehrt richtigen Verhältnisse der Anlage der meisten
hohen Gebürgsketten, zu diesem Theil von Amerika,
möchte ich beynahe glauben, daß diese amerikanische
Granitreihe ehemals eine höhere Stellung gehabt habe,
daß sie, wie andere Granitreihen über ihre benachbarte
Gebürge der zweyten Ordnung nach erhaben sind, es
auch einst über das endlose Gebürge war. Dieses angenommen, finden sich sodann alle jene ursprüngliche Gebürgsarten an ihren gewöhnlichen Orten, und
man wird sich nicht einfallen lassen, Spuren von See-
produkten auf Bergreihen zu suchen, die vorhin höher
gelegen haben, als die ehemals niedrigern, nun aber
höhern Berge, auf denen sie sich noch wahrnehmen
lassen.

Freylich ist es kühn, mit der Anordnung von Wel-
ten nach Belieben zu schalten; da Erdstriche sinken zu
lassen,

laſſen, und dort andere an die Sonne zu bringen, um
das zu erklären, was wir beobachten. Es iſt dieſer
arme Erdenkloß ſchon ſo viel mit allerley Hypotheſen
durchwühlet, und wieder durchwühlet, gehoben, geſenkt, geborſten, geſchmolzen und auf allerley Arten
umgeſchaffen worden, daß alles, was in der Art ge-
ſagt iſt, zulezt darauf hinausläuft, daß jeder uns er-
zählt, wie er es würde angefangen haben, um die Erſcheinungen hervorzubringen, die er beobachtet hat.
Ich geſtehe es, daß ich mich hier in dem nemlichen
Falle befinde. Um dem Granit mit ſeinem Gefolge
nichts von dem Range zu vergeben, den er in der
übrigen Welt auf den erhabenſten Gipfeln behauptet,
möchte ich glauben, daß ſich ehemals ein ihm unmittelbar oſtwärts anſtoſſendes Gebürg, oder Theil der
Erdrinde, in die Tiefe geſenkt habe, um die Waſſer
aufzunehmen, die hinter den amerikaniſchen Granit-
und Gneisreihen, und über den endloſen Gebürgen
geſtanden; daß bey dieſer wichtigen Veränderung
ſich die Grundveſte der Granit- und der anſchlieſſenden
andern Mittelreihen ſelber dermaſſen geſenkt habe, daß
der nunmehrige ganze öſtliche Theil von Nordamerika,
zwiſchen dem Granit- und dem Hauptgebürge, aus einer vormals nach Weſten abhängenden Pläne, nun
eine oſtwärts abhängende worden iſt.

L 4

Faſt

Faſt alle bekannte feſte Länder ſtunden ehemals bis
zu einer gewiſſen Höhe an die Urgebürge unter Waſſer.
Dieſe Waſſer, wenn man ſie nicht ſchlechterdings nur
will verdünſten laſſen, mußten ſich in tiefere Becken zurück gezogen haben, die vor dieſer Veränderung nicht
da waren. Das Entſtehen dieſer Becken ſetzt Vertiefungen durch Einſenkung eines groſſen Theils des Bodens der alten Meere voraus, um Raum zur Aufnahme ſo vieler tauſend Quadratmeilen (*) von Waſ-
ſern zu machen, die vorhin über den nun trocknen
Erdflächen geſtanden haben. Bey einer ſo wichtigen
Veränderung konnte es wohl nicht fehlen, daß auſſer
dem Sinken eines Theils des ehemaligen Meergrundes
ſelber, auch noch ein Theil des vorhin feſten Landes,
das den Gegenden, wo die Senkung ſich ereignete, am
nächſten war, theils mitſinken, und die angränzenden
ſich neigen mußten. Da nun das Atlantiſche Meer einen Theil der t rhin über Amerika geſtandenen Waſſer muß aufgenommen haben, und dieſes aufzunehmen,
mußte ſelber vertiefet werden, ſo iſt es nicht ganz unmöglich,

---

(*) Buffon rechnet, daß die Gewäſſer die Fläche der
itt bewohnten Erdkugel bis auf 2000 Toiſen hoch bedeckt haben; die zum wenigſten 300 Millionen Kubikmeilen Waſſer
geben.

möglich, daß der östlich abhangende Theil von Nordamerika sich von einer vormaligen beträchtlichen Höhe
abwärts geneigt, und daß die Granitreihe das wurde,
was sie vorhin nicht war, nemlich die Gränze des zurück gewichenen Meeres.

Alle Gebürgsarten beynahe, die in den vordern
Gegenden und hinter dem Granit von Nordamerika
vorkommen, haben einen mehr oder mindern Abhang
nach Südosten. Auch in der Tiefe hat man noch bis
daher das nemliche beobachtet; die Erzgänge in der
Jersey streichen sämmtlich von Nordost nach Südwest,
und fallen alle Ostwärts ab, und werden in dieser
Richtung mächtiger; und denselben Abhang beobachtet
das todte liegende.

Zunächst hinter der Granitreihe finden sich in
Pensylvanien bey Swedesford, und vielfach anderwärts, blätterict angelegte Marmor- und Kalchschichten, die beynahe senkrecht stehen; so wie die nemliche
fast senkrechte Stellung auch an den schwarzen Kalch-
schiefern, bey Quebec und andern Orten in Canada,
vom Herrn Kalm (*) bemerkt worden. Die Beobachtungen

£ 5

(*) Kalm Reisen, 3ter Theil, S. 551.

tungen des Herrn von Saußûre in der Schweiz sind
zwar der Meynung, daß ähnliche vertical stehende
Schichtungen von Flözgebürgen, durch eine Art von
Einstürzung in diese Stellung gekommen, ungünstig (*),
die er lieber durch eine Art verwirrter Krystallisation
erklärt.   Ich bin eben so wenig geneigt, das Gegentheil hartnäckig zu behaupten; aber verhindern konnte ich nicht, daß bey dem öftern Anblick solcher stehender, oder stark nach Osten abhängender Schichten, die
Vorstellung eines Einsturzes sich mir immer aufdrang. Und
das um so mehr, da dergleichen Erscheinungen mir nur
in den Mittelreihen, nemlich zwischen dem Granit und
dem Hauptgebürge, vorgekommen sind.   Die auf dem
Rücken der Hauptgebürge aufgeschichteten Wezsteine ⁊c.
haben meistens eine horizontale Lage; und so beobachten auch die zwischen dem Granit und der See liegende
Sand- Thon- und Muschelbetten, wo man sie immer
siehet, eine wagerechte Stellung.

Dieses Senken der vordern Gegenden konnte sich
auch so allmählich ereignen, daß die Wirkungen eines
gewaltsamen Einsturzes weniger bemerkbar blieben, und
den Wassern, die sich von den hintern Gegenden darüber
hin-

(*) Saußûre Reis. durch die Alpen, 1ster Theil, §. 239.

hinweg nach den Ocean zogen, Gelegenheit gaben,
noch. andere Veränderungen auf dieser Fläche zu be-
wirken, und Sand und Leimen darüber zu schlemmen,
die ich, um nicht weitläuftig zu seyn, übergehe.

44.

Findet man es wahrscheinlich, daß eine Vertiefung,
ein Niedersinken des östlichen Theils von Nordamerika,
ihm seinen gegenwärtigen Abhang gegeben, und
die nächst der See streichende Granitreihe, (die einzige
vielleicht von mehreren parallel mit ihr streichenden,
nun über der Wasserfläche sichtbar gebliebene,) von einer vorhin gehabten Höhe, dem Mittelpunkt der Erde
näher gebracht hat; so folgt es von selber, was anfangs schon (§. 12.) wahrscheinlich war, daß nemlich
alles vor der jezigen Granitreihe herliegendes Land,
von neuerem Ursprung sey. Dahin nun gehört die
oben beschriebene vordere Gegend, von York herab bis
nach Florida. (§. 4. und folgende.) Ihre Beschaffenheit und Anlage läßt keinen Zweifel, daß sie nicht vom
Meer erzeugt wären; und daß sie von keinem sehr
hohen Alter seyn mögen, zeugen die Weichheit und
Lockerheit ihrer Schichten im Ganzen, die nur hie und
da, aus Lokalumständen vielleicht, eine grössere Härte
erlangt haben, als allgemein.

Es

Es konnten also die Mittelgegenden, zwischen dem
Granit und dem Hauptgebürge, schon lange trocken seyn,
als noch die See unmittelbar an sie stieß, und die weiten Plänen von Virginien und Karolina noch wirklich
unter Waſſer ſtanden. Und auf dieſe vordere Gegenden eingeſchränkt, bin ich mit der Meynung derer ein-
verſtanden, die Amerika für ein jüngeres Land anſehen.
Wenn aber Abbé Raynal und andere glauben, daß
der Ocean Amerika erſt lange nachher verlaſſen habe, nachdem unſer Welttheil ſchon bevölkert geweſen;
ſo kann ich ihm unmöglich beypflichten. Nach dem allgemeinen Geſetze der Gravitation, kann die See an
keinem Ort der öſtlichen Küſte von Amerika beträchtlich höher ſtehen, als ſie an der unter gleicher Parallele entgegen geſetzten weſtlichen Küſte von Europa
ſtehet; wenn man auch eine mehrere Anhäufung der
Waſſer in Weſten, von dem Schwung der Erde nach
Oſten, zugeben wollte. Sollte daher der Continent von
Amerika länger unter See geſtanden haben, als der
europäiſche, ſo hätte die See dort müſſen um viele
Lachtern höher ſtehen, als die niedrigſten Gegenden
des ſchon trocknen, und, nach Raynals Meynung, bewohnten Europa; welches aber anzunehmen ungereimt
wäre. Amerika konnte vielleicht ſpäter ſeyn bevölkert
worden, als Europa; aber die See mußte es zu glei-

cher

cher Zeit verlaffen haben, als es sie von den übrigen
festen Ländern sich zurückzog, wenn anders die Gesetze
des Gleichgewichts beobachtet werden sollten, Kraft
welcher die Oberfläche des Oceans, (die von auffen auf
ihn wirkende Ursachen abgerechnet,) überall den nemlichen Abstand vom Mittelpunkt der Erde haben muß.

Daß der Continent von Amerika zu gleicher Zeit
unverhältnißmäffig kälter und wärmer als Europa ist,
rührt nicht von der, nach dem Rückzug der See, zu-
rückgebliebenen Feuchtigkeit her, sondern hat seine Ursachen theils in dem Abhang nach Südosten, welcher
der Sonne mehr Einfluß gestattet; und in der Ausdehnung nach Norden und den nordwestlichen Seen,
welche die daher kommenden Winde kühlen. Daß ein
Land eine mit Sümpfen und Morästen angefüllte
Wildniß ist, beweißt nur, daß keine Einwohner ihre
Industrie darauf verwandt haben; aber nicht, daß die
Natur selber in ihrer Kindheit sey, die doch ihre ein-
heimische Produkte in derselben Vollkommenheit hervor-
bringt, als andere Länder die ihrigen.

Für das Alter von Amerika zeugen überdies die
Tiefen der Flußbetten, besonders in den Gebürgen, und da wo sie die Gebürgsreihen durchgegraben
haben,

haben, um sich Südostwärts zu wenden. Der Augenschein lehrt es, daß sie nicht weniger Zeit damit müssen zugebracht haben, als die Flüsse der übrigen Welt
mit Vertiefung ihrer Betten. Anders nicht, als wenn
das feste Land aus der Tiefe wäre heraufgehoben worden, könnte Amerika jünger seyn; da sich aber dieses
von den Gegenden zwischen dem Granit und dem Gebürge nicht vermuthen läßt, weil es nicht das Gepräge
eines Meeresbodens hat, wie das höher gelegene Gebürg, und die niedriger gelegene Plänen, so kann dies
auch nicht der Fall seyn. Amerika wird daher gewiß
eben so alt seyn, als Europa; oder wenigstens viel
älter, als man es zu seyn angenommen hat.

45.

Ohne an die Voraussetzung des Sinkens der mittlern Gegenden von Amerika gebunden zu seyn, könnte
man wohl die nemliche Erscheinung durch andere Hypo-
thesen ebenfalls erklären. Man könnte mit Herrn
Silberschlag annehmen, daß die Hauptgebürge durch
unterirrdisches oder Central-Feuer in die Höhe wären
gehoben worden; dann mußten freylich auch die vorliegenden Reihen verhältnißmässig dadurch erniedriget
werden. Oder man könnte zugeben, daß die Mittelreihen, wie die Hauptgebürge, ehemals mit blätterichten

ten Sandsteinen überlegt waren, bey dem Ablauf des
Meeres aber davon gewaltsamer Weise entblösset worden sind. Ich will nicht weiter für eine oder die andere
Meynung streiten; es müssen erst noch weitere Beobachtungen darüber gesammlet werden, ehe man mit
etwas mehr Zuverlässigkeit zu entscheiden wagen darf.
Welche Meynung man aber auch darüber annehmen
mag, so bleibt noch immer eine wichtige Frage übrig.
Welche Ursache hat der vermuthlich ältesten Granitreihe, und allen übrigen Gebürgsreihen, die merkwürdige und parallele Richtung von Nordost nach Südwest
gegeben; die sich in diesem Theil von Amerika noch besonders, durch ihre grosse, beynahe ununterbrochene
Länge, auszeichnen? In Absicht auf diese Richtung,
stimmt diese amerikanische niedrige Granitreihe, mit der
Anlage anderer erhabener Granitketten, im mittäglichen
Europa überein; mit der Centralkette der Schweizer-
Alpen, des Fichtelbergs, des Riesengebürgs, und mehr
anderer überein. Ueberhaupt genommen nähern die
höchsten Gebürge der Erde sich der Richtung von Norden nach Süden; und genauer in der Richtung streichen die nördlicheren Gebürge von Europa, wie die
Norwegischen ꝛc. (*) Aber auch die nördlichern in
Ameri-

_____

(*) *Buffon* Supplem. à l'hist. nat. Tom. IX. p. 440.

Amerika kommen diesen hierinnen gleich, wie aus der Folge erhellen wird. — Eine zusammenhängende Kette hoher Berge läuft nach Buffon (*) durch die Mitte von Afrika von Norden nach Süden, und in eben der Richtung streicht die hohe Kette im mittäglichen Amerika.

Da alle diese höchsten Gebürge aus ursprünglichen Felsarten bestehen, unter denen der Granit die erste Stelle einnimmt; so ist zu vermuthen, daß die Richtung der Granitreihen aller Orten, die der übrigen gewissermassen bestimmen, ungeachtet niemand wird die Ursache angeben können, die dem Granit seinen Weg vorgezeichnet.

Aus der Uebereinstimmung und Aehnlichkeit in der Gestalt mehrerer Länder, wird es zwar wahrscheinlich, daß eine gewaltige Ueberschwemmung oder Strömung der Wasser von Südwesten her irgend einmal statt gefunden habe; und diese Meynung wird von mehreren Naturforschern begünstiget, und jeder schließt es aus andern ihm vorgekommenen Beobachtungen. Aus der Betrachtung der vielen nach Süden gekehrten grossen Landspitzen nimmt Buffon (**) an, daß das

Wasser

(*) Ebendaſ.

(**) Supplem. à l'hiſt. natur. Tom. IX.

Waſſer vom Südpol in groſſerer Menge als vom
Nordpol hergekommen ſey; und dieſe Meynung beſtäti-
get Herr Forſter in ſeinen Bemerkungen auf ſeiner
Reiſe um die Welt (*). Aus ſeinen Beobachtungen
über die Berge des ruſſiſchen Reiches (**) urtheilet
Pallas, daß die Ueberſchwemmung, welche jene betroffen, aus Süden gekommen ſeyn müſſe. Aus den
Farrnkräutern und andern indianiſchen Pflanzen, die
ſich in den europäiſchen Schiefern abgedruckt finden,
folgert Juſſieu eine Ueberſchwemmung aus Süden, oder
aus den Meeren um Indien. Aus der Beſchaffenheit
der Holländiſchen, Friesländiſchen und anderer Torfgruben, und den darinn nicht ſelten vorkommenden um-
geſtürzten Bäumen, die einerley Lage, ſo daß ſie ihre
Krone oder Gipfel nach der Gegend zwiſchen Oſt und
Nord, ihre Wurzeln gegen Südweſten zukehren, läßt
ſich auch in dieſen Gegenden eine ſtarke Ueberſchwemmung

(*) Joh. Reinb. Forſters Bemerk. auf ſeiner Reiſe
um die Welt, Berlin 1783. S. 3.

(**) Pallas Beobacht. über die Berge ꝛc. Sammlung
zur Phyſik und Naturgeſch. Leipzig, 1ſter Band ates Stück,
Nro. 1.

Schöpfs min. Beytr.   M

mung aus Südwesten vermuthen (*). Die Richtung
der beschriebenen Gebürgsreihen und Thäler in Amerika giebt diesen Meynungen ferner noch viele an-
scheinende Wahrscheinlichkeit. Denn daß die langen
Thäler dieser Gegenden nicht als bloße von Flüssen
ausgehölte Kanäle können angesehen werden, beweißt,
daß die Flüsse zwar eine Strecke lang in ihnen fort-
gehen, aber dann in anderen Richtungen sich nach Südosten abwenden, da die Thäler selber doch ihre südwestliche Richtung behalten. Von dem großen Kalch-
thale habe ich angemerkt, daß es gegen Süden breiter
werde; ob dieses aber auch von den übrigen zutrifft,
weiß ich nicht, und eben so wenig konnte ich erfahren,
ob sich die übrigen Thäler, und besonders die engern
des Hauptgebürges, so weit und so ununterbrochen verfolgen lassen, als jenes große Kalchthal, so daß man
mit einiger Zuverläßigkeit, ihre Entstehung den von
Süden und Südwesten her strömenden Wassern zu-
schreiben könnte. Man müßte sich auch über ihren
wahren Abhang nach dieser Gegend erst berichtigen,
welches aber schon schwerer seyn dürfte, weil in den
nachfolgenden Zeiten die Thäler auf verschiedene Weise
von den Materien der höheren Gegenden überschlemmt,

abge-

(*) v. Beroldingen Beobacht. die Mineral. betr. S. 34.

abgeſchnitten und ungleich angefüllt werden konnten, ſo daß
man ihren urſprünglichen Gang nicht unverändert finden
dürfte. So viel Uebereinſtimmung man nun aber auch
zwiſchen den erwähnten allgemeiner angenommenen aus
Süden kommenden Ueberſchwemmungen, und der Richtung der amerikaniſchen Gebürge fände, ſo ſtehen wieder viele andere Umſtände im Wege, es für ausgemacht anzunehmen. Und viele Einwürfe würden erſt
zu beantworten ſeyn; ja, man würde hier mit eben
ſo vielem Rechte fragen können: ob nicht die Waſſer
ſich vielmehr 'n der ſüdweſtlichen Richtung, nach dem
Mexikaniſchen Meerbuſen zurückgezogen haben? —
Wenigſtens wird mir es aus andern Betrachtungen
wieder unwahrſcheinlich, daß die Bildung der Gebürgsreihen einen Bezug auf jene Ueberſchwemmung aus
Süden habe. Dieſe kann und will ich darum nicht ab-
läugnen. Sie erfolgte aber muthmaßlich ſpäter; nachdem die Gebürge ſchon in ihrer gegenwärtigen Geſtalt
geordnet waren. Als einen vorzüglichen Beweis der
Richtung jener Ueberſchwemmungen aus Süden nimmt
Herr **Pallas** die Ueberbleibſel von Landthieren, die
nur zwiſchen den Wendekreiſen leben, und die man
doch bis in die nordiſchen Länder hinein haufenweiſe
begraben findet (*). Dieſe Ueberbleibſel finden ſich

M 2 nun

(*) **Pallas** über die Gebürge, Leipz. Samml. S. 188.

nun auch bekanntermaſſen in Amerika (*), aber nur ſo
ſeichte unter der Oberfläche, daß man daher nicht glauben kann, daß die Gewäſſer, die ſie in jene Gegenden geſchwemmt haben, eine groſſe Wirkung auf die
Gebürge konnten gehabt haben; da es blos eine kurze
vorübergehende und auſſerordeutliche Ueberſchwemmung
geweſen zu ſeyn ſcheint, die ſchon eine bewohnte Welt
in Amerika vorausſezte; und eben ſo ſchon eine ge-
wiſſe Anordnung in der Oberfläche des überſchwemm-
ten Bodens vermuthen läßt, die dem Waſſer geſtat-
tete nach Norden zu flieſſen. Denn hätten ſie ein
hohes, von Oſt nach Weſten ſtreichendes Gebürg gefunden, ſo würden ſie ſolches vielleicht wohl hie und
da durchbrochen, aber ſeine Richtung nicht geändert
haben.

Nimmt

(*) Man wußte vor wenigen Jahren nur eine Stelle am
Ohio, wo ſich ein groſſer Haufen ſolcher Knochen fand; ſeit
kurzem aber hat man auch an der Oſtſeite der Gebürge, in
Nordkarolina, in Penſylvanien, in Neuyork, einzelne aber
ähnliche Knochen gefunden. Sie finden ſich auch in Canada.
Jene Ueberſchwemmung mußte alſo den ganzen Continent be-
troffen, und die Gebürge, wo nicht über — doch von allen
Seiten umfloſſen haben.

Nimmt man an, daß, früher als diese, eine lang
anhaltende Ueberschwemmung, die blätterichten Sandsteine mit Muschel-Abdrücken, auf den endlosen Gebürgen abgesezt habe; so fragt sich, warum dieses
blos Reihenweise auf schmalen Bergrücken geschehen
sey, und warum die davor und dazwischen liegende
Kalchthäler nicht mit dem nemlichen Bodensaz bedeckt
wurden? Und warum diese Kalchthäler, wo nicht gar
keine, doch äusserst selten ähnliche Ueberbleibsel von
Seethieren als die Hauptgebürge liefern? Es wird dadurch die Vermuthung eines nach Osten gesenkten Landes vermehret, und eben dadurch auch noch weiter
wahrscheinlich, daß der Kalch, der zunächst an der
Granitreihe, und zwischen den folgenden gneis- und
quarzichten Reihen, eigentlicher Urkalch (§. 31.) und
nicht aus Schaalthieren entstandener sey; und es folgt
daher, nach meiner Meynung, daß ursprünglich schon
jene quarzichte Reihen, mit den zwischen und anliegen-
den Urkalchschichten, abgesondert und neben einander
sind angelegt worden. Darüber aber hat uns, meines
Wissens, noch niemand die Ursache angegeben, daß der
Urkalch, der keine Spuren von Seekörpern enthält,
dennoch in andern hohen Gebürgen immer niedriger
als die Grundspitzen, und ihnen gleichförmig, gleich-

M 3

lau-

laufend angelegt ist, wie ihn Saußüre am Buet und
andern Schweizer-Alpen bemerket, und wie er auch
anderwärts vorkommt, wohin vorzüglich der weiße
Marmor zu rechnen ist. Daß dieser aber sowohl als
die andern mit Urkalch gefüllten Thäler, in Amerika
höher als der Granit liegen, führt immer wieder auf
die Voraussetzung einer Erniedrigung dieses Striches
zurück. Sollten die grossen amerikanischen Kalchthäler
der Bodensaz einer lange darüber gestandenen See seyn,
warum ließ diese See nicht auch Kalch über die Mit-
telgebürge, über den South-Mountain fallen, die
niedriger als die Hauptgebürge sind? — Sollte der
Kalch dieser Thäler ein Produkt der See seyn, ohne
daß diese die Höhe der sie umgränzenden Berge erreicht
hätte, so müßten die gneis- und quarzichten Reihen
schon Thäler zwischen sich gehabt haben, um jene See
darinn aufzunehmen, und mit ihrem kalchichten Bodensaz angefüllt zu werden, und das zu einer Zeit, da
diese See noch keine Schaalthiere, oder äusserst wenige
gehabt hätte. War aber dieser Theil von Amerika
vorhin ein erhabenes Land, das erst nach Westen abhängend war, und bey nachfolgenden Veränderungen
auf der Rinde der Erde, sich ostwärts stürzte, so mußten die Kalchreihen, die zunächst an der Granitreihe und

zwi-

zwischen den Mittelgebürgen sind, auch schon mit ihnen zugleich entstanden gewesen seyn, und durch mir unbekannte grosse und allgemeine Ursachen, ihre mit mehr andern Gebürgen so merkwürdig übereinkommende Richtung erhalten haben.

Noch könnte man vielleicht die Wirkung verschiedener, aus Süden und Südwesten kommender Seeströme annehmen, die während der langwierigen Ueberschwemmung konnten statt gefunden, und die Thäler in ihrer gegenwärtigen Richtung ausgegraben haben, und sich bey der Gelegenheit auf das Daseyn eines noch in der Richtung ich äussernden Meerstroms (§. 11.) stützen. Man würde allerdings einige Erscheinungen daher erklären können, aber auch wieder zu gleicher Zeit andere Zweifel rege machen.

Aus allem aber erhellet zur Genüge, daß mehr als eine, und zu sehr verschiedenen Zeiten wirkende Ursachen müssen angenommen werden, um die Anlage und das Gebäude dieses östlichen Theils von Nordamerika, mit allen darauf vorkommenden Erscheinungen näher zu erörtern. Es müssen noch viele Gegenden und alle Theile des Gebürges aufmerksam untersucht werden, ehe dies geschehen kann.

M 4

46.

46.

Ich habe mich bisher, wie ich anfangs es bestimmte, blos auf den südlichen Theil von Nordamerika
eingeschränkt, weil ich nur den kannte, der südlich vom
Hudson liegt. Die Gebürge auf der Ostseite dieses
Flusses, die zwischen Neuyork und Canada, laufen wie
jene, meist parallel mit der See. Nach Evans bestehen sie aus zwey Etagen: „Die erste, wenn man
„von Boston aus über das Gebürg gerade gegen
„Westen reiset, fängt in der Gegend von Water-town
„an, und enthält ungleichen hügelichten Grund bis
„über Western. Von hier an bis 20 Meilen inner-
„halb des Hudsonflusses hat man die zweyte Etage
„vor sich; diese bestehet aus mehrentheils kleinen Ber-
„gen, die hier in langen Ketten und Reihen, Nord
„und Süd laufen, und sich nach Süden bis an den
„Sund, der Long-Eyland vom festen Land trennt,
„erstrecken, wo sie jene Klippen, und die Reihen von
„gebrochenen steinichten Boden machen, die man auf
„dem Wege längst dem Ufer von Connektikut bemerkt,
„und wodurch zugleich die Anlegung einer bessern
„Strasse weiter Landeinwärts verhindert wird. Der
„grössere Antheil von Connektikut liegt auf dieser zwey-
„ten Etage, und hat reiches und gutes Land, in den
„Thälern, zwischen seinen Reihen. Die ansehnlichste

„Kette

„Kette davon läuft längst des Connektikut-Flusses, und
„ist nahe an 20 Meilen breit. Die Richtung dieser
„Berge und Hügel bestimmt den Lauf der verschiede-
„nen Flüsse und Ströme. Oestlich von der ersten
„Etage ist einiges Land durch Anschlemmung des
„Sandes von der See gemacht und aufgehäuft, wel-
„ches durch das Zusammenstossen und Widerprallen der
„Meeresfluth von Nordost mit der von Südost be-
„wirkt wird; dadurch ist beynahe alles Land vom Kap
„Cod, östlich von Massachusetsbay, entstanden (*).

Diese Gebürge bleiben also eine Strecke lang mehr
in einer nördlichen Richtung; fangen in einiger Entfernung vom Hudson an, und erstrecken sich längst den
Seen St. George und Champlain nach dem St. Lorenzfluß hin; doch scheinen sich die weißen Berge,
von denen der Connektikut, der Kennebec 2c. entspringen, wieder etwas nach Nordosten zu wenden, in der
nemlichen Maaße, als die Ufer vom Kap Cod erst nördlich und dann wieder von Casco-Bay nordöstlich nach
Fundy-Bay sich ziehen. Beynahe alle Flüsse dieser
Abtheilung, der Connektikut, Thames, Sagadahock,
Kennebec, Penobscot, St. Croix, St. John 2c. haben
ihre Hauptrichtung von Norden nach Süden.

M 5 Wir

(*) Evans Analysis, 1. S. 6.

Wir haben noch keine Nachrichten über die Anordnung und die Verschiedenheiten der Bergreihen dieser
Gegenden, und in wie ferne sie den südlichern ent-
sprechen. Evans klagt, daß er nichts darüber erfahren können, ausgenommen, daß ein Berg (*), der die
Fortsetzung der hohen Berge um den See Sr. Sacrament macht, nachdem er den Wood-Krick und Otter-
Krick passirt, Nordostwärts fortgehet, bis er 15 Meilen unterhalb Quebec, am Lorenz sich erniedriget. Damit stimmen Herrn **Kalms** Nachrichten überein, der
einige der Gebürge um Fort Friederich, längst des
Woodkricks von Süd-Südwest zu Nord-Nordost streichen sahe (**), die verschiedene Gattungen von Granit, Gneis (***), und Norrke (†) enthielten. Zwischen ihnen bestunden die Hügel, auf welchen Fort
Frederic steht, aus kohlschwarzen schieferichten Kalchstein, die höheren Schichten aber aus grauem dichten
Kalchstein. Der erste schwarze Kalchschiefer enthielte
eine Menge Versteinerungen (††). Der See Champlain
ist

(*) Analysis, S. 9.
(**) **Kalms** Reisen, 3ter Theil, S. 290.
(***) Ebendas. S. 311.
(†) Ebendas. S. 316.
(††) Ebendas. S. 312.

ift von beyden Seiten mit hohen Gebürgswänden in
einer kleinen Entfernung umgeben, die von Nord nach
Süd laufen, und aus nicht geschichteten Felsen von
grauem Quarz und dunklem Glimmer bestehen, an
welche grauer oder schwarzer Kalchstein mit Versteinerungen angelegt ist (*). Weiter hin, um Quebec,
traf Herr Kalm noch sehr häufig schwarze Kalchschiefer, aber gänzlich ohne alle Versteinerungen an, und
aus andern Umständen erhellet, daß diese Kalchlagen
verschiedenes und ungleichzeitigen Ursprungs mit den
erst erwähnten seyn mögen. „An der südöstlichen Seite
„des Lorenzflusses zeigt sich eine lange Reihe von hohen
„Bergen, welche mehrentheils mit dem Flusse gleich-
„laufend, obgleich viele Meilen von demselben weg,
„waren. Nach Westen wiederum verwandelten sich
„die Berge, in einiger Entfernung von diesen Anhöhen,
„in eine andere Reihe von sehr hohen Bergen, davon
„der eine fast neben den andern lag. Diese liefen
„gleichfalls parallel mit dem Flusse, oder ungefähr
„von Norden nach Süden. Diese hohen Berge be-
„stehen aus grauem Fels, der aus verschiedenen Stein-
„arten zusammengesezt ist. Von diesen scheinet man
„einen Beweis nehmen zu können, daß der Kalchschie-
„fer

(*) Ebendaf. S. 311.

„fer eben so alt, als der graue Fels, und nicht in
„den spätern Zeiten erst entstanden sey. Denn hier
„liegen diese ungeheuren grossen grauen Felsen zu oberst
„auf diesen Höhen, welche aus dem schwarzen Kalch-
„schiefer bestanden (*). „ Von diesem schwarzen Kalchschiefer erinnert er aber noch öfter, daß man niemals (**)
Versteinerungen in ihm antrifft, und daß seine Schichten zwar hie und da in horizontaler Lage angetroffen
werden, aber doch öfter noch sehr schräg liegend, so
daß sie der senkrechten Richtung am nächsten kamen,
sich mit dem oberen Ende nach Nordwest neigten, mit
dem untern aber gegen Südost stützten (***). An einigen Stellen kommen aber auch Schichten vor, welche
sich gegen Norden neigten, ob sie gleich ebenfalls der
senkrechten Linie am nächsten waren (†); wieder anderwärts stunden die Schichten gleichsam neben einander aufgestellt, fast ganz senkrecht, ausgenommen, daß
sie sich etwas gegen West - Südwest neigten (††). Wo

immer

(*) Kalm 3ter Theil, S. 450. — Gegend zwischen Quebec und Lorette.

(**) Ebendas. S. 532. und S. 552.

(***) Ebendas. S. 551. 509.

(†) Ebendas. S. 552.

(††) Ebendas. S. 514.

immer dieser schwarze Kalchschiefer, weiterhin angetroffen
wurde, an der Bay St. Paul, auf der Insel Orleans,
um Montreal ꝛc. (*) hatte er gestürzte Schichten, und
niemals Versteinerungen, mit welchen doch der häufig
um und neben ihn in horizontalen Lagen liegende
graue Kalchstein zahlreich versehen war (**). Die
Steinart der übrigen hohen Canadischen Berge um den
Lorenzfluß, waren mit Glimmer und Quarz vermischte
Kalchhaltige graue Felssteine (***), die zu den Bergen der zweyten Ordnung zu gehören scheinen, „denn
„ein grosser Theil von diesen grauen Felsen in Canada
„steh,t auf jenem schwarzen Kalchschiefer (†), und
„enthält sogar zuweilen Eindrücke von Versteinerun-
„gen (††). „ Es fallen aber alle diese Gegenden
schon westwärts, von der Richtung die das Hauptgebürge, zu dessen Hauptstamm ich die weissen Berge
rechne, beobachtet; und die Bestimmung der Einrich-
tung und Verbindung der Hauptketten dieser nördlichern
Geburgsgegenden bleibt noch zu berichtigen. In Absicht

(*) Ebendas. S. 506. 509. 593.

(**) Ebendas. S. 594.

(***) Ebendas. S. 503. 517. 522.

(†) Ebendas. S. 527.

(††) Ebendas. S. 532.

ſicht auf die Schichtungen überhaupt aber will man ſchon längſtens gefunden haben, daß ſie ſich in Canada eben ſo verhalten, wie in der Schweiz (*).

48.

Wahrſcheinlich mochte ſich ehemals das feſte Land von Amerika viel weiter nach Oſten erſtrecken; es mag nun als trockenes Land, oder als überfloſſenes da geweſen ſeyn. Der öſtlichſte Theil von Neufundland fällt bey- nahe in dieſelbe Linie mit den öſtlichſten der Inſeln unter dem Winde; in Weſtindien, und in der Mitte dieſer

(*) „La nature après avoir produit, dans le nouveau „monde, tant de végétaux et d'animaux abſolument in- „connus dans l'ancien, n'a rien changé au regne minéral: „plus on fait des recherches, plus on decouvre, que „les métaux et l'arrangement des couches terreſtres „ſont les mêmes en Amérique que dans notre conti- „nent ſous les mêmes latitudes; *au point que Mr.* „*Guettard* (*) *a prouvé que, dans le Canada, la diſpo-* „*ſition intérieure de la terre eſt préciſement comme en* „*Suiſſe.* „ Defenſe des Recherches philoſoph. ſur les Américains Tom. III. Chap. XXI.

(*) Voyez les Memoir. de l'Academie des Scienc. de Paris. l'an. 1752.

dieser Linie liegen — gleichsam als Ueberbleibsel eines festeren Bodens — zwischen diesen Nord- und Südinseln die Bermudischen. Was man auf dem dermaligen festen Lande vom östlichen Nordamerika vergebens bisher gesucht hat, nemlich Spuren von Vulkanen, findet sich in diesen zerbrochenen südlichen Gegenden. — Der Schwefelberg auf Guadeloupe, der noch beständig raucht, Schwefelgruben und heisse Quellen enthält, und der Elendsberg (Mount-Misery auf St. Christopher, der wie jener, Schwefel und warme kochende Wasser hat,) sind noch bestehende Beweise für die Möglichkeit, daß unterirrdische Feuer in diesen Gegenden ehemals ansehnliche Verwüstungen anrichten konnten; deren Wirkungen sich eben sowohl noch weiter Nordwärts erstrecken mochten, als diese Gruppe von Inseln ihr Daseyn in gegenwärtiger Gestalt vorzüglich mit von daher erhalten zu haben scheint. Lava ähnliche Steine finden sich auf beynahe allen diesen Caribischen Inseln; und wenn man mich recht berichtet hat auch auf den Bermuden.

Erwäget man ferner, daß, ausser den Spuren von verloschenen, und noch übrig gebliebenen Vulkanen an dieser Westseite des Oceans, den noch häufigen und zerstörenden Erdbeben, und oft schrecklichen Orkanen,

die

die diese Himmelsstriche so vielmals von Grund aus
erschüttern, daß ausser diesen, auch an der Ostseite des
Oceans, unter den Inseln des grünen Vorgebürges
auf Fogo, unter den Canarischen auf Teneriffa, Vul-
kane noch wirklich da sind, daß diese Inseln, und die
noch weiter nordwärts und fast in der Mitte des
Oceans gelegenen Azoren, gar nicht selten von unter-
irdischen Erschütterungen heimgesucht werden, so wird
die Vermuthung, daß der gegenwärtige Boden des
Atlantischen Meeres ehemals höher gelegen, nachher
aber gesunken seyn könnte, immer wahrscheinlicher. —
Wir wissen nicht, ob nicht eine Menge anderer Vul-
kane bey dieser Ereigniß mit gestürzt und ausgelöscht
worden sind. Es ist auch der Grund des atlantischen
Meeres gar nicht durchgehends von einer ausserordent-
lichen und gleichen Tiefe. In der Seecharte des West-
indischen Piloten sind viele Stellen mitten im Ocean
angezeichnet, wo man versunkene Felsen (Sunken Rocks)
bemerkt haben will; und ich habe es mehrmalen erwähnen hören, daß einst eine englische Fregatte, auf
der Nachhausreise von Westindien, so oft es möglich
war, im offnen Ocean, um die Tiefe zu messen,
beygelegt, und solche auch an sehr vielen Stellen un-
erwartet erreicht habe. Wenn man nun die Möglichkeit einer Einstürzung annimmt, so hält es auch gar

nicht

nicht schwer einzusehen, daß die Linie, in der dieses
geschah, viel von der Richtung ursprünglicher Gebürgsreihen abhangen mußte. — Da nun diese so allgemein
von Norden nach Süden laufend angetroffen werden,
so würde auch daher noch vielleicht einiges zur Aufklärung des Abfalls der amerikanischen Küste in der Eingangs erwähnten Richtung geschlossen werden können.

In so ferne die ältesten Traditionen sich immer
auf einige wirkliche, aber durch die Länge der Zeit ver-
unstaltete Begebenheiten gründen, darf ich, im Vorbey-
gehen wenigstens, meine Leser an die uralte Sage
von dem verlornen Lande Atlantis erinnern.

Bey Gelegenheit von Südamerika bemerkt Herr
Forster, daß eine auffallende Aehnlichkeit zwischen der
südlichen Landspitze dieses Welttheils mit allen südlichen
Landspitzen anderer Welttheile statt finde. Unter Ein-
schränkung läßt sich diese Bemerkung auch auf Nordamerika anwenden. Noch mehr aber kommen beyde
Hälften von Amerika in Absicht auf ihren ganzen Umriß überein. Das feste Land von Nordamerika ist, wie
jenes, im Norden zwischen Berings-Straße und der
Küste von Labrador von ansehnlicher Breite, und ver-
schmälert sich, wie jenes, gegen Süden. — Die Gebürge

von Nordamerika haben übrigens in ihrer Richtung
keinen Bezug auf die Cordilleras von Südamerika.
Wenn man die Linie, in der sie streichen, südwärts
durch den Gulf von Mexico fortsetzet, so trift sie genau auf die Provinz Yucatan vor Neu-Mexico, die
mit einem schmalen Strich Landes, weit in den Mexikanischen Busen herein, den Gebürgen der nördlichen
Hälfte entgegen zu gehen scheinet. Da ich aber von
diesen Gegenden nichts weiter kenne, so enthalte ich
mich auch, blosse Wahrscheinlichkeiten weiter zu verfolgen, und begnüge mich, das wenige, aus eigner Erfahrung bekannte, angezeigt zu haben. Der Unvoll-
kommenheit obiger Anmerkungen ungeachtet, werden
solche doch von einigen Nutzen seyn, wenn sie andere
Reisende zu weiteren Beobachtungen anleiten, und
durch Berichtigung oder Bestätigung der meinigen, die
Kenntniß dieses Welttheils befördern werden.

Druckfehler.

Seite 3. Z. 14. l. erften, ftatt veften.

— 17. Z. 1. l. Flußbette, ftatt Fußbette.

— 18. Z. 15. l. feft weiche, ft. faft weiche.

— 82. Z. 22. l. reiner, ft. reicher.

— 86. Z. 17. nach Schaalen, ift das Punktum hinwegzuthun.

— 112. Z. 6. l. Bogen, ft. Lagen.

— 113. Z. 7. nach Karten, ift hinzuzufezen: von.

— 122. Z. 15. l. Fuß, ft. Fluß.

— 127. Z. 16. l. Littleton, ft. Bittleton..

— 129. Z. 14. l. breiter, ft. breiten.

— 140. Z. 4. nach ꝛc. ꝛc. ift hinzuzufezen: gefunden.

— 165. Z. 13. nach find: und.

— 175. Z. 17. ift: überein, auszuftreichen.